The Specificity of
Cell Surfaces

PRENTICE-HALL, INTERNATIONAL, INC., *London*
PRENTICE-HALL OF AUSTRALIA, PTY., LTD., *Sydney*
PRENTICE-HALL OF CANADA, LTD., *Toronto*
PRENTICE-HALL OF INDIA (PRIVATE) LTD., *New Delhi*
PRENTICE-HALL OF JAPAN, INC., *Tokyo*

The Specificity of
Cell Surfaces

A symposium held under the auspices of
The Society of General Physiologists
at its annual meeting at
The Marine Biological Laboratory
Woods Hole, Massachusetts, September 1-4, 1965

Bernard D. Davis
Leonard Warren, Editors

Prentice-Hall, Inc.
Englewood Cliffs, New Jersey

©1967 by
Prentice-Hall, Inc.
Englewood Cliffs, N.J.

Library of Congress Catalog Card Number 66-29268
Printed in the United States of America
82657C

Current printing (last digit):
10 9 8 7 6 5 4 3 2 1

Preface

Recent years have witnessed spectacular advances in the analysis of a variety of fundamental biological processes at a molecular level: the biosynthesis of cellular building blocks; their polymerization into informational macromolecules (proteins and nucleic acids) and into structural macromolecules; the regulation of gene function; and the regulation of enzyme action. The occurrence of these processes in all living organisms strikingly reflects the unity of biology at a molecular level; and since microbes have often served as model cells in such studies it has proved fruitful, in many recent symposia on these topics, to bring together those working with microbes and those working with higher organisms.

While the macromolecules involved in these intracellular processes are made of essentially the same monomers in all organisms, the surface structures of cells, in contrast, present much greater diversity. This "ektobiological" realm, to use Kalckar's phrase, includes not only unique macromolecular patterns but also the incorporation of a great variety of different monomers in different organisms. The reason for the evolution of such variety is evident, for it is at their surfaces that cells and viruses interact with their special environments. A multiplicity of cell surface structures have evolved in response to many environments—"social" actions that are essential for survival and reproduction. With microbes such interactions include their attack on host cells, or their relations with phagocytic cells, as well as the exchange of genetic material between microbial cells. With animal cells these interactions govern cell aggregation, in both normal morphogenesis and the aberrant morphogenesis seen in neoplastic growth and metastasis; and they also govern such specialized reactions as fertilization, diapedesis, phagocytosis, tissue graft rejection, and probably antibody formation.

In many of these examples the existence of specific surface macromolecules can be inferred only from the specificity of cell behavior or
from immunological evidence of antigenic specificity. With certain bacterial
wall polysaccharides, however, and with the ABO blood group substances
(isoantigens) of the membranes of many human cells, it has been possible
to purify the material and thus to translate antigenic specificity into terms
of detailed carbohydrate chemistry. In the hope of promoting the extension
of such molecular studies to additional systems it has seemed worthwhile
to bring together investigators from diverse disciplines to consider several
related topics: our knowledge of those surface macromolecules that have
lent themselves to chemical analysis; some of the systems of surface interaction that are yet groping toward such analysis; and techniques that are
being developed for the purification of animal cell membranes. In addition,
since the biologically specific interactions of these surface molecules all
apparently involve weak, noncovalent bonds, we have included, as a model,
a review of immunological specificity, which is the best understood of these
classes of interactions. The diversity of the structures under consideration
prevents, of course, the degree of generalization that has proved possible in
comparative studies of molecular genetics, but it is hoped that the Symposium, and this volume, will promote some valuable cross-fertilization.

The Symposium was organized by a committee consisting of Dr.
Herman M. Kalckar (Harvard Medical School and the Massachusetts
General Hospital) and the two editors. We are grateful for helpful sugges-
tions from a number of colleagues, and in particular from Dr. Salvador
E. Luria and Dr. Phillips Robbins of Massachusetts Institute of Technology.

The Symposium was held during the annual meeting of the Society of
General Physiologists, at the Marine Biological Laboratory, Woods Hole,
Massachusetts, on September 1-4, 1965. We are grateful to the Marine
Biological Laboratory for the facilities they generously provided, and we
are indebted to the U.S. Public Health Service for Research Grant GM
13238-01, which defrayed the expenses of the Symposium.

BERNARD D. DAVIS*
LEONARD WARREN†

    * Bernard D. Davis, Department of Bacteriology and Immunology, Harvard Medi-
cal School
    † Leonard Warren, Department of Therapeutic Research, University of Pennsyl-
vania School of Medicine

Contents

SECTION III. The Molecular Basis of Complementarity

SESSION CHAIRMAN—*Salvador E. Luria*

The Specificity of
Cell Surfaces

section I

Bacterial Cell Walls
and Membranes

Bacterial Cell Wall—Deep Layers

Hiroshi Nikaido

Biochemical Research Laboratory
Massachusetts General Hospital
and
Department of Bacteriology and Immunology
Harvard Medical School
Boston, Massachusetts

Introduction

In recent years the bacterial cell surface has attracted the attention of bio-chemists, microbiologists, and geneticists as a model for the surface of mammalian cells. Obviously, the thick and rigid cell walls of bacteria are entirely different from thin and frail mammalian cell membranes in their physical architecture as well as in their chemical composition. However, they definitely have one common feature: both bacteria and mammalian cells interact with their environment through the cell surface, and consequently the surface has acquired, during evolution, many structures of elaborate design that serve as specific tools in these interactions. External agents "recognize" these specific surface structures, become attached to them, probably through complementary sites, and bring about various consequences on the life of the cell.

Kalckar (1965) called these cell-surface structures, and cellular interactions with the environment through these structures, "ektobiological." He stated that ektobiological features are a "luxury" for the cells, since individual cells can amply survive without such features, and that ektobiological structures are thus needed only for the social aspects of cellular activity — or for cellular interaction with the environment, excepting, of course, such essential and primitive functions as the ingestion of nutrients, excretion of waste products, and so forth.

Ektobiological interactions obviously involve two different stages. First, there has to be an attachment of external agents to the ektobiological structures on the cell surface. This attachment could be either specific or nonspecific, although specific interactions would be much more important. Second, the attachment affects the activity of the cell; this step can also be either specific or nonspecific.

As examples of such external agents exerting influence upon bacteria, antibodies, bacteriophages, bacteriocins, or other bacterial cells can be cited. As is well known, specific antibodies attach to the bacterial surface, and in the presence of complement, the bacteria are frequently lysed. Cellular death also ensues after the interaction of bacteria with bacteriophage "ghosts" or with bacteriocins through specific structures ("receptors") on the bacterial surface. These examples might be taken to imply that the consequence of bacterial interaction with external agents is rather nonspecific — it always leads to killing — and cannot be used as a model for the behavior of mammalian cell surfaces, where highly complex reactions such as contact inhibition are seen. Recent studies on the mode of action of bacteriocins, especially those by Nomura (1963), indicate that this is not the case, however. Nomura showed that after the specific attachment to the bacterial surface bacteriocins remain on the surface, and at the same time exert powerful effects on the intracellular metabolic processes. These effects are strikingly specific; for example, one bacteriocin specifically inhibits protein synthesis while another interferes with DNA metabolism. The truly remarkable finding is that these effects can be reversed by destroying, through tryptic digestion, the bacteriocin molecules attached to the surface. Thus it appears, at least in this case, that external agents exert *specific* influences on the intracellular processes *while staying on the surface*. The role of the bacterial surface in the mating process also serves to illustrate the specificity of the ensuing reaction. Here, specific structures on the surface of male bacteria, probably the "F-pili" (Brinton *et al.*, 1964), "recognize" and attach to the surface of female bacteria, and this induces a succession of highly complex processes resulting in the injection of the male chromosome.

To understand the nature of these surface interactions it is essential to know the chemical architecture of the ektobiological structures of the bacterial surface. An attempt to define this chemical architecture will be made here. The nature of the reactions following the attachment of external agents to the cell surface will undoubtedly become an exciting field of research in the near future, but at present the paucity of data precludes any meaningful discussion of this field.

Constituents of the Bacterial Cell Wall

The common constituents of the bacterial cell wall are listed in Table 1. Among these, mucopeptide is the component responsible for the most basic function of the cell wall, that is, its rigidity. It has not been shown that mucopeptide takes part in such specific interactions with external agents as we have been describing here. Obviously mucopeptide is the target of attack for various enzymes causing lysis of the cell wall, but no antibody against mucopeptide has been prepared, and no bacteriophage requiring mucopeptide itself as receptor has been described. In contrast, other components of the cell wall are known to have varied biological functions including the participation in "ektobiological" interactions. Teichoic acids in *Staphylococci*, polysaccharides in *Streptococci*, and lipopolysaccharides (LPS) in *Enterobacteriaceae* are major antigens of these bacteria. Some of these substances, such as teichoic acids and lipopolysaccharides are commonly believed to form an outer layer of cell walls, because antibodies specific for these substances can attach to the surface of intact cells. It is equally possible, however, that these substances are embedded mostly in the deeper layers of the cell wall and that antibodies attach only to the occasional protrusions of these structures (Weidel *et al.*, 1960).

TABLE 1

MAJOR CONSTITUENTS OF BACTERIAL CELL WALL

Gram-positive bacteria	Gram-negative bacteria
Mucopeptide	Mucopeptide
Teichoic acids	Proteins
Polysaccharides	Lipopolysaccharides
Teichuronic acid	Phospholipids

Lipopolysaccharides (LPS) of Gram-negative Bacteria

Detailed chemical studies have been published on teichoic acids (for review, see Baddiley, 1962) and on the polysaccharide antigen of *Streptococci* (McCarty, 1956); but probably LPS of enteric bacteria are the best group of compounds for the purpose of illustrating the correlation of chemical structure and ektobiological specificity, and I shall therefore limit my discussion to these LPS. Although more attention will be paid to the structure of the central portion of LPS, no deliberate effort will be made to exclude its peripheral portion from the discussion. This paper and the following paper by Drs. P. W. Robbins and J. M. Keller will differ not so much in the areas covered as in the methods of approach to the problem.

LPS constitutes about 2-4% of the dry weight of gram-negative enteric bacteria, or 20-30% of the dry weight of their cell wall. It is responsible for the O-antigenic specificity of these bacteria, and presumably contains receptor sites for many bacteriophages. It also shows the powerful biological activity of an endotoxin. Since the O-antigenic specificity of *Salmonella* has been the object of detailed and systematic studies (Kauffmann, 1954), chemical studies of *Salmonella* LPS may be expected to produce particularly fruitful results.

LPS of *Salmonella* has a highly complex chemical composition, as shown by the pioneering studies of Westphal's group (Kauffmann *et al.*, 1960a) and by the more recent studies from other laboratories (Heath and Ghalambor, 1963; Osborn, 1963; Grollmann and Osborn, 1964). For example, LPS of *Salmonella typhimurium* contains eight different sugars, phosphate, and ethanolamine in its polysaccharide portion, and various additional components in its lipid portion called lipid A (Table 2). Obviously, the structure of such complex macromolecules is extremely difficult to establish, though the fact that mild acid hydrolysis splits the LPS molecule into polysaccharide and lipid A (Westphal and Lüderitz, 1954) gives us an idea about the over-all organization of LPS.

TABLE 2*

CONSTITUENTS OF LPS FROM *S. typhimurium*

Polysaccharide (PS)	Lipid A
3-deoxyoctulosonate (KDO)	KDO
L-glycero-D-mannoheptose	D-glucosamine
D-glucose	phosphate
D-galactose	fatty acids
N-acetyl-D-glucosamine	
D-mannose	
L-rhamnose	
abequose (3.6-dideoxy-D-galactose)	
phosphate	
ethanolamine	

* For reference, see Westphal and Lüderitz (1954); Kauffmann *et al.* (1960a); Osborn (1963); Heath and Ghalambor (1963); Grollman and Osborn (1964); and Sutherland *et al.* (1965).

Earlier Chemical Studies of the S-R Mutation

The polysaccharide is known to carry all of the O-antigenic specificity of LPS. The first clue concerning its structure came from the study of mutant strains in Westphal's laboratory. It was known that the wild-type strains of enteric bacteria, which form smooth colonies and have O-antigens, give rise to mutants forming rough colonies and having none of the O-antigenic specificities. Westphal and his associates analyzed the sugar composition of LPS from wild-type strains (S-forms) and from their mutants (R-forms) (Lüderitz *et al.*, 1960; Kauffmann *et al.*, 1961), and found that LPS of all the R-forms analyzed contained only four sugars: glucose, galactose, heptose, and glucosamine,[1] whereas LPS of S-forms frequently contained many more additional sugars, as already noted for the *S. typhimurium* LPS. From these results they proposed the following hypothesis: (*a*) the polysaccharide is composed of two parts, an "R_{II} core,"[2] and "S-specific side-chains" that are attached to the surface of the core; (*b*) the R_{II} core contains only the aforementioned four sugars, whereas S-specific side-chains contain various other sugars; (*c*) biosynthesis of the polysaccharide begins from the R_{II} core; (*d*) R-forms (actually a particular type later defined as R_{II} forms) can synthesize the R_{II} core normally but either cannot synthesize or cannot attach S-specific side-chains, presumably owing to a defect in certain enzyme(s). This proposal was indeed a remarkable advance in the study of LPS: it gave us, for the first time, a clear idea of the structure of the polysaccharide and more important, it gave us the principle — the use of defective mutants — by which the structure of this material could be studied; all the predictions of the hypothesis have turned out to be correct during subsequent years.

UDP-galactose 4-epimeraseless Mutants

Westphal's hypothesis could not be put to a direct test until very recently, and could offer little help in the elucidation of LPS structure beyond the general outlines just mentioned, because the nature of the postulated enzyme defect in R mutants was completely unknown. Thus, it is no wonder that the next development in this field was brought about by the studies of mutants with known metabolic defects; but such studies were, in reality, initiated by a succession of what may properly be called accidents.

Many years ago Massini described a peculiar type of *Escherichia coli* strains, which were lactose-nonfermenting but mutated with a high frequency to lactose-fermenting cells. Thus, when the strains were plated on a lactose-containing medium, most colonies were found, on prolonged incubation, to carry several lactose-fermenting papillae. These strains were named *Bacterium coli mutabile* (Massini, 1907). Years later Murase in Japan isolated, from old broth cultures of various enteric bacteria, mutants which formed colonies very similar to Massini's *B. coli mutabile* on plates containing lactose, and he named them "mutabile-type variants" (Murase, 1932). It was soon found that these mutants were different from the classical *B. coli mutabile*: in contrast to the *lactose*-nonfermenting *B. coli mutabile*, these mutants were actually *galactose*-nonfermenting strains producing galactose-positive or galactose-resistant papillae; furthermore Murase's mutants were "galactose-sensitive" and were killed by growth in the presence of galactose.

[1] More recently, 3-deoxyoctulosonate was also found to be present (Heath and Ghalambor, 1963).

[2] This nomenclature will be defined later.

More than twenty years after Murase's original discovery Dr. Toshio Fukasawa and I decided to investigate the nature of Murase's mutants. We were particularly encouraged at that time by the elucidation of the pathway of galactose metabolism by Kalckar and his associates and by their finding that galactose was toxic to certain galactose-negative mutants — galactose-1-phosphate uridyl transferaseless — of both man and *E. coli* (Anderson *et al.*, 1957; Kurahashi and Wahba, 1959). It was soon found that our *E. coli* and *Salmonella* mutants were defective in still another enzyme, UDP-galactose 4-epimerase (Nikaido, 1961), which is required for the biosynthesis of the activated form of galactose, UDP-galactose, from carbon sources other than galactose. Thus when these cells are grown in the absence of galactose they should be defective in the synthesis of cellular components containing galactose.

Since LPS of both S-form and R_{II}-form *Salmonella* was known to contain galactose, it was of interest to examine the sugar composition of LPS from these mutants. We found that heptose and glucose (and also 3-deoxyoctulosonate discovered more recently) were the only constituent sugars of their LPS, aside from glucosamine, which was present in lipid A (Nikaido, 1961; 1962a). The other sugars present in S-form LPS, i.e., galactose, mannose, rhamnose, and abequose in *S. typhimurium*, were completely absent. By analogy with the R-form LPS, we could postulate the presence in LPS of an inner core, which represents the entire LPS from the epimeraseless mutants, and of more peripheral portions containing all the sugars which are present in S-form LPS and lacking in the LPS of mutants (see Fig. 1). In other words the "inner core" portion of LPS would be synthesized normally in these mutants; but the synthesis of LPS would stop there, because the next sugar to be attached to this core is galactose, which has to come from UDP-galactose. Thus, all the sugars missing in the mutant LPS must be located distal to this galactose moiety in the S-form LPS (Fig. 1).

Two predictions can be made from such a hypothesis. First, if we could add UDP-galactose to the LPS-synthesizing machinery of the mutants, galactose should be transferred to the defective LPS. Second, if this transfer of galactose could be done in the presence of other nucleotide-sugars, it would result in the successive addition of other sugars distal to the galactose moiety, and complete S-form-type LPS would eventually be synthesized. These predictions were fulfilled easily *in vivo*, because the mutants can make UDP-galactose readily *from exogenously given galactose*. Thus, when the mutants were grown for a short period in the presence of galactose, they were found to have synthesized an LPS indistinguishable in qualitative composition from the LPS of S-forms (Fukasawa and Nikaido, 1961).

These predictions were also verified by experiments *in vitro*. Broken cell preparations of the mutants were found to transfer ^{14}C-galactose readily from added UDP-^{14}C-galactose onto the "inner core" LPS (Nikaido, 1962;

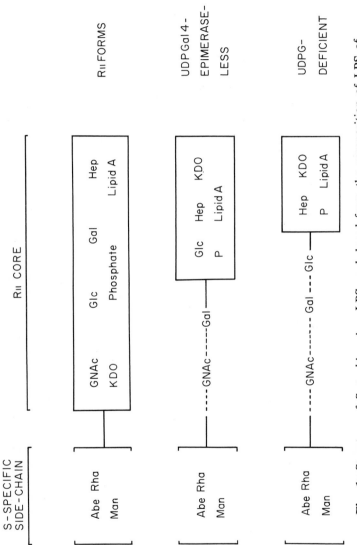

Fig. 1. Structure of *S. typhimurium* LPS as deduced from the composition of LPS of R_{II}, UDP-galactose 4-epimeraseless, and UDP-glucose-deficient mutants. Abbreviations: Glc, D-glucose; Gal, D-galactose; GNAc, N-acetyl-D-glucosamine; Hep, L-glycero-D-manno-heptose; KDO, 3-deoxyoctulosonate; Abe, abequose; Rha, L-rhamnose; Man, D-mannose.

Osborn *et al.*, 1962). Furthermore, these preparations were found to transfer several sugars to LPS after the initial attachment of galactose (Osborn *et al.*, 1964).

Mutants Defective in UDP-glucose Synthesis

The second type of mutants utilized were those unable to synthesize a glucosyl donor, UDP-glucose. They lack either UDP-glucose pyrophosphorylase (Fukasawa *et al.*, 1962; Sundararajan *et al.*, 1962), or phosphoglucoisomerase (Fraenkel *et al.*, 1963). When grown under appropriate conditions they synthesize LPS containing only heptose and KDO residues (plus glucosamine in lipid A). Obviously this LPS is even more simplified in its structure than the LPS of epimeraseless mutants; it can safely be assumed that there should be at least one glucose moiety between the galactose moiety first attached to epimeraseless LPS and the defective LPS synthesized by these UDPG-deficient mutants (Fig. 1).

Structure of Core LPS

Detailed chemical studies of the LPS produced by various mutants, as well as incorporation experiments *in vitro*, enabled investigators to draw a tentative structure for R_{II} form LPS (for review, see Osborn *et al.*, 1964), as is shown in Fig. 2. When we start from the most central portion, it is evident from the composition of the LPS of UDPG-deficient mutants that heptose, KDO, phosphate, and O-phosphorylethanolamine are present in this region (Fukasawa *et al.*, 1962; Sundararajan *et al.*, 1962; Fraenkel *et al.*, 1963; Grollman and Osborn, 1964). The structure of this portion is at present not well understood; however, the recent isolation of *Salmonella* mutants which do not contain even heptose in their LPS (Lüderitz, personal communication; Osborn, personal communication) should be of great help for the elucidation of this problem.

Broken cell preparations of UDPG-deficient mutants transfer glucose from UDP-glucose onto their defective LPS, but the linkage between the glucose moiety and the acceptor has not been elucidated so far (Rothfield *et al.*, 1964). The linkage of glucose to heptose is suggested, however, because by partial acid hydrolysis of the LPS of an epimeraseless *S. enteritidis* an α-glucosyl-heptose disaccharide has been isolated (Nikaido, unpublished).

LPS of epimeraseless mutants has one more glucose residue than the LPS of UDPG-deficient mutants, and it is presumably this glucose which is incorporated *in vitro* by the cell-free preparations of UDPG-deficient mutants. As we have seen, broken cell preparations of epimeraseless mutants incorporate galactose onto their LPS. That this galactose is transferred onto

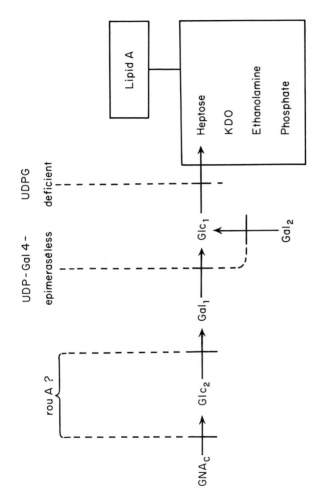

Fig. 2. Structure of R$_{II}$ core LPS. For reference see Osborn *et al.* (1964) and Sutherland *et al.* (1965).

the 3-position of the glucose moiety previously mentioned was shown by the elegant work of Rosen *et al.* (1964). Osborn and her collaborators have further demonstrated the successive *in vitro* transfer of glucose and N-acetyl-glucosamine to the galactosyl-LPS, using a particulate fraction from epimer-aseless *S. typhimurium* (Osborn *et al.*, 1964).

Biochemical Studies of Rough Mutants

Since the structure of the central region of LPS had been clarified by studies of mutants with known metabolic blocks in the biosynthesis of nucleotide-sugars, we then considered mutants known to synthesize defective LPS, and tried to elucidate the biochemical nature of the defects. In these studies we were very fortunate to have the collaboration of Dr. Bruce Stocker's group at the Lister Institute, London, and of Dr. P. H. Mäkela at the University of Helsinki, Finland.

About the only group of mutants previously known to synthesize defective LPS were the so-called R-forms. R-forms have been defined as those mutants which lack specific O-antigens; it is evident, however, that there can be many kinds of metabolic blocks leading to the loss of the S-specific side-chain portion of LPS which determines the O-antigenic specificity.[3] It was, therefore, imperative to have methods of classifying these mutants. Stocker and his associates used genetic mapping and the resistance to several bacteriophages to classify many rough mutants they had isolated from an S-form strain of *S. typhimurium*. At present, there are four major classes of mutants, *rou A*, *rou B*, *rou C*, and *rou D*.

Of these four classes the last two are not, strictly speaking, R-forms, because their LPS shows weak O-antigenic specificities. We shall discuss these mutants later.

When LPS of *rou A* and *rou B* mutants were examined by Dr. I. Beckmann in Freiburg, Germany, it was found that LPS from *rou A* and *rou B* were typical R-type LPS in that they did not contain any of the side-chain sugars, such as mannose, rhamnose, or abequose. Most *rou A* mutants examined belonged to a homogeneous group in that their LPS showed extensive immunological cross reactions; the same was true with all *rou B* mutants examined, and there was practically no cross reaction between these two groups.

[3] According to the classical definition, both epimeraseless and UDPG-less mutants have to be classified among R-forms; and, as we shall see later, there are many other classes of mutants belonging to R-forms. This confusion is mostly due to the negative quality of the classical definition of R-forms. Although an attempt at a more systematic classification has been made (Lüderitz, *et al.*, 1966), it is still not entirely satisfactory. Until all the steps in the biosynthesis of LPS have been completely elucidated and mutants defective in each step studied in detail, the nomenclature of various mutants must remain tentative.

The immunological specificity of *rou A* LPS was called R_I, that of *rou B* LPS, R_{II}.

Moreover, they found in *rou A* mutants a soluble haptenic polysaccharide with the O-antigenic specificity of the S-form, whereas such material was always absent from *rou B* mutants (Beckmann *et al.*, 1964*b*). This hapten contains all the constituent sugars of the S-specific side-chains of S-form LPS, and it is believed to represent side-chains that have not been added to the "core." These findings suggested that *rou B* mutants had defects in the building-up of the side-chains and were left only with the "R_{II} core" portion of LPS, whereas *rou A* mutants could synthesize side-chains normally but could not attach them to the core because their core LPS itself was incomplete and lacked the proper terminal units, to which side-chains could be transferred.

We have examined *rou A* and *rou B* mutants for their ability to synthesize various nucleotide sugars, i.e., UDP-glucose, UDP-galactose, GDP-mannose, TDP-rhamnose, and CDP-abequose[4] (Nikaido *et al.*, 1964). All *rou A* mutants could synthesize all the nucleotide sugars tested for, which is in agreement with their ability to synthesize complete side-chains. Among six *rou B* mutants, only one strain had a defect in TDP-rhamnose synthesis; in no other strains was any defect in nucleotide-sugar synthesis observed. The TDP-rhamnose-deficient strain would not be able to synthesize side-chains because of the lack of their essential component, rhamnose, and it is left with an LPS representing the complete "core" without any side-chains. Since the LPS of other *rou B* mutants are immunologically indistinguishable from the LPS of the TDP-rhamnoseless mutant, presumably they also have defects in the synthesis of side-chains, and consequently they synthesize LPS corresponding to the complete "R_{II} core."

Chemical studies of *rou A* and *rou B* LPS led to the same conclusion. The polysaccharide from *rou A* strains contained heptose, KDO, glucose, and galactose as monosaccharide units; that from *rou B* strains contained N-acetylglucosamine in addition to these components (Sutherland *et al.*, 1965). Obviously *rou A* strains must have defects at an earlier step of the biosynthesis of LPS than do *rou B* strains, i.e., before the addition of the N-acetylglucosamine residue. Furthermore, from the structure of oligosaccharides obtained by partial acid hydrolysis of *rou A* and *rou B* LPS, Sutherland *et al.* (1965) found that the structure of *rou B* LPS could be represented as in Fig. 2, which was drawn essentially according to the *in vitro* biosynthesis studies of Osborn *et al.* (1964). One important difference was that the second galactose residue (Gal_2 of Fig. 2), whose existence had not been suspected in the previous *in vitro* incorporation studies, was found to be linked to the most proximal glucose.

---

[4] The conversion of CDP-glucose into CDP-abequose was not studied because of technical reasons.

It is interesting that the structure of core LPS appears very similar, if not the same, in different serotypes of salmonella, as judged by the analysis of oligosaccharides after acid hydrolysis (Sutherland *et al.*, 1965) or by immunological cross reaction (Beckman *et al.*, 1964a). This result is in marked contrast to the variety in structure of the side-chain portion found among different serotypes (Kauffmann *et al.*, 1960a).

In Vitro Synthesis of Side-Chains

The structure of side-chains was much clarified by the studies of Robbins and Uchida (1962), who found them to be composed of oligosaccharide repeat units in group E salmonella. Taken together with the chemical and immunochemical studies by Staub and her coworkers (Staub, 1964), it could be assumed that side-chains of LPS from group B salmonella, such as *S. typhimurium*, are composed of the following repeat unit.

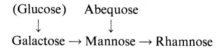

The TDP-rhamnose-deficient *rou B* mutant was as valuable for the study of *in vitro* synthesis of side-chains as were the epimeraseless mutants for the study of the R_{II} core. Broken cell preparations of the mutant synthesized the most proximal portion of the side chain, when they were incubated in the presence of a mixture of appropriate nucleotide sugars (Nikaido, 1965; Nikaido and Nikaido, 1965). An example is given in Table 3. It is clear that sequential addition of sugars is suggested from the results; for the incorporation of mannose both UDP-galactose and TDP-rhamnose must be present, and for the incorporation of abequose UDP-galactose, TDP-rhamnose, and GDP-mannose must be all present. Although the incorporation of galactose and that of rhamnose were interdependent and did not fit into the sequential pattern, analysis of the incorporation products showed that galactose is the first sugar attached to the R_{II} core, and that rhamnose is transferred onto the galactose moiety. Therefore, a sequence of abequosyl-mannosyl-rhamnosyl-galactosyl-core is indicated for the beginning of side-chains (Fig. 3).

The situation was actually found to be a little more complicated than this. It is seen in Table 3 that for the maximal incorporation of any sugar, all four nucleotide sugars were necessary. This is difficult to explain by the sequential-addition hypothesis. In addition, the curious interdependence between galactose and rhamnose incorporation lacked an explanation. These points were clarified by the discovery that sugars in the side-chains are assembled on an intermediate carrier of presumably lipid nature (Wright *et al.*,

TABLE 3*

INCORPORATION OF VARIOUS SUGARS INTO TCA-INSOLUBLE FRACTION
CATALYZED BY A PARTICULATE FRACTION FROM TV208

Labeled nucleotide	Nonlabeled nucleotide	Incorporation (mμmoles)	
		Exp. 1	Exp. 2
UDPGal†	None	2.3	0.9
	TDPRh	3.3	2.9
	TDPRh, GDPM	4.2	3.3
	TDPRh, GDPM, CDPA	7.9	5.3
	GDPM, CDPA	2.2	1.5
TDPRh	None	0.4	0.7
	UDPGal	3.1	3.0
	UDPGal, GDPM	3.3	3.3
	UDPGal, GDPM, CDPA	5.0	5.6
	GDPM, CDPA	0.5	0.7
GDPM	None	<0.1	0.1
	UDPGal	<0.1	0.1
	UDPGal, TDPRh	1.3	2.1
	UDPGal, TDPRh, CDPA	3.4	3.4
	TDPRh, CDPA	0.1	0.5
CDPA	None	<0.01	<0.01
	UDPGal	<0.01	<0.01
	UDPGal, TDPRh	<0.01	<0.01
	UDPGal, TDPRh, GDPM	0.17	0.25
	TDPRh, GDPM	0.06	0.05

* From Nikaido and Nikaido (1965).

† Abbreviations: UDPGal, uridine diphosphate D-galactose; TDPRh, thymidine di-phospate L-rhamnose; GDPM, guanosine diphosphate D-mannose; CDPA, cytidine di-phosphate abequose.

1965 and Weiner et al., 1965). In the system studied by Wright et al. oligo-saccharides are built up on the intermediate but are not transferred to LPS until a complete repeat unit is formed. In our case, galactose alone probably cannot be transferred to the R_{II} core, but if TDP-rhamnose is added to the incubation mixture, a rhamnosyl-galactose linkage would be formed on the intermediate, and this disaccharide is presumably transferred as such to the R_{II} core. Since the addition of GDP-mannose has little effect on the incor-poration of rhamnose or galactose, the rate of transfer of mannosyl-rham-nosyl-galactose from the intermediate to LPS would not be too different from that of rhamnosyl-galactose. Further addition of abequose enhanced the incorporation very much; hence an abequosyl-mannosyl-rhamnosyl-galac-tose tetrasaccharide might be the best (and probably the natural) substrate for the transferase.

Presumably the discrepancy between the results of Wright *et al.* (1965) and our own is due, in part, to the difference of strains. Another factor is the method of breaking the cells, which is done by sonication in our case. Even with our own strains, when the cells were broken by freeze-thawing in EDTA solution as described by Wright *et al.* (1965), and were incubated with TDP-rhamnose- [14]C and UDP-galactose alone, a large proportion of ^{14}C was incorporated into the lipid intermediate, but failed to be transferred to LPS. That this is closer to the situation *in vivo* is suggested by the observation that LPS of a GDP-mannose-deficient mutant contained very little rhamnose (Osborn *et al.*, 1964), although in this mutant rhamnosyl-galactose should be synthesized on the intermediate and should be ready for transfer to LPS.

Biochemical Studies of Semirough Strains

The sequence of the sugars attached to the R_{II} core *in vitro* is exactly the sequence of sugars in the repeat units,[5] and thus presumably the same repeat unit repeats itself for the entire length of the side-chains. It will be noticed that the first repeat unit has to be attached to the R_{II} core, whereas all the subsequent repeat units have to be added onto another repeat unit. Naturally it can be assumed that the "first-unit transferase" would be a different enzyme from the "subsequent-unit transferase." If the latter enzyme is lost by mutation, we should have a mutant whose LPS has very short side-chains, each containing only one repeat unit. Such mutants were indeed isolated (Naide *et al.*, 1965). They are the *rou C* mutants of Stocker's classification. Their LPS contain all the side-chain specific sugars — mannose, rhamnose, and abequose — but their amount is very small compared with the amount present in S-form LPS. They show O-antigenic specificity, but the amount of antibody precipitated by this LPS is much smaller than the amount precipitated by an equivalent amount of S-form LPS. Because of these properties, the mutants were called "semi rough." Their LPS, however, does not react at all with an anti-R_{II} serum that presumably has specificity directed against the terminal units of the R_{II} core (*cf.* Lüderitz *et al.*, 1965). These results are in agreement with the assumption that *all* the terminal units in *rou C* LPS carry short side-chains.

Strains with defects at the *rou C* locus can be prepared by genetically crossing two different serotypes of *Salmonella* (Mäkelä, 1966): the chromosome of group B *Salmonella* was introduced into group C *Salmonella* whose

---

[5] Although our sequence, "natural" repeat unit, terminates with a reducing galactose, Staub's repeat unit, whose structure is based on the product of partial acid hydrolysis, terminates with rhamnose. This is simply because of the acid-lability of rhamnosyl linkages, and it has no biological significance. When polymerized, both types of repeat units will give an identical sequence, except at the very ends.

LPS has an entirely different structure; when those recipients which had received the *his* region[6] of the donor chromosome were selected, more than half of these recombinants were found to make *rou* C-type LPS. This is interpreted as meaning that almost all the information necessary for the synthesis of group B-type LPS is contained in a gene cluster — called *O* cluster — close to *his* and thus is acquired by most of these recombinants, but that the gene for the "subsequent-unit transferase" is located far from *his* and has much less chance of being integrated into the recombinant genome. Locus *rou C* was indeed mapped far from *his*, i.e., between *gal* and *try*, in Stocker's mutants (Gemski, Wilkinson and Stocker, personal communication).

More recently we have tried to establish the structure of *rou C* LPS by partial acid hydrolysis. The results, shown in Table 4, are clearly consistent with our hypothesis, and exclude the presence of side-chains containing two or more repeat units; if such side-chains were present one should be able to isolate galactosyl-mannosyl-rhamnose (*cf.* Fig. 3), which was not found at all in the partial acid hydrolyzates of *rou C* LPS. In another experiment, *rou C* LPS was specifically labeled with C^{14} in the mannose moiety, and a partial acid hydrolysis experiment was performed to isolate longer oligosaccharides. Again, no longer oligosaccharide was detected, except for small amounts of an oligosaccharide that may contain a portion of R_{II} core together with the short side-chain.

TABLE 4

ISOLATION OF OLIGOSACCHARIDES FROM
PARTIAL ACID HYDROLYZATES OF LPS

Oligosaccharides isolated	LPS from		
	S-form (147,000)	*rou C* (185,000)	*rou D* (345,000)
Rha → Gal	*	600	200
Man → Rha	1200	2630	560
Gal → Man → Rha	4150	<70	2010

* Isolation not attempted in this experiment.

Figures represent the amounts of oligosaccharides isolated (in cpm) from LPS uniformly labeled with ^{14}C. Hydrolysis was performed in 1 N H_2SO_4 for 16 min. at 100°.

Stocker and his associates isolated one more class of mutants with semi-rough-type biological properties. These *rou D* mutants also show weak O-antigenic specificity, and their LPS contains only small amounts of side-chain-specific sugars (Naide *et al.*, 1965). But the locus of mutation is far from the *rou C* locus in these mutants (Gemski, Wilkinson, and Stocker,

[6] Symbols for genetic loci are listed in Fig. 4.

personal communication). Moreover, their LPS reacts strongly with an anti-R_{II} serum (Naide *et al.*, 1965); therefore, most of the R_{II} terminal units in *rou D* LPS presumably are still unsubstituted. To explain the results of quantitative sugar analysis we assumed that *rou D* LPS has *long* but *few* side-chains, in contrast to *rou C* LPS, known to have *uniformly short* but *numerous* side-chains.

Our recent studies of *rou D* LPS by partial acid hydrolysis (Table 4) amply support this hypothesis; also the pattern of longer oligosaccharides released from *rou D* LPS specifically labeled in the mannose moiety was indistinguishable from that of S-form. Unfortunately, we have not been able to offer a reasonable explanation as to why this type of unusual LPS is produced by *rou D* mutants.

Genetics of LPS Biosynthesis

Having examined the biochemistry of various mutants of LPS synthesis, we can review the genetics of LPS synthesis, particularly in group B *Salmonella*, such as *S. typhimurium*. In these organisms the genes concerned with LPS biosynthesis are known to be clustered in three distinct regions of the chromosome (Fig. 4).

(1) *rou A region.* The genes determining the synthesis of the R_{II} core seem to be located in this region. As we have seen, the *rou A* mutation, which presumably results in the loss of the enzyme transferring the N-acetyl-glucosamine or the glucose residue preceding it (glc$_2$ of Fig. 2), is located in this region (Subbaiah and Stocker, 1964). The existence of two groups of *rou A* mutants with different phage resistance patterns (Subbaiah and Stocker, 1964) suggests that there probably are *rou A* mutants that are blocked at different steps in the synthesis of the R_{II} core.

Recently, another group of mutants were isolated by Stocker and associates and were studied biochemically by Osborn's group. Some of them lack the enzyme transferring a glucose residue (glc$_1$ of Fig. 2), and produce an LPS indistinguishable from that of UDPG-deficient mutants. Others lack the enzyme transferring a galactose residue (gal$_1$ of Fig. 2), and their LPS is very much like that of epimeraseless mutants (Osborn, personal communication). Interestingly, these mutations were also mapped at the *rou A* region (Stocker, personal communication).

Thus, out of five transferases presumably necessary to synthesize R_{II} core LPS starting from the "backbone" LPS of UDPG-deficient mutants, at least three, and probably four, appear to be determined at the *rou A* cluster. This region, then, determines the synthesis of the R_{II} core.

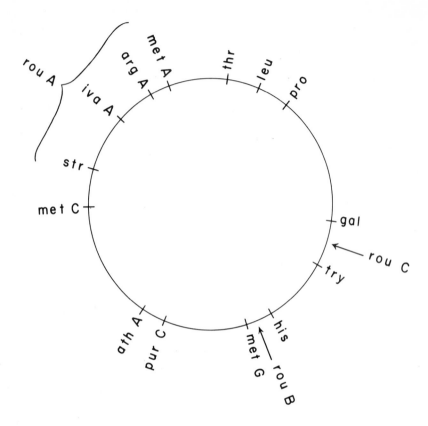

Fig. 4. Location of "rough" mutations on *S. typhimurium* chromosome. (Gemski, Wilkinson and Stocker, personal communication). Symbols for genetic loci: *his, met, pur, ath, iva, arg, thr, leu, pro, try,* biosynthesis of histidine, methionine, purine, adenine-thiamine, isoleucine-valine, arginine, threonine, leucine, proline, and tryptophan, respectively; *gal,* fermentation of galactose; *str,* streptomycin resistance.

(2) *rou B region.* For the synthesis of side-chains, various sugars must be provided in the form of nucleoside diphosphate sugars. Fig. 5 shows the known pathways for the biosynthesis of side-chain specific sugars in these "activated" forms. Of eleven necessary enzymes,[7] enzyme E was proved to be determined at the *rou B* locus because a TDP-rhamnoseless mutant

---

[7] Although reactions E and H undoubtedly require, respectively, more than one enzyme, they were here assumed as requiring one "enzyme" each for the simplicity of argument.

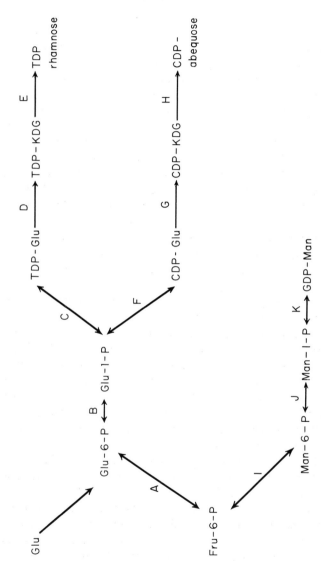

Fig. 5. Pathways of nucleotide-sugar synthesis. [Ginsburg (1964); Nikaido and Nikaido, to be published.] Abbreviations: Glu, D-glucose, Fru, D-fructose; Man, D-mannose; KDG, 4-keto-6-deoxy-D-glucose; TDP, thymidine diphosphate; CDP, cytidine diphosphate; GDP, guanosine diphosphate.

which lacks this enzyme was shown to have a lesion in this gene cluster (Subbaiah and Stocker, 1964; Nikaido *et al.*, 1964).

In joint studies with Dr. P. H. Mäkelä, recombinants of intergroup crosses of salmonella were examined as to the level of various enzymes (Fig. 5). The results, which have been published elsewhere (Nikaido, Nikaido, and Mäkelä, 1966), indicated clearly that at least seven other enzymes (C, D, F, G, H, J, and K) are determined in this region, and also confirmed the conclusion regarding the location of the gene for enzyme E.

Stocker's group has mapped the genes for enzymes A and I, using mutants defective in these enzymes. (The mutants were characterized biochemically by Osborn and her associates: see Osborn *et al.* (1964) for review). Both of the genes were located far from the *rou B* region: the gene for enzyme A close to *met A* locus, and the gene for enzyme I between *gal* and *try* (Fraenkel *et al.*, 1963; Stocker, personal communication) (see Fig. 6). This is not surprising as both these enzymes are also active catabolic enzymes, in contrast to the enzymes C-H and J-K which presumably are engaged solely in the biosynthesis of LPS. The gene for enzyme B has not been mapped.

Thus it appears that among the eleven enzymes, eight definitely are determined at the *rou B* locus, and one has an unknown location, whereas the remaining two, which have mixed catabolic-anabolic functions, are determined at other loci.

We found that most *rou B* strains did not have defects in nucleotide-sugar synthesis (Nikaido *et al.*, 1964). Since none of these *rou B* strains produce any side-chain material, they must be defective in one or more of the transferases necessary for the synthesis of side-chains. According to the mechanism proposed by Wright *et al.* (1965) for the synthesis of side-chains, a defect in any one of the several necessary transferases would result in the complete loss of side-chains. (There is one important exception, that is, the "subsequent-unit transferase.") There has been no indication of the existence of mutants which lack transferases for side-chain synthesis and which map outside of the *rou B* cluster (*cf.* Subbaiah and Stocker, 1964); therefore most, if not all, of these transferases are presumably determined by the *rou B* cluster. We may thus conclude that the *rou B* region determines all the enzymes *solely* engaged in the biosynthesis of side-chains, except the one enzyme determined by the *rou C* locus. In other words, since side-chains determine the O-antigenic specificity of LPS, we may say that the *rou B* cluster determines O-antigens, and is the same as the so-called *O*-cluster. The results of the interspecific crosses of salmonella (Mäkelä, 1966) also indicate that *all* information necessary for the synthesis of group B-type side-chains, except that for the "subsequent-unit transferase," is contained in the *O*- or *rou B*-cluster. It is interesting to note that the *O*-cluster has been mapped at a place close to *his* in *Escherichia coli* (Orskov and Orskov, 1962).

(3) *rou C locus.* While direct proof is still lacking, all the evidence already discussed points to the conclusion that the *rou C* locus controls the synthesis of the "subsequent-unit transferase." As was pointed out, recombinants lacking this gene can be obtained by crossing group B male salmonella with group C female salmonella (Mäkelä, 1966). The finding that similar, semirough recombinants were not produced by the reverse cross (Mäkelä, 1966) may mean, assuming the side-chain of LPS of group C salmonella to be also synthesized by the same mechanism as the LPS of group B salmonella, that the gene for the "subsequent-unit transferase" is located close to the *rou B* or *O*-region in group C strains. Another interesting point is that crosses of group B males with group D females did not produce *rou C*-type or semirough recombinants; this presumably indicates that the "subsequent-unit transferase" of group D can transfer the repeat units of group B LPS equally well (Mäkelä, 1965). This is not improbable because the side-chains in these two groups are known to be very similar in structure, except for the nature of the 3, 6-dideoxyhexose present — abequose in group B and tyvelose in group D (Staub, 1964).

Structure of E. coli Lipopolysaccharides

The studies of LPS from *E. coli* 0111:B4 appear to indicate that the sequence of monosaccharides in the R_{II} core is the same as that in salmonella (Edstrom and Heath, 1964). The nature of the linkage between monosaccharides, however, might be different.

Kauffmann *et al.* (1960b), in a systematic investigation of LPS from various *E. coli* strains, noted that LPS from a few strains did not contain any detectable galactose. Since, as we have seen, galactose is an essential constituent of the R_{II} core in salmonella, the structure of the core in these *E. coli* strains must be very different from that in salmonella or that in *E. coli* 0111:B4.

Another interesting observation was made by Rapin and Mayer (1965). They found that UDP-galactose 4-epimeraseless mutants of E. coli K-12 lost only half the galactose of the LPS as a result of the mutation, in contrast to the salmonella mutants, which are known to lose all of their galactose. Thus, the nucleotide specificity of galactosyl transferases appears to be different in E. coli K-12 from that in salmonella.

These results serve to emphasize that the structure of the R_{II} core may be different in *E. coli* from that in *Salmonella*, and that it may vary even among different *E. coli* serotypes. The latter observation is in accord with the heterogeneity of *E. coli*, in contrast to the homogeneity of *Salmonella* as a taxonomic group, the view of many bacteriologists.

To reach a definite conclusion we obviously need much more detailed studies on the structure of R core and LPS in various enteric bacteria. It appears, however, that the structure of the core tends to be constant within each larger taxonomic group, for example, genus *Salmonella*, whereas the structure of side-chains varies very much from one serotype to the other within such a group. Probably the structure of the core (determined by the *rou A* region in *S. typhimurium*) became fixed much earlier than the structure of side-chains during the course of evolution.

It is known, from the strong serological cross reactions frequently encountered between members of different genera, that the side-chain structure of such members may be very similar, and possibly even identical. Thus LPS from two different *Salmonella* serotypes may be entirely different in the structure of their side-chains, but would probably contain the same core, whereas LPS from a *Salmonella* serotype and an *E. coli* might contain very similar side-chains, but their core would probably be very different. A striking example of such relationships was demonstrated by Lüderitz *et al.* (1964).

Correlation of LPS Structure with the Biological and Ektobiological Properties of the Cells

The alterations of LPS structure in mutants affect their biological behavior to various degrees. One marked characteristic, however, is that these extensive alterations do not interfere with the normal growth and proliferation of the mutant cells, as was stressed in the definition of ektobiological phenomena earlier in this discussion.

In contrast, the pattern with which the cells interact with external agents undergoes a profound change after mutation. Some of the properties in the following list are quite nonspecific and might not belong to the category of ektobiological phenomena; nevertheless they will be discussed, because they might illustrate an important correlation between the structure of the cell surface and the biological behavior of the cell.

(1) *Spontaneous agglutination.* Quantitatively, in many *Salmonella* and *E. coli* serotypes, side-chains comprise the major portion of the polysaccharide, which is probably one of the main hydrophilic components on the cell surface. Therefore, the loss of side-chains by mutation produces a profound change in the physico-chemical properties of the bacterial surface. All R-forms, including UDP-galactose 4-epimeraseless mutants, agglutinate spontaneously in saline and form rough colonies with a granular surface when grown on agar plates.

(2) *Virulence and toxicity.* It has long been known that living cells of R-forms are much less virulent against laboratory animals than the corresponding S-forms. UDP-galactose 4-epimeraseless mutants are also avirulent. It is not well understood how the loss of side-chains reduces the virulence,

but a few interesting observations, described below, might be pertinent to this problem.

   a. R-forms are killed much more rapidly by serum than are the corresponding S-forms.

   b. It is said that R-forms are phagocytized more readily than the corresponding S-forms.

   c. Kauffmann *et al.* (1960a) noted that most of the *Salmonella* serotypes causing severe disease contain LPS of complex composition, in which 3, 6-dideoxyhexose and rhamnose were always present. The actual role of such side-chains for pathogenesis is not clear, but the foregoing seems to suggest that these side-chains are at least important for virulence.

   Killed enteric bacteria are toxic when injected into animals, presumably because of LPS, the "endotoxin" of gram-negative bacteria. When isolated LPS is used, there is no significant difference in toxicity between R-forms and S-forms. This is true even with an LPS of highly simplified structure such as that from UDP-galactose 4-epimeraseless mutants. The toxicity of the heat-killed cells of these mutants was, however, remarkably reduced compared with that of the S-forms (Nakano, 1962). One explanation would be that most of the incomplete LPS of these mutants are buried deeply in the cell wall and are released less readily than the LPS of S-forms. In any event, this observation indicates that there can be a change in the toxicity of whole killed cells when their antigenic side-chains are modified.

(3) *Antigenicity.* Specific structural features of side-chains are recognized by antibodies, and this interaction provides a good example of the ektobiological recognition of fine surface patterns (Staub, 1964). Various mutants show different antigenic patterns, as shown in Table 5. Obviously it would be interesting to prepare antibodies specific for other mutants and to examine their properties.

TABLE 5

SEROLOGICAL REACTIONS OF LPS FROM S-, R_{II}-, AND R_I-FORMS

Antiserum	LPS from				
	rou A	*rou B*	*rou C*	S-form	*rou D*
Anti-S	−	−	+	+++	+
Anti-R_{II}	−	+++	−	−	+++
Anti-R_I	+++	−	−	−	±

Quantitative complement fixation test was used (Naide, Nakane, and Nikaido, unpublished). Some of the results confirm earlier observations by Beckmann *et al.* (1964b) and Lüderitz *et al.* (1964), obtained by the use of hemagglutination inhibition and hemagglutination tests.

(4) *Adsorption of bacteriophages*. As the first step of infection, bacteriophages have to attach to a specific structure on the bacterial surface. Various components of the cell wall are known to serve as phage receptors: it was through the pioneering studies of Goebel and Jesaitis (1952) and of Weidel *et al.* (1954) that we learned the function of LPS as receptors. Goebel's group isolated an O-antigen preparation from a *Shigella sonnei* phase-II organism and found that it could inactivate several T-series phages. Moreover, a similar preparation from a mutant resistant to T3, T4, and T7 was unable to inactivate these phages, and was quite different in its sugar composition from the preparation obtained from the wild type. Glucose, galactose, glucosamine, and heptose were all present in the O-antigen from wild-type organism, whereas the mutant preparation contained only a hexosamine.

Very similar results were obtained by Weidel and his associates with *E. coli* B. They found that a cell-wall preparation, whose lipoprotein layer was removed with 90% phenol, was a good receptor for T3, T4, and T7 phages, and that such a preparation contained a large amount of LPS. A similar preparation from a phage-resistant organism, B/3, 4, 7, was qualitatively different in its composition from that of the parent strain; the former contained only glucosamine (plus a trace of glucose), while the latter contained considerable amounts of glucose, a heptose, and glucosamine.

The significance of these pioneering studies could not be fully understood at the time they were published. But we can now appreciate these results in the light of much more advanced knowledge on the structure and biosynthesis of LPS. It seems clear that the mutation to a T3, 4, 7-resistant organism involved the loss of heptose, which we know to be a constituent of the inner-most, "backbone" region of LPS. It is not known whether this loss of heptose is due to defects in the biosynthesis of the heptose moiety or to defects in its transfer, but obviously the loss of the "backbone" resulted in the failure of attachment of the remainder of the polysaccharide which contains glucose and galactose. Thus these mutants were the first heptose-deficient mutants described, and their LPS probably consists mostly of lipid A.

Because the mutations involved the complete loss of the polysaccharide portion of LPS, it is difficult to pinpoint the structure that would have been necessary for the adsorption of phages to the LPS of wild-type strains. A working hypothesis, however, can be proposed. The LPS-rich layer of *E. coli* B contains only heptose and glucose, besides glucosamine, which probably is contained in lipid A. If the core LPS in this *E. coli* is built up according to the same principle as that of *Salmonella*, the results would indicate that *E. coli* B has the same type of LPS as the UDP-galactose 4-epimeraseless mutants of *Salmonella*.[8] Since this LPS has a polysaccharide of extremely simplified structure, there are not many probable candidates for the receptor structure except one containing glucosyl-heptose units or unsubstituted heptose units. Although the results of Weidel's and of Goebel's groups indicate the heptose units are more important for receptor activity, the observation that the loss of UDPG makes *E. coli* B resistant to T3, T4, and T7 (Luria and Human, 1952; Hattman and Fukasawa, 1963) seems to suggest the glucose residue plays a crucial role in the adsorption of these phages.

Wilkinson and Stocker (personal communication) made a detailed study of phage sensitivity patterns in various mutants of LPS synthesis in *S. typhimurium*. Although in most cases it was not proven rigorously that the alteration in phage sensitivity was due to the changes in adsorption, this conclusion is most probable because the strains usually differed only in the structure of LPS and were otherwise isogenic. These results, shown in Table 6, demonstrate clearly how subtle changes in LPS structure affect the adsorption of various phages.

TABLE 6

PHAGE SENSITIVITY OF VARIOUS MUTANTS OF *S. typhimurium* LT2*

| Phage | \multicolumn{6}{c}{Mutant} |
	epi⁻	*rou A*†	*rou B*	*rou C*	S-form	*rou D*
C21	+	−	−	−	−	−
Ffm	+	+	+	−	−	+
6O	+	+	+	−	−	+
P221C₁	−	+	+	+	−	+
6SR	−	−	+	−	−	+
Felix O	−	−	+	+	+	−
P22hC₂	−	−	−	−	+	+
P22C₁	−	−	−	−	+	−

$$\text{Hep} - \text{Glc} \genfrac{}{}{0pt}{}{}{} \text{Gal} \vdash \text{Glc} \vdash \text{GNAc} \dashv \text{Gal-Rha-Man} \vdash \left(\text{Gal-Rha-Man} \right)_n$$

Abe | Abe

Gal ? ?

The scheme at the bottom of Table 6 shows the location of block in the synthesis of LPS in various mutants. For the defect in *rou D* strains, see text; for the abbreviations for the sugars, see the legend to Fig. 1.

* (Wilkinson and Stocker, personal communication.)

† Another group of *rou A* mutants show exactly the same pattern as *rou B* mutants.

[8] This hypothesis is also supported by the observation that *E. coli* B is susceptible to phage C21, which is known to attack only the organisms having the epimeraseless-type or UDPG-deficient-type LPS.

Although we do not have any direct evidence on the structure of receptors for various phages, we can postulate from these results fairly precise structures that would be necessary. For example phage C21 is specific solely for UDP-galactose 4-epimeraseless, UDPG-deficient, or the transferaseless mutants making LPS similar to these two; thus its adsorption may require the presence of either glucosyl-heptose units, which probably are present in small numbers also in UDPG-deficient mutants (which are usually leaky), or heptose units and glucosyl-heptose units, but not galactosyl-glucosyl-heptose units. Phages Ffm and 6O can attack all R mutants; its receptor is probably deep in the LPS, and the attachment is completely inhibited by the presence of S-specific side-chains. Phage 6SR is probably the most specific of phages studied; aside from *rou D*, it can adsorb only to *rou B*. Its receptor therefore must be related to the terminal unit of *rou B* LPS, and the receptor function is lost by any substitution on the unit or, obviously, by the loss of such a unit.

The phage-sensitivity pattern of *rou D* mutants deserves special comment. We have assumed earlier that *rou D* LPS has a few long side-chains plus many unsubstituted N-acetylglucosamine terminal units of *rou B* LPS. This hypothesis is strongly supported by the phage-sensitivity pattern of *rou D* mutants; it can be regarded as the pattern of *rou B* mutants and S-forms combined. Thus *rou D* mutants are sensitive to phages Ffm, 6O, P221C$_1$, and 6SR probably owing to their unsubstituted terminal units of *rou B* type, and also to P22hC$_2$, presumably because of their side-chains. P22C$_1$, which can attack only the S-form, might require for attachment longer side-chains or a larger number of side-chains than found in *rou D* LPS; its host range mutant P22hC$_2$ might have a greater affinity for the side-chains (Stocker, personal communication), and thus may be able to attack the *rou D* mutants. The behavior of Felix O phage, however, cannot be explained at present.

These explanations are only working hypotheses at the present stage of our knowledge. Obviously it is necessary to study the interaction of isolated LPS and phages, and it may also be possible to specifically inhibit such interactions by adding oligosaccharides related to the receptor structure. When such studies are completed, they may furnish one of the most interesting examples of ektobiological recognition at the molecular level.

ACKNOWLEDGMENT

The author is indebted to Drs. B.A.D. Stocker, P. H. Mäkelä, M. J. Osborn, and O. Lüderitz for permission to quote their unpublished results. He is also grateful to Drs. A. M. C. Rapin and Y. Naide for their help in the preparation of the manuscript. The author's own studies were supported by U. S. Public Health Service grant AI-05729.

REFERENCES

Anderson, E. P., H. M. Kalckar, and K. J. Isselbacher. 1957. *Science.* 125: 113.

Baddiley, J. 1962. *J. Royal Inst. Chem.* 366.

Beckmann, I., O. Lüderitz, and O. Westphal. 1964a. *Biochem. Z.* 339: 401.

Beckmann, I., T. V. Subbaiah, and B. A. D. Stocker. 1964b. *Nature.* 201: 1299.

Brinton, C. C., Jr., P. Gemski, Jr., and J. Carnahan. 1964. *Proc. Natl. Acad. Sci. U. S.* 52: 776.

Edstrom, R. D., and E. C. Heath. 1964. *Biochem. Biophys. Res. Commun.* 16: 576.

Fraenkel, D., M. J. Osborn, B. L. Horecker, and S. M. Smith. 1963. *Biochem. Biophys. Res. Commun.* 11: 423.

Fukasawa, T., K. Jokura, and K. Kurahashi. 1962. *Biochem. Biophys. Res. Commun.* 7: 121.

Fukasawa, T., and H. Nikaido. 1961. *Biochim. Biophys. Acta* 48: 470.

Goebel, W. F., and M. A. Jesaitis. 1952. *J. Exptl. Med.* 96: 425.

Grollman, A. P., and M. J. Osborn. 1964. *Biochem.* 3: 1571.

Hattman, S., and T. Fukasawa. 1963. *Proc. Natl. Acad. Sci. U. S.* 50: 297.

Heath, E. C., and M. A. Ghalambor. 1963. *Biochem. Biophys. Res. Commun.* 10: 340.

Kalckar, H. M. 1965. *Science.* 150: 305.

Kauffmann, F. 1954. *Enterobacteriaceae*, 2nd ed. Copenhagen: Munksgaard.

Kauffmann, F., O. Lüderitz, H. Stierlin, and O. Westphal. 1960a. *Zentr. Bakteriol. Parasitenk., Abt. I, Orig.* 178: 442.

Kauffmann, F., O. H. Braun, O. Lüderitz, H. Stierlin, and O. Westphal. 1960b. *Zentr. Bakteriol. Parasitenk., Abt. I, Orig.* 180: 180.

Kauffmann, F., L. Krüger, O. Lüderitz, and O. Westphal. 1961. *Zentr. Bakteriol. Parasitenk., Abt. I, Orig.* 182: 57.

Kurahashi, K., and A. J. Wahba. 1958. *Biochim. Biophys. Acta* 30: 298.

Lüderitz, O., F. Kauffmann, H. Stierlin, and O. Westphal. 1960. *Zentr. Bakteriol. Parasitenk., Abt. I, Orig.* 179: 180.

Lüderitz, O., I. Beckmann, and O. Westphal. 1964. *Biochem. Z.* 339: 416.

Lüderitz, O., H. J. Risse, H. Schulte-Holthausen, J. L. Strominger, I. W. Sutherland, and O. Westphal. 1965. *J. Bacteriol.* 89: 343.

Lüderitz, O., A.-M. Staub, and O. Westphal. 1966. *Bacteriol. Rev.* 30: 192.

Luria, S. E., and M. L. Human. 1952. *J. Bacteriol.* 64: 557.

Mäkelä, P. H. 1965. *J. Gen. Microbiol.* 41: 57.

Mäkelä, P. H. 1966. *J. Bacteriol.* 91: 1115.

Massini, R. 1907. *Arch. Hyg.* 61: 250.

McCarty, M. 1956. J. *Exptl. Med.* 104: 629.

Murase, W. 1932. *Japan. J. Bacteriol.* No. 440. 975.

Naide, Y., H. Nikaido, P. H. Mäkelä, R. G. Wilkinson, and B. A. D. Stocker. 1965. *Proc. Natl. Acad. Sci. U. S.* 53: 147.

Nakano, M. 1962. *Nature* 196: 1119.

Nikaido, H. 1961. *Biochim. Biophys. Acta* 48: 460.

Nikaido, H. 1962a. *Proc. Natl. Acad. Sci. U. S.* 48: 1337.

Nikaido, H. 1962b. *Proc. Natl. Acad. Sci. U. S.* 48: 1542.

Nikaido, H. 1965. *Biochem.* 4: 1550.

Nikaido, H., and K. Nikaido. 1965. *Biochem. Biophys. Res. Commun.* 19: 322.

Nikaido, H., K. Nikaido, and P. H. Mäkelä. 1966. *J. Bacteriol.* 91: 1126.

Nikaido, H., K. Nikaido, T. V. Subbaiah, and B. A. D. Stocker. 1964. *Nature* 201: 1301.

Nomura, M. 1963. *Cold Spring Harbor Symp. Quant. Biol.* 28: 315.

Ørskov, F., and I. Ørskov. 1962. *Acta Pathol. Microbiol. Scand.* 55: 99.

Osborn, M. J. 1963. *Proc. Natl. Acad. Sci. U. S.* 50: 499.

Osborn, M. J., S. M. Rosen, L. Rothfield, and B. L. Horecker. 1962. *Proc. Natl. Acad. Sci. U. S.* 48: 1831.

Osborn, M. J., S. M. Rosen, L. Rothfield, L. D. Zeleznick, and B. L. Horecker. 1964. *Science* 145: 783.

Rapin, A. M. C., and H. Mayer. 1965. *Federation Proc.* 24: 479.

Rosen, S. M., M. J. Osborn, and B. L. Horecker. 1964. *J. Biol. Chem.* 239: 3196.

Rothfield, L., M. J. Osborn, and B. L. Horecker. 1964. *J. Biol. Chem.* 239: 2788.

Subbaiah, T. V., and B. A. D. Stocker. 1964. *Nature* 201: 1298.

Sundararajan, T. A., A. M. C. Rapin, and H. M. Kalckar. 1962. *Proc. Natl. Acad. Sci. U. S.* 48: 2187.

Sutherland, I. W., O. Lüderitz, and O. Westphal. 1965. *Biochem. J.* 96: 439.

Staub, A.-M. 1964. In *Bacterial Endotoxins*, ed., M. Landy and W. Braun. New Brunswick, N. J.: Rutgers University Press.

Weidel, W., G. Koch, and F. Lohss. 1954. *Z. Naturforsch.* 9b: 398.

Weidel, W., H. Frank, and H. H. Martin. 1960. *J. Gen. Microbiol.* 22: 158.

Weiner, I. M., T. Higuchi, L. Rothfield, M. Saltmarsh-Andrew, M. J. Osborn, and B. L. Horecker. 1965. *Proc. Natl. Acad. Sci. U. S. 54:* 228.

Westphal, O., and O. Lüderitz. 1954. *Angew. Chem.* 66: 407.

Wright, A., M. Dankert, and P. W. Robbins. 1965. *Proc. Natl. Acad. Sci. U. S.* 54: 235.

Salmonella O-Antigen and Lipopolysaccharide Biosynthesis

P. W. Robbins and **J. M. Keller**

Division of Biochemistry
Department of Biology
Massachusetts Institute of Technology
Cambridge, Massachusetts

The lipopolysaccharide of gram-negative enteric bacteria is a macromolecular aggregate of complex heteropolysaccharide chains linked covalently to the lipid A of Westphal through a basal or "core" polysaccharide. It is known that the lipopolysaccharide carries a major part of the antigenic specificity of the cell surface, and recent experiments suggest that the bacterial membrane plays a major role in its synthesis. For these reasons lipopolysaccharide is of interest not only in relation to bacterial structure and function, but also as a model for the complex materials the biochemist and molecular biologist must deal with in considering general problems of membrane function and cell surface specificity.

Much of the recent progress in studies on the structure and biosynthesis of lipopolysaccharide is based on fundamental isolation and chemical studies of Westphal and coworkers and on the work by Staub on the relation of chemical structure to O-antigen specificity. No attempt will be made here to review in detail the chemistry or immunochemistry of the *Salmonella* O-antigen. The recent review by Lüderitz *et al.* (in press) is an excellent summary of both classical and more recent work. In addition, no attempt will be made

31

to deal with the genetic aspects of lipopolysaccharide synthesis. Since bacteria growing under laboratory conditions seem to be able to dispense with the synthesis of at least a major part of the lipopolysaccharide, it has been possible to apply the very powerful tools of genetic analysis to the problems of structure and biosynthesis. The preceding paper in this symposium by Nikaido summarizes much of the recent work in this field.

Since studies on the enzymatic synthesis of lipopolysaccharide are still in the early stages of development and major structural questions are still unsettled, it is impossible to describe the mechanics of step by step assembly. Rather, we propose in this brief review to give illustrations of the types of enzymatic reactions that have been found in studies on lipopolysaccharide biosynthesis and to suggest how the various types of reactions may be related and coordinated.

Synthesis of Lipopolysaccharide "Core". As stated above the typical lipopolysaccharide of pathogenic or "smooth" *Salmonella* strains consists of long heteropolysaccharide chains linked to lipid A by way of "core" polysaccharide material. From the work of Subbaiah and Stocker (1964) and Beckmann *et al.* (1964) it seems clear that "rough" mutants may result from the loss of the ability to form the heteropolysaccharide chains or from defective core synthesis. In the latter case it is assumed that the defective core will not allow the attachment of the antigenic heteropolysaccharide chains to the lipopolysaccharide structure. Although the detailed structure of the core polysaccharide is far from clear it is often pictured schematically as follows:

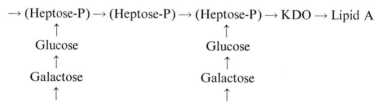

Ketodeoxyoctonate (KDO) is linked directly to lipid A (Osborn, 1963) and it is therefore of interest that Edstrom and Heath (1964) have observed the transfer of KDO moieties from CMP-KDO to preparations of degraded lipid A. These degraded lipid acceptors were prepared by treating lipopolysaccharide with 0.2 N NaOH followed by acid hydrolysis. Although intact lipopolysaccharide and lipid A were not effective acceptors of KDO it is possible that these materials are the natural acceptors under *in vivo* conditions in the cell wall-membrane complex where lipopolysaccharide assembly is taking place. Hopefully, such questions will be answerable by experimental techniques now being developed.

Of special interest in this respect are the glucosyl and galactosyl transfer reactions being studied by Rothfield *et al.* (1964a; 1964b; 1964c). These reactions may be described as follows:

Glucose-deficient lipopolysaccharide + UDP-glucose
→ glucosyl-lipopolysaccharide + UDP
Glucosyl-lipopolysaccharide + UDP-galactose
→ galactosyl-glucosyl-lipopolysaccharide + UDP

Since at least part of the enzymatic activity in each case has been found in the cytoplasmic fraction of the cell, it has been possible to study the substrate specificity of the enzyme and binding of the enzyme to its macromolecular substrate. This significant work has shown that while purified lipopolysaccharide is inactive, a complex prepared by mixing lipopolysaccharide with phosphatidyl ethanolamine under appropriate conditions will serve as an excellent substrate for the enzyme. The active complex is generated by heating the appropriate lipopolysaccharide with membrane phospholipid at 60° for 30 min and allowing the mixture to cool slowly to room temperature. Although other explanations are possible the requirement for such an "annealing" operation in the *in vitro* system suggests that during lipopolysaccharide assembly *in vivo*, the partially synthesized lipopolysaccharide may exist within or on the cytoplasmic membrane and that enzymes such as the glucosyl transferase and galactosyl transferase may interact with the entire complex rather than with the lipopolysaccharide itself. It seems possible, in fact, that many "membrane enzymes" are simply globular proteins that associate with membranes or membrane fragments. An analogous situation exists with the enzymes glycogen phosphorylase and UDPG-glycogen synthetase. Both of these enzymes are present in the insoluble glycogen-containing fraction of cellular homogenates but both are readily "solubilized" after digestion of the glycogen with amylase.

It is anticipated that isolation and further study of the glucosyl and galactosyl lipopolysaccharide transferases will add significantly to our understanding of "membrane enzymes." Further chemical and electron micrographic studies of the lipid-lipopolysaccharide complexes may add substantially to concepts of lipopolysaccharide biosynthesis and the relation of lipopolysaccharide to the cell membrane and other components of the cell wall.

Synthesis of antigenic determinant chains. The structure of the "smooth" O-antigen of many of the *Salmonella* A, B, D, and E group strains may be represented by the generalized formula:

$$-(\text{D-mannosyl-L-rhamnosyl-D-galactosyl})_n^-$$

dideoxyhexose   O-acetyl
                                 D-glucosyl

in which n may be as large as 80. Exactly how the long chains are linked to the core polysaccharide is, at present, obscure. The mannosyl residues may be substituted with dideoxyhexose moieties and the galactosyl residues may carry O-acetyl or glucosyl residues. Specific examples of O-antigen repeating unit structures are shown in Fig. 1.

The three enzymes just discussed in connection with the synthesis of the polysaccharide core all catalyze the direct single-step transfer from the nucleotide sugar precursor to lipid A or lipopolysaccharide. In contrast to these reactions, the assembly of the O-antigen chains appears to involve a complex sequence of events that includes the preassembly of the repeating unit on a lipid carrier or coenzyme. Following the suggestions made by Anderson *et al.* (1965) from their studies of mucopeptide synthesis, Weiner *et al.* (1965) and Wright *et al.* (1965) have shown that synthesis of the man-nosyl-rhamnosyl-galactose chain can probably be pictured as follows:

UDP-Gal + lipid → lipid-P-Gal + UMP
lipid-P-Gal + TDP-Rh → lipid-P-Gal-Rh (+TDP)
lipid-P-Gal-Rh + GDP-Man → lipid-P-Gal-Rh-Man (+GDP)
n lipid-P-Gal-Rh-Man → (Gal-Rh-Man)$_n$ + n lipid + n Pi

In antigens carrying dideoxyhexose, present evidence suggests that the dideoxyhexose is added to the lipid trisaccharide intermediate before the

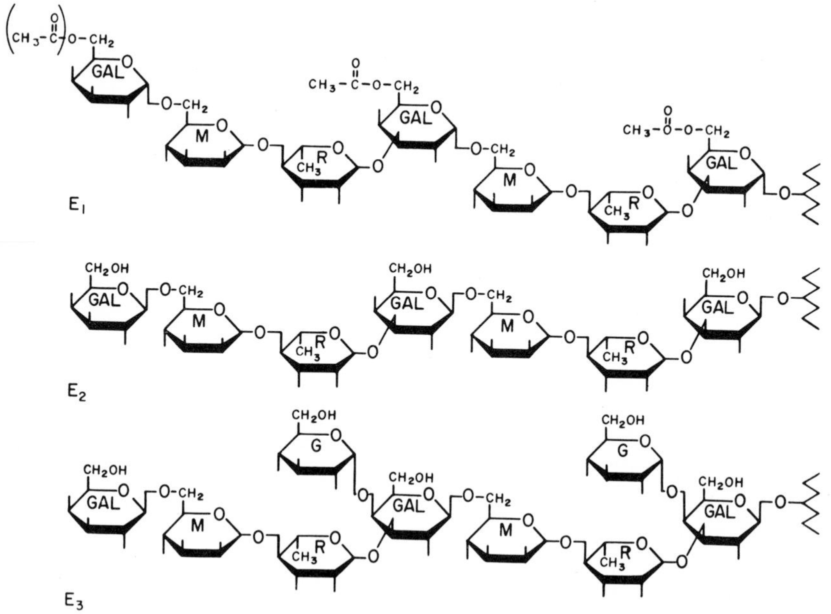

Fig. 1. O-antigen repeating units of three E-group *Salmonella* strains. The *S. anatum* antigen is shown at the top (E-1). The E-2 antigen differs in the anomeric configuration of the galactosyl residues and lacks O-acetyl groups. The E-3 antigen carries glucosyl residues attached to galactosyl moieties of the main chain.

final polymerization step(s). Studies of the lipid intermediate and of the detailed mechanism of the reactions are still in the early stages of development. It is clear, however, that the synthesis of the O-antigen chain involves a number of steps carried out independently of lipid A and polysaccharide core synthesis. This concept is in accord with the finding that mutants with defective polysaccharide core structures accumulate O-antigen "soluble hapten" chains unattached to lipopolysaccharide (Beckmann, *et al.* 1964a; Beckmann, *et al.* 1964b). Although O-antigen synthesis goes on independently of core synthesis, the two processes may well be related and coordinated in some way *in vivo*. At least it is clear that both processes involve the functioning of "membrane enzymes." In addition, the lipid intermediate that participates in the assembly of O-antigen chains may well be considered a "membrane coenzyme."

Modifying enzymes. Another distinct group of enzymes that is associated with the cell envelope and is important in the formation of lipopolysaccharide is that group adding to, or modifying, the polysaccharide structure. The only enzyme studied in detail in this group is 0-10 transacetylase, the enzyme of *S. anatum* that catalyzes the transfer of acetyl residues from acetyl coenzyme A to preformed polysaccharide chains. As shown in Table 1 when a particulate preparation from the cell envelope of *S. anatum* is incubated with radioactive acetyl-CoA under conditions where lipopolysaccharide is not being synthesized, acetyl groups are transferred to endogenous preformed lipopolysaccharide present in the enzyme preparation. It would be of interest to know whether the transacetylase, like the galactosyl transferase of Rothfield *et al.* (1964a; 1964b; 1964c), requires a specific type of lipid-lipopolysaccharide complex as substrate. Although the finding that particulate enzyme will acetylate added oligosaccharides indicates that this may not be so, a clear-cut answer cannot be given at the present time since soluble enzyme is not available for appropriate tests.

Coordination and control of synthesis. From the picture just outlined, it is clear that the assembly of the lipopolysaccharide may give a reflection of the type of processes that occur during the synthesis and organization of complex macromolecules at the cell surface. Since all components of the system — enzymes, polysaccharides, and coenzymes — seem to form specific associations with the phospholipids of the cytoplasmic membrane, it seems likely that a deeper understanding of the architecture of the membrane will be required before a detailed picture of enzyme and substrate interactions will be possible. Enzymes with complex substrate and allosteric sites, and substrates "dissolved" in a phospholipid matrix, offer more than enough potential control systems to account for the orderly assembly of the lipopolysaccharide molecule. The glucosyl and galactosyl transferases of Rothfield *et al.* (1964a, b, c) discussed in the foregoing probably offer the greatest promise for direct answers to these questions at the present time. Beyond this point, however, remain the problems of assembly and coordination of the cell wall as a whole, and the relation of cell-wall synthesis to the known framework of protein synthesis and biochemical genetics.

TABLE 1

INCORPORATION OF ACETYL GROUPS INTO LIPOPOLYSACCHARIDE
FROM ACETYL-CoA

Fraction	Percent of radioactivity
Washed particles	(100)
Phenol extract	87
Dialyzed phenol extract	91
Precipitate after ultracentrifugation	70
Antibody precipitate	54–62

The particle fraction (Robbins et al., 1965; Robbins and Uchida, 1965) from S. anatum (7.9 mg protein/ml; 1.2 ml) was incubated with 0.1 ml of 0.5 M phosphate buffer pH 7.4 and 0.1 ml of 2.1 mM C^{14}-acetyl-CoA for 120 min at 37°. The reaction was stopped by the addition of 0.2 ml of neutral 2 M NH_2OH and 0.4 ml of 2 M acetic acid. The particles were isolated by centrifugation for 30 min at 30,000 g and were washed twice with 0.05 M phosphate buffer pH 7.4. The techniques used for the extraction and precipitation of lipopolysaccharide have been described previously (Robbins et al., 1965; Robbins and Uchida, 1965).

REFERENCES

Anderson, J. S., M. Matsuhashi, M. A. Haskin, and J. L. Strominger. 1965. Proc. Natl. Acad. Sci. 53: 881.

Beckmann, I., O. Lüderitz, and O. Westphal. 1964a. Biochem. Z. 339: 401.

Beckmann, I., T. V. Subbaiah, and B. A. D. Stocker. 1964b. Nature 201: 1299.

Edstrom, R. D., and E. C. Heath. 1964. Biochem. and Biophys. Res. Comm. 16: 576.

Lüderitz, O., A. M. Staub, and O. Westphal. Bacteriol. Rev. In press.

Osborn, M. J., 1963. Proc. Natl. Acad. Sci. 50: 499.

Robbins, P. W., J. M. Keller, A. Wright, and R. Bernstein. 1965. J. Biol. Chem. 240: 384.

Robbins, P. W., and T. Uchida. 1965. J. Biol. Chem. 240: 375.

Rothfield, L., and B. L. Horecker. 1964. Proc. Natl. Acad. Sci. 52: 939.

Rothfield, L., M. J. Osborn, and B. L. Horecker. 1964. J. Biol. Chem. 239: 2788.

Rothfield, L., and M. Takeshita. 1965. Biochem. Biophys. Res. Commun. 20: 521.

Subbaiah, T. V., and B. A. D. Stocker. 1964. Nature 201: 1298.

Weiner, I. M., T. Higuchi, L. Rothfield, M. Saltmarsh-Andrew, M. J. Osborn, and B. L. Horecker. 1965. Proc. Natl. Acad. Sci. 54: 228.

Wright, A., M. Dankert, and P. W. Robbins. 1965. Proc. Natl. Acad. Sci. 54: 235.

Contributions of Pili to the Specificity of the Bacterial Surface, and a Unitary Hypothesis of Conjugal Infectious Heredity

Charles C. Brinton, Jr.

Microbiology Section
Department of Biological Sciences
University of Pittsburgh
Pittsburgh, Pennsylvania

I. Introduction

Pili (from the Latin for hairs or hair-like structures) (Brinton, 1954; 1959), also called fimbriae (Duguid *et al.*, 1955), are a class of long thin appendages that grow out from the surface of most gram-negative bacteria. They participate in highly specific interactions with viruses, bacteria, and antibodies, and in nonspecific adhesive interactions with any hydrophobic surface. So far, eight morphological types of pili have been discovered. Of these, Types I and F have been studied in detail, and have been found to differ in their structure, function, genetic control, and phenotypic expression. Pili are optional surface structures, since nonpiliated bacteria can grow and divide normally under the usual laboratory growth conditions. However, the frequent occurrence of richly piliated bacteria among gram-negative strains isolated from natural sources implies that pili perform important special functions under certain conditions.

Interest in pili is increased by the observation (Crawford and Gesteland, 1964; Brinton *et al.*, 1964) that one class, the F pili, are found only on male

37

Bacterial Pili

TABLE 1

A PARTIAL AND TENTATIVE MORPHOLOGICAL CLASSIFICATION OF PILI

Reference	Morphological type	Bacterial strain where originally observed	Diameter	Typical length in microns	Typical number on cell	Distribution on cell	Genetic control	Function
(*)	I	E. Coli	70Å	0.5-2	100-200	Uniform	Chromosomal	1. Adhesiveness 2. Enhances growth in oxygen-limited dense suspensions
Duguid, 1959	II	Klebsiella aerogenes	48Å	0.5-2	100-200	Uniform	Unknown	Unknown
Brinton, 1965; Hoeniger, 1965	III	Proteus	30-40Å	2-6	200-500	Uniform	Unknown	Unknown
Brinton, 1965	IV	Proteus	About 70Å (helical)	1-2	100-200	Uniform	Unknown	Unknown
Brinton, 1965	V	E. coli	About 250Å	1-2	1-2	Uniform	Unknown	Unknown
Marx & Heumann, 1962 Heumann & Marx, 1964	VI	Pseudomonas	About 50Å	2-10	1-5	Polar	Unknown	Unknown
Marx & Heumann, 1962 Heumann & Marx, 1964	VII	Pseudomonas	100-200Å	0.2-0.5	10-20	Polar	Unknown	Adhesiveness
Brinton, 1965 Brinton et al., 1964	F	E. coli genetic donors	85Å	1-20	1-4	Uniform	Episomal	1. Nucleic-acid conduction 2. Adhesiveness

* References for this type are as follows: Brinton, 1959; Brinton, 1965; Brinton et al., 1954; Brinton & Baron, 1960; Brinton et al., 1961; Brinton & Stone, 1961; Wohlhieter et al. 1962; Brinton & Huang, 1962; Cawal, 1965; Brinton & Stone, 1961

cells and adsorb male-specific phages. The purposes of this paper are to give a brief general survey of pili and, in particular, to present a unitary hypothesis of infectious heredity in bacteria involving the conduction of nucleic acids by F pili.

II. Morphology and Distribution on the Cell Surface

A partial and tentative classification of the various kinds of pili, based mainly on morphology, is presented in Table 1; metal-shadowed electron micrographs of some of these pili types are shown in Fig. 1. The diameter of a given type of pilus is a characteristic value, although lengths are quite variable even among pili on the same cell. A single cell may have two or more kinds of pili in addition to flagella and capsular material. Populations of cells

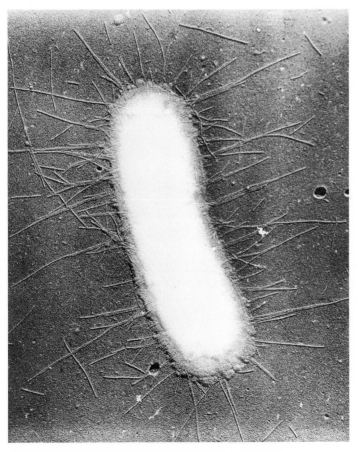

Fig. 1a. Type I piliated cell of *E. coli* K12 F⁻.

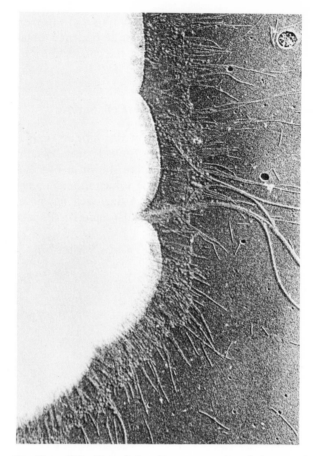

Fig. 1b. Type IV pili and flagella on a strain of *Proteus* from infected urine.

in pure cultures are usually not uniformly piliated; the number of pili per cell can vary from none to several hundred within the same culture.

Unattached pili are often seen in growing cultures. Some of these may arise from mechanical breakage, but they are probably produced by natural outgrowth from the cell, since more violent mechanical agitation is required to remove them from bacteria than the agitation of aeration during growth. Even unagitated broth cultures can contain large numbers of unattached pili.

III. Natural Occurrence

The majority of gram-negative bacteria isolated from nature are piliated. An example of an ecological niche that frequently contains richly piliated

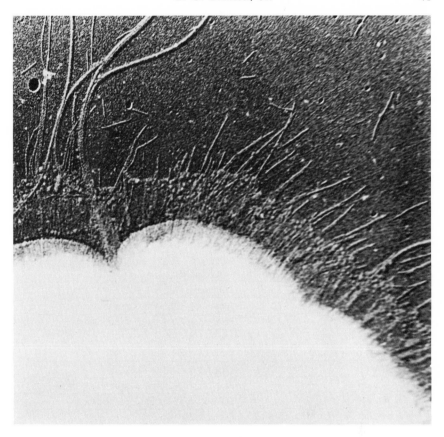

Fig. 1c. Type III pili (very thin, upper right), Type IV pili, and flagella on a strain of *Proteus* from infected urine.

bacteria is the infected human urinary tract. An electron microscopic survey of infected urine specimens from patients in the Pittsburgh Children's Hospital showed that 65 of 72 specimens produced piliated bacteria when inoculated into glucose broth and aerated overnight (Brinton and Carnahan, unpublished [c]). In 20 of the 72 specimens, piliated bacteria could be seen in the urine itself. All 12 specimens containing *Proteus* and all 17 specimens containing *Klebsiella* produced piliated bacteria. Of 33 specimens containing *E. coli*, 29 produced piliated bacteria; of 12 specimens containing *Pseudomonas* 10 produced piliated bacteria.

A partial list of strains reported to be piliated without regard for type of piliation is given in Table 2. Frequency of occurrence is shown when available. Although a systematic search has not been carried out, no piliated gram-positive bacteria have been reported.

TABLE 2

PARTIAL LIST OF PILIATED GENERA AND SPECIES OF
GRAM-NEGATIVE BACTERIA

Strain	Fre-quency	Reference
Escherichia coli		Brinton, 1959; Brinton *et al*, 1954; Brinton *et al*, 1964; Houwink & van Iterson, 1950
Escherichia coli	29/33	Brinton & Carnahan, unpublished
Escherichia coli	31/47	Duguid *et al*, 1955
Salmonella typhosa		Brinton & Baron, 1960
Salmonella typhimurium		Brinton *et al*, 1964
Salmonella spp.	65/81	Duguid & Gillies, 1958
Proteus vulgaris		Brinton & Carnahan, unpublished; Weibull & Hedvall, 1953
Proteus mirabilis		Hoeniger, 1965; Brinton & Carnahan, unpublished
Proteus spp.	35/35	Duguid & Gillies, 1958
Proteus spp.	12/12	Brinton & Carnahan, unpublished
Klebsiella spp.	17/17	Brinton & Carnahan, unpublished
Klebsiella spp. (encapsulated)	109/140	Duguid & Gillies, 1958
Klebsiella spp. (nonmotile)	125/154	Duguid, 1959
Shigella flexneri	103/145	Duguid & Gillies, 1957
Shigella flexneri		Duguid, 1959; Gillies & Duguid, 1958
Shigella spp.		Brinton & Carnahan, unpublished
Aerobacter cloacae	10/13	Constable, 1956
Aerobacter cloacae		Duguid, 1959
Aerobacter aerogenes		Brinton & Carnahan, unpublished
Serratia marcescens		Duguid, 1959
Pseudomonas spp.	10/12	Brinton & Carnahan, unpublished
Pseudomonas echinoides		Marx & Heumann, 1962
Pseudomonas pyocyanea		Houwink & van Iterson, 1950
Chromobacterium prodigiosum	10/10	Duguid & Gillies, 1958
Flavobacteria		Brinton & Carnahan, unpublished
Photobacterium splendidum		Houwink & van Iterson, 1950

IV. Detection and Assay

A. Electron microscopy. The usual method of detecting pili is by electron microscopy of metal-shadowed specimens prepared by the collodion agar filtration technique (Kellenberger and Arber, 1957), which permits quantitative visualization of attached surface structures as well as unattached structures in the culture fluid (Fig. 1). The total number and length of pili in the

Fig. 1d. Type I, Type V, and F pili on *E. coli* K12 Hfr Cavalli.

culture, the morphological type or types, the number per cell, the distribution within the cell population, and the distribution over the cell surface can be estimated with reasonable accuracy. The advantage of this method is that structures which project out from all parts of the surface are constrained to lie in the plane of the collodion film and are almost completely visible. The negative contrast technique is also useful; surface structures are confined to one plane and a certain amount of internal fine structure can be discerned (Figs. 2 and 3) as a result of penetration of the stain between subunits. Pili are far more difficult to detect in thin sections owing to the low probability of a given pilus being in the plane of the section.

B. Electrophoresis. Since the net surface electric-charge density of Type I pili is lower than that of the outermost cell wall layer, and since Type I pili contribute a large amount of surface area to the piliated cell, piliated bacteria move at about one-third to one-half the velocity of their nonpiliated mutants in an electric field (Brinton *et al.*, 1954; Brinton and Lauffer, 1959). Microscope electrophoresis can be used to count relative numbers of piliated and

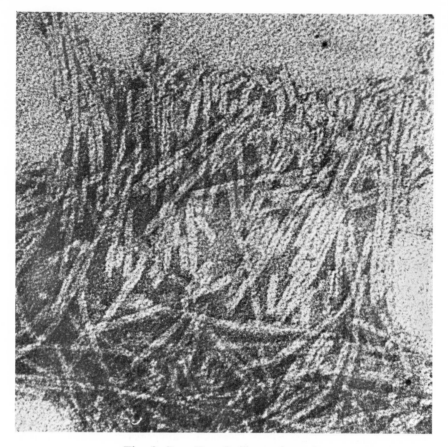

Fig. 2. Pure Type I pili-negative stain.

non-piliated cells in a culture and to determine the total amount of pili on individual cells, since difference in electrophoretic mobility is related to extent of piliation. This method is only useful for detecting pili that occur in large numbers per cell. The mobility of an F-piliated culture is not detectably different than that of a non-F-piliated culture, since the average number of F pili per cell is one or less.

C. *Colonial form.* Some strains having Type I pili (*E. coli* Bam and *E. coli* B-L (E), for instance) mutate to a form that has lost its piliation (Brinton, 1959). The piliated form (P+) grows on solid medium as a smaller, more opaque colony than the nonpiliated form (P−). The difference in colonial growth may be due to the hydrophobic nature of pili, which causes piliated cells to adhere more tightly to each other than do nonpiliated cells. However, not all strains having P+ and P− forms exhibit a colony difference.

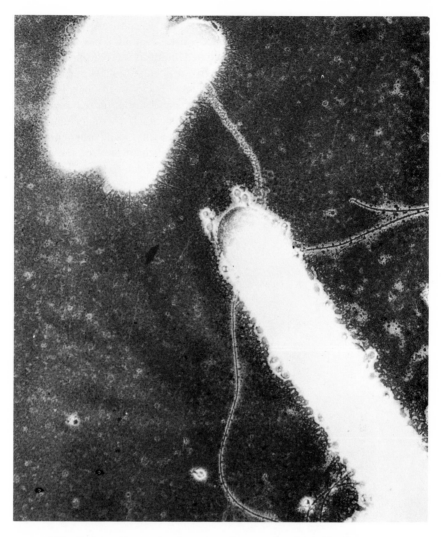

Fig. 3. Negative stain electron micrograph of an F pilus connected male-female pair presumed to be a mating pair since it was present in a mating mixture. The male cell is Type I piliated and the female cell has T_6 phage adsorbed to its surface. M12 RNA male phage are adsorbed to the F pilus.

D. Particle agglutination. The adhesiveness of pili causes piliated bacteria to adhere not only to one another but to polystyrene latex particles (Brinton, 1965), red blood cells (Duguid *et al.*, 1955), and air-water interfaces. A simple slide hemagglutination test performed by mixing a saline suspension of guinea-pig red blood cells with a bacterial colony or a few drops of liquid culture is a useful screening method for the detection of piliated cultures or for detecting piliated colonies if no colony difference exists. Not all types of pili hemagglutinate, however, and sparsely piliated cultures or colonies having a small fraction of piliated cells will not give a positive test. A rapid method of differentiating well-piliated from nonpiliated bacterial colonies is to flood colonies on agar plates with a concentrated suspension of red blood cells and to wash off the excess after a few minutes of contact. Strongly hemagglutinating colonies will retain a red layer of blood cells, while nonhemagglutinating colonies will not. Precautions must be taken to prevent the colonies from floating away from the agar; either gentle heat fixation or a superimposed filter paper disk can be used.

Fig. 4 shows the orientation of Type I pili in a network of pili-aggregated

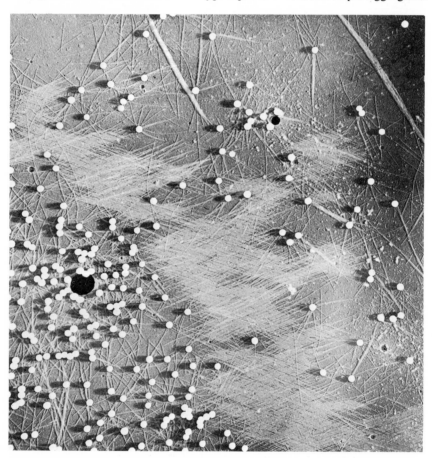

Fig. 4. Type I pili with polystyrene latex spheres; PSL spheres are agglutinated by endwise attached pili; no PSL spheres are attached to sides of pili in the angled layer crystal.

polystyrene latex spheres. The ends of the pili are the adhesive sites under these conditions: no latex spheres adhere to the sides of pili in the angled layer crystal, and free pili adhere endwise to latex spheres.

E. Chemical and physical properties of pure concentrated suspensions. Type I pili are pure proteins with a characteristic amino acid composition. Pure concentrated suspensions of Type I pili have characteristic ultraviolet (UV) (Fig. 5) and infrared absorption spectra. The UV spectrum is conveniently used as a measure of concentration, purity, and intactness of tertiary and quaternary structures (Brinton, 1965). Concentrated suspensions also exhibit strong streaming birefringence in 0.1 M magnesium chloride. Any of these properties (see Sections V-A, V-B, V-C) may be used to detect and assay Type I pili. Large volumes of piliated cells are necessary to produce enough pure pili for such assays.

F. Antibody agglutination, precipitation, and inhibition. Pili are antigenic: specific antibodies are formed after injection of either piliated bacteria (Brinton, 1959; Gillies and Duguid, 1958; Ørskov and Ørskov, 1960; Old, 1963) or free pili (Brinton, 1959) into animals. Gillies and Duguid (1958) prepared antisera that agglutinated only piliated strains. For this purpose, antisera prepared against piliated *Shigella flexneri* cultures were absorbed with cultures of the same strain grown under conditions in which little or no pili were produced. These antisera also inhibited hemagglutination by the piliated *Shigella* strains. Brinton (1959) prepared an antiserum against isolated, semipurified *E. coli* B-L(E) pili that agglutinated only the piliated

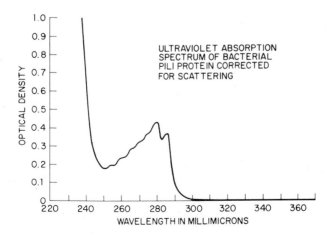

Fig. 5. Ultraviolet absorption spectrum of Type I pili.

form of this strain. Old (1963) used agar double diffusion to estimate the amount and degree of purity of *E. coli* pili preparations. Ørskov and Ørskov (1960) were able to define an antigen, termed f⁺, present only on male strains of *E. coli*, which was undoubtedly F pili, although direct confirmation of this is still lacking.

Studies of the specificities of pili antigens carried out with absorbed antisera (Gillies and Duguid, 1958) showed that all strains of *Shigella flexneri* had pili of the same antigenic composition. *Shigella* pili antigens cross reacted strongly with only one piliated strain of *E. coli* and showed no cross reaction with strains of *Salmonella, Aerobacter cloacae*, or *Proteus*. Campbell (1961) divided *Salmonella* pili antigens into five classes using cross-agglutination tests with absorbed sera.

Clear-cut antigenic classification based on antisera absorbed with phenotypically nonpiliated cultures is difficult because:

(1) Cultural conditions that change piliation can affect other surface antigens.
(2) Cultures judged nonpiliated by hemagglutination or electron microscopy may still contain small amounts of antibody-absorbing pili.
(3) Cultures containing no visible pili might still contain microscopically invisible antigenically active pilin subunits.
(4) The presence of one kind of pilus (Type I, for instance) can interfere with specific antibody agglutination of another kind (F pili, for instance).
(5) Different kinds of pili are often expressed under different cultural conditions.
(6) The same pilus type, controlled by the same structural gene, can have different genetic stabilities and different conditions for phenotypic expression, depending on the host cell that carries the gene (Gemski, 1964).

A reliable antigenic classification of pili could best be achieved using antisera produced against isolated pure pili. The multiplicity of structurally different pilus types, varying genetically and phenotypically in complex ways, makes concomitant genetic, structural, and cultural characterization obligatory. Genetic studies are especially important since a given antigenic type of pilus may be present in more than one genus and species. Brinton and Baron (1960) have shown that *E. coli* K-12 Type I pili are antigenically identical to *E. coli* B-L(E) Type I pili and remain so when genetically transferred to *Salmonella typhosa*. F pili can be produced by many different genera and species (Brinton *et al.*, 1964) and are genetically transferable to most gram-negative bacteria.

In view of the widespread occurrence of pili in nature, identification of pili-antigenic determinants would be of great value in the classification and identification of gram-negative strains. This enormous task is hardly begun.

G. Genetic donor ability. The establishment of an F pili requirement for genetic donor ability (Section VI-D-1) allows the use of this property for the detection and assay of F-piliated cells. This is a sensitive test as selective techniques for isolating recombinant clones can be used to detect very small fractions of donor cells in a given population. A negative test does not necessarily mean absence of F pili, however, since other requirements for genetic donation or recombinant formation may not be fulfilled.

H. RNA male phage sensitivity. The establishment of an F pili requirement for RNA male phage infection (Brinton, 1965) (Section VI-D-4) permits the detection and assay of F-piliated cells by phage sensitivity tests. Types of tests include plaque formation, cross streaking, phage adsorption, and titer increase (Brinton *et al.*, 1964; Brinton, 1965).

Plaque formation by RNA phage requires that a fairly large proportion of the indicator cell population be F piliated and therefore sensitive. The larger the fraction of sensitive cells, the clearer the plaques.

If the proportion of sensitive cells is too low to form plaques, or if the strain releases phage particles with little or no lysis, the ability of the culture to increase the phage titer can be used as an assay for F-piliated cells (Brinton *et al.*, 1964). The culture is infected with RNA phage and titered as a function of time, using bacteria having a high degree of efficiency of plating for the phage as indicators. The increase of titer is a sensitive measure of the number of F-piliated cells since a single infected cell can produce as many as 20,000 phage particles (Loeb and Zinder, 1961). The sensitivity can be increased further by careful elimination of unadsorbed phage (Meynell and Datta, 1965).

The adsorption of plaque-forming units or radioactivity of labeled phage particles can also be used to detect and assay F pili (Brinton, 1965; Valentine and Strand, 1965). A convenient method of eliminating unadsorbed phage is to trap the bacterial culture or the suspension of free F pili on a millipore filter. The proper adsorption medium must be used to prevent free phage from adsorbing to the filter (Lodish and Zinder, 1965).

Testing RNA male phage sensitivity by cross streaking bacteria and phage on the surface of a dry agar plate is a rather insensitive test, since production of F pili by bacteria is relatively poor under these conditions. The use of moist plates usually improves sensitivity.

V. Type I Pili

A. Isolation and purification. Pure Type I pili can be prepared in yields of 1-2 mg per liter of culture by growing a richly piliated strain, *Escherichia coli* BamP⁺, in a minimal lactose medium overnight with aeration. Since this strain spontaneously segregates a completely nonpiliated form [BamP⁻, whose colonies can be distinguished from those of BamP⁺ (Brinton, 1959)], the inoculum for this culture must be grown from isolated BamP+ colonies to ensure a well-piliated culture. Two minutes of agitation in a large-volume high-speed mixer are sufficient to remove all pili from the bacteria. The depiliated cells are removed by centrifugation. Concentration is achieved by iso-electrically precipitating the crude pili suspension at pH 3.92 overnight in the cold and centrifuging at low speed. The resuspended and neutralized preparation is then made 0.1 M with $MgCl_2$ in the cold. The pili rods crystal-lize longitudinally and strong streaming birefringence appears. The crystals are removed by centrifugation and resuspended in distilled water. Two more recrystallizations yield a pili preparation which is pure by the criteria of UV spectroscopy, electron microscopy, chemical analysis, crystallinity, electro-phoresis, ultracentrifugation, and agglutinating activity. Electron micro-graphs of pure suspensions are shown in Fig. 6 (metal shadowed) and Fig. 2 (negative stain). The presence of an axial hole 20-25 Å in diameter can be seen in Fig. 2.

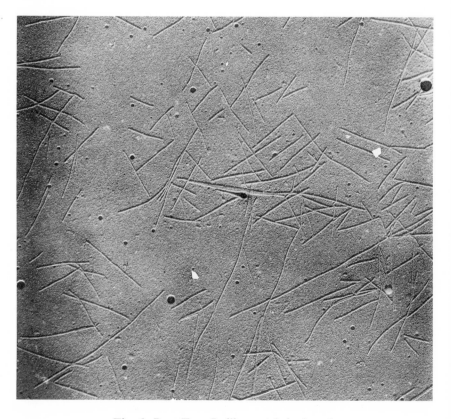

Fig. 6. Pure Type I pili—metal shadowed.

B. Chemical composition. Chemical analysis of Type I pili showed no detectable amounts of carbohydrate, lipid, or nucleic acid. More than 99% of the weight could be accounted for as known amino acids. Studies with D-amino acid oxidase demonstrated that at least the major amino acids were "L" isomers. The results of a series of amino acid analyses of pure pili preparations acid-hydrolyzed for various times are presented in Table 3 as the number of residues. The *pilin* molecule has a minimum molecular weight, according to the analyses of 16,600, and contains at least 163 amino acid residues. Pilin contains a high proportion of amino acids with hydrocarbon side chains and a low proportion of basic amino acids. In addition, the number of ammonia residues indicates that the proportion of free carboxyl groups is low. The preponderance of nonpolar side-chains may help to account for the distinctive hydrophobicity of Type I pili.

C. Molecular structure. The structure of Type I pili determined by electron microscopy, crystallography, and X-ray diffraction is shown in Fig. 7. The axial hole of 20–25Å is drawn to conform to the size estimated by electron microscopy; the pitch distance (23.2 Å) and the number of subunits per turn

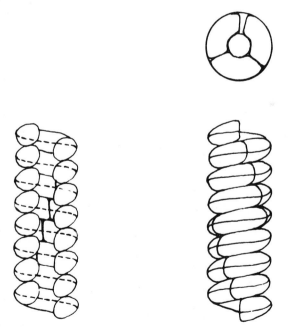

Fig. 7. Model of Type I pili; side view, end view, and cross section. Outer diameter = 70 Å; inner diameter = 20–25 Å; pitch distance of helix = 23.2 Å; 3⅛ subunits per turn; 17,000 = molecular weight of subunit.

($3\frac{1}{8}$) were determined by X-ray diffraction. Subunits of this size having the density of pili protein would have a molecular weight of about 16,000, which is in good agreement with the minimum molecular weight of 17,000 calculated from the amino-acid analyses.

Type I pili can be depolymerized into pilin subunits by treatments that break hydrogen or hydrophobic bonds. The pilin subunits can repolymerize spontaneously to form pili indistinguishable in electron micrographs from native pili. The rate and extent of the polymerization reaction is dependent upon protein concentration, temperature, pH, salt concentration, and ionic species.

D. *Genetic control.* Type I pili are genetically controlled by a structural gene located on the chromosome and by regulator genes which have not yet been mapped. Type I pili were first transferred genetically from *E. coli* K12 to *Salmonella typhosa* (Brinton and Baron, 1960). By recombinational and interrupted mating analysis using an *E. coli* K12 donor, HfrC, and several *E. coli* K12, *E. coli* B, and *E. coli* B/r recipients, the structural gene for Type I piliation was located two minutes from the threonine locus on the side away from leucine on the *E. coli* chromosome (Brinton *et al.*, 1961; Gemski, 1964). Depending upon the recipient, P+ recombinants ranging from completely stable to very unstable could be isolated.

TABLE 3

AMINO ACID COMPOSITION OF TYPE I PILIN

ala	34	iso	4*
thr	20	lys	3*
asp	20	arg	3*
gly	17	his	2*
val	13	tyr	2*
glu	13	½ cys	2
leu	10	pro	2*
ser	10	try	0
phe	8*	met	0
	NH_3^+ 30		

* These residues have been analyzed with sufficient accuracy to ascertain that they occur in simple molar ratios, demonstrating that pilin is a homogenous molecular species.

The stability of Type I piliated strains has been studied in detail (Brinton, 1959; Wohlhieter *et al.*, 1962; Gemski, 1964). The P+ to P⁻ genetic change in *E. coli* B-L (E) or *E. coli* Bam is mutational in nature, being an all-or-nothing, sudden, random, spontaneous, reversible event. A cell is either P+ (hundreds of pili) or P⁻ (no pili). The rate of P+ to P⁻ mutation can be as high as 10^{-2} per cell division, but in these strains the P⁻ to P+ change occurs at a low rate.

The rate of P⁺ to P⁻ mutation is strongly affected by the environment; measurements carried out in the absence of any selection showed a hundredfold change in mutation rate with an 18°C change in incubation temperature. These studies led to the hypothesis that mutator genes, whose action could be influenced by environmental conditions, were involved in the control of Type I pili.

E. Synthesis. Microscope electrophoresis and electron microscopy have been used to study the effects of growth conditions and inhibitors upon the outgrowth of Type I pili. Figure 8 shows the change in mobility as Type I pili regenerate from depiliated *E. coli* B placed in fresh 37°C nutrient broth. This rapid regeneration is prevented by growth-inhibiting concentrations of streptomycin but not by growth-inhibiting concentrations of chloramphenicol. After four cycles of pili removal and regeneration in the continued presence of chloramphenicol, regeneration could still occur. Since Type I pili are pure proteins, the inability of chloramphenicol to inhibit their regeneration probably means that their growth is an assembly of presynthesized subunits rather than *de novo* protein synthesis. In support of this, radioactively labeled amino acids do not appear in Type I pili protein in the presence of chloramphenicol. Low temperature (0°C) and formaldehyde also prevent regeneration.

F. Function. Measurements of relative growth rates demonstrate that Type I piliated cells can grow and survive at different rates than their non-piliated forms (Brinton, 1959; Gemski, 1964). Under aeration in the usual laboratory media the difference is small but significant; the P⁺ form can grow either faster or slower than the P⁻ form, depending upon the temperature.

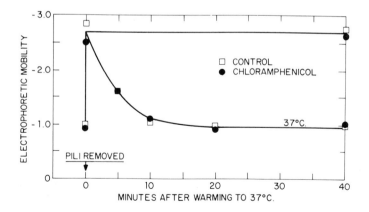

Fig. 8. Removal and regeneration of Type I pili assayed by change in cell electrophoretic mobility.

Under conditions of limiting oxygen and high cell concentration, piliated cells can grow twice as fast as nonpiliated cells. During the decline phase of growth, viable piliated cells can increase in number while nonpiliated cells are dying. The reason for the growth advantage conferred by Type I pili is not clear. Figure 9 shows the increase in the number of viable piliated cells and decrease in the number of viable nonpiliated cells as the culture ages at high cell density with limiting oxygen. It should be noted that these conditions are closer to those of the intestinal habitat of enteric bacteria than the usual laboratory conditions of rapid aerobic growth.

VI. F pili

A. Genetic control. F pili are defined as those pili genetically controlled by the fertility factor of gram-negative bacteria. Since they also serve as receptors for the RNA male bacteriophages, they have been operationally defined as pili capable of attaching these phage particles. This definition is not all-inclusive, however, since RNA male phage sensitivity can be lost by mutation without loss of F pili.

The evidence that F pili are genetically controlled by the F factor is shown in the work of Brinton *et al.* (1964):

(1) Male strains of bacteria (Hfr, F^+, F') are F piliated and female strains (F^-) are not.

(2) Elimination of the F factor by acridine orange curing also eliminates F pili.

(3) Genetic transfer of the F factor into non-F-piliated strains confers the ability to produce F pili on the recipient strains.

B. Phenotypic control. The expression of F pili genes is controlled by mechanisms not yet well understood. Overnight aerated cultures of Hfr cells in broth have few or no F pili, while overnight still broth cultures have nearly maximal F piliation (Brinton, 1965). When overnight aerated cultures are diluted into fresh medium and grown with aeration, F pili begin to appear at the time cell mass begins to increase; maximum F piliation is reached near the end of the exponential growth phase. The number of F pili per cell declines to a low level about 8 hrs after dilution into fresh medium. Overnight cultures on nutrient agar plates have very few F pili.

The maximum (3-4) and average (about 1) numbers of F pili per cell in fully expressed populations of Hfr, F^+, or F' cells correspond approximately to the number of integrated or autonomous F factors present in these cells. This one-to-one correspondence could be caused by the F factor DNA itself being part of the F pilus, although other possibilities are not excluded.

F piliation can be phenotypically repressed by the presence of drug resistance transfer factors (RTF) (Hirota *et al.*, 1964) (Section VI-D). F

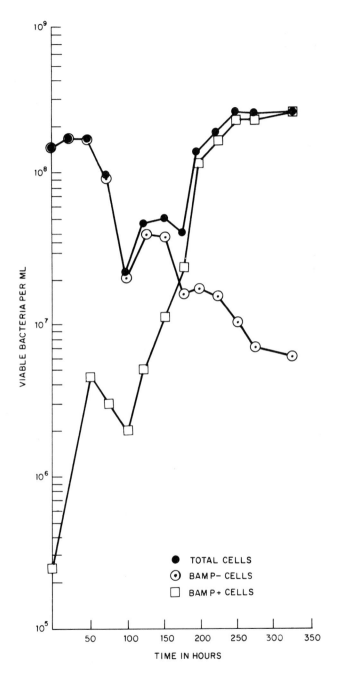

Fig. 9. Growth of piliated and non-piliated cell of *E. coli* Bam at high cell density and low oxygen tension.

piliation returns upon removal of RTF by acridine orange. These facts suggest the existence of genes on RTF capable of repressing F piliation and genes on the F factor sensitive to this repression. Mutants of RTF exist that have lost the capacity to repress F piliation.

C. Structure and synthesis. F pili are usually considerably longer than Type I pili and about 20% thicker (85 Å). Detached F pili are almost always aggregated in large bundles of parallel rods (Beer *et al.*, unpublished). These bundles appear as needle-like crystals under phase or dark field microscopy. F pili may be solubilized by adding small concentrations of organic solvents to aqueous suspensions, indicating that hydrophobic bonds have a role in the maintenance of their structure. Negatively stained electron micrographs show an axial hole 25–30 Å in diameter. Analysis of semipurified preparations indicates that F pili are mainly if not entirely protein. They are trypsin sensitive as judged by electron microscopy. The UV absorption spectrum shows no indication of nucleic acid. Thus, the structure and composition of F pili are similar to Type I pili; determination of molecular structure awaits complete purification in adequate yields.

The rapid generation of new F pili by mechanically depiliated cells and the presence of large numbers of detached F pili in growing cultures demonstrate that F pili grow out from and are released by the cell (Brinton, 1959; Brinton *et al.*, 1964). Under a variety of regeneration conditions maximum numbers of F pili per cell (equal to about 50% of the nondepiliated cells) are regenerated in 5 to 10 min. Formaldehyde, streptomycin, and 0°C prevent regeneration of F pili, while chloramphenicol has only a slight effect, indicating that F pili may be formed by polymerization of previously synthesized subunits. Although detached F pili contain little or no DNA, the structure of F pili and the manner of their release by the cell are remarkably similar to the structure and release of the DNA male phages (Hofschneider and Preuss, 1963).

D. Function. 1. Transfer of fertility factor and chromosomal DNA. The evidence implying a role of F pili in DNA transfer is sufficiently strong to justify restatement of the essential steps in the bacterial mating process. This will be done in the form of a generalized working model, the "F pili conduction model" (Brinton, 1965), which will be depicted here in some detail, although direct experimental evidence for certain of its features has not yet been obtained. It represents an attempt to formulate a unitary hypothesis of DNA transfer. The evidence currently available in support of it will be summarized after the model has been presented.

In this model the specific organelle of DNA transfer is the F pilus, synthesized and assembled by the donor cell *before* contact with the recipient cell. Its structure and synthesis are under the control of genes which are part of the DNA of the fertility factor. The synthesis of F pili protein subunits and their assembly into the F pilus structure are presumed to occur in a manner similar to virus maturation in which the protein coat is formed around the DNA of the transferable genetic element. The F pilus-DNA complex then exits from the donor cell without lysing it by passing through the wall-membrane barrier. If, before the F pilus has detached from the donor cell, its distal end contacts a receptor on a sensitive recipient cell, an event occurs at the receptor site causing the F pilus to attach to the site and initiating injection of the genetic element's DNA. The DNA is then conducted into the recipient cell through the axial hole of the F pilus.

Both the attachment of the F pilus to form a mating pair and the subsequent DNA transfer require energy (Brinton, 1965; Fisher, 1957a, b). It is not yet clear why energy should be required for attachment, but the transfer may require replicative release of DNA.

If the DNA of the transferable genetic element has become associated with the chromosomal DNA of the donor cell by recombination (Adelberg and Pittard, 1965), chromosomal genes may also be transferred. Although the intercellular F pilus connection is strong enough to resist dilution, pipetting, and thermal agitation, it has a high probability of spontaneous disruption and can be broken artificially by vigorous agitation. One consequence of spontaneous separation of mating pairs is that rather long pieces of newly donated DNA can apparently be withdrawn from the recipient cell (de Haan and Gross, 1962). The newly donated DNA can recombine with the chromosome of the recipient cell to produce stable recombinants if the region in question is not withdrawn during spontaneous separation, leaked back out after blending, or destroyed intracellularly by the recipient before the event leading to the production of stable recombinants occurs.

According to this model, the events involved in the formation of genetic recombinants may be divided into three periods: precontact, transfer, and postzygotic. These events may be briefly summarized as follows:

(A) Precontact period

(1) a. Replication of fertility factor's DNA.
   b. Association of fertility factor with donor chromosome (if DNA region whose transfer is being assayed is on chromosome).
   c. Synthesis of F pili protein.
(2) Assembly of F pili protein and fertility factor DNA.
(3) Exit of F pilus–DNA complex from the donor cell through the wall-membrane barrier. (Spontaneous detachment of the F pilus from the donor cell can eventually occur.)

(B) Transfer period

(1) Collision of F-piliated donor cell with recipient cell.
(2) Contact of F pilus attached to donor cell with receptor site on recipient cell surface.

(3) Attachment of F pilus to receptor site.

(4) Signal to donor to begin transfer.

(5) Initiation of transfer by donor.

(6) Replication of donatable DNA by donor (may precede and/or be simultaneous with transfer).

(7) Conduction of DNA through F pilus interior into the recipient.

(8) Spontaneous separation of donor and recipient (constant probability per unit time) that interrupts transfer and may be accompanied by either:

    a. Withdrawal of DNA by uncoupled donor cell *or*

    b. Breakage of DNA strand.

(*C*) *Postzygotic period*

(1) Possible loss of the newly transferred selective marker by one or more of the following processes:

    a. Internal inactivation of DNA.

    b. Back leakage of DNA into the medium following breakage.

    c. Withdrawal of DNA by the uncoupled donor cell.

    d. Death of the zygote before the first division.

(2) If DNA is not lost: recombination of the DNA region in question with the recipient chromosome.

(3) Replication and segregation of nonintegrated DNA, may occur before, during, or after recombination.

(4) Replication and segregation of integrated DNA, phenotypic expression of the characteristic controlled by the DNA region in question, and division of the zygote to form a recombinant clone.

The principal feature of this model is that F pili are necessary for DNA transfer. The evidence for this requirement is as follows (Brinton, 1965; Brinton *et al.*, 1964):

(1) F factor DNA genetically determines both donor ability and F piliation. Genetic loss of F pili results in loss of F piliation. Genetic gain of functional F pili results in gain of donor ability.

(2) Phenotypic loss of F pili caused by a change in cultural conditions results in loss of donor ability. When a change in cultural conditions allows F pili to be produced, donor ability is regained at the same time and at the same rate as F pili.

(3) Removal of F pili by an amount of mechanical agitation which does not affect viability or growth rate of the donor cells results in loss of donor ability. Donor ability returns at the same rate and to the same extent as F pili regenerate.

An F pili requirement might only mean that these structures are needed for specific contact or for the induction of sensitivity in the recipient, DNA transfer occurring at another site. Although no direct demonstration of DNA transfer through the F pilus has yet been made, some indirect evidence and structural arguments in favor of F pili conduction may be summarized as follows (Brinton, 1965):

(4) Light microscopy of mixtures of living donor and recipient cells under conditions of medium and temperature optimal for mating pair formation demonstrates the existence of pairs of cells that are not in wall-to-wall contact, but are connected by an invisible strand the same length as an F pilus. This connection is implied by the behavior of cell pairs with one motile partner that can be observed to tow the other partner through the medium or to move rapidly from side to side, and stop suddenly at a constant distance of separation. Female cultures have none of these pairs and male cultures only a few. The number of visible pairs in a mating mixture 3 to 5 min after mixing is approximately equal to the maximum number of genetic recombinants eventually obtained by plating on selective medium. The number of cells in clumps and in wall-to-wall pairs is far too small to account for the number of recombinants observed. Strand-connected pair formation is prevented by lowering the temperature to 0°C or by adding $10^{-3}M$ dinitrophenol, treatments which also prevent mating pair formation as measured genetically. Strand-connected pairs form in 1 or 2 min as do genetically competent pairs, and separate spontaneously at the same rate as genetically competent pairs.

(5) F-pili-connected pairs can be visualized by electron microscopy (Fig. 3).

(6) F pili are required for the conduction of male specific phage RNA into the male cell (Section VI-D-4). In effect, F pili serve as the "tail" for these tailless phages. They may also conduct the DNA of the rod-shaped male phages (Section VI-D-3). The fact that F pili can conduct other nucleic acids makes the conduction of bacterial DNA by F pili seem more plausible.

(7) The average number of F pili per cell corresponds approximately to the number of F factors per cell. This is consistent with the feature of the model that assumes that each F pilus contains F factor DNA. If F pili were required only for specific pair formation, many more per cell might be expected.

(8) Many long unattached F pili are found in cultures of male bacteria grown under gentle aeration. Since quite violent mechanical agitation is required to remove F pili from cells, and regeneration experiments show that about 50% of depiliated cells grow out new F pili very rapidly, the free F pili must be produced by natural outgrowth. This is consistent with the idea that the F pilus–F factor complex is a virus-like infectious particle that can leave the cell without lysing it in a manner analogous to the release of the rod-shaped DNA male phages (Hofschneider and

Preuss, 1963). However, infectivity of free F pili has not been demonstrated. Infectivity may be lost when the F pilus detaches from the donor cell.

It may be of interest to point out that the spontaneous detachment of F pili from donor cells during normal growth is sufficient to account for the spontaneous separation of F-pili-connected mating pairs as both processes occur at about the same rate (probability of about 0.05/min at 37°C in liquid medium).

 (9) The F pilus is topologically well suited to the protected conduction of long DNA molecules since it appears in negative contrast electron micrographs to have an axial hollow region 20–25 Å in diameter. The interior of the F pilus could be considered as a precisely constructed molecular tunnel, free of obstruction, providing a smooth path through the disorder of thermally agitated liquid media. The moving DNA molecule would not need to expend energy to deform or drag its environment. The transfer of DNA through F pili might represent a "biological superconduction" requiring little or no energy.

(10) Rapid DNA conduction through protein tubes is not without precedent. The tails of at least some tadpole-shaped phages have tubular protein cores, with about the same inner and outer diameters as the F pilus, through which the phage DNA is presumed to pass from the phage head into the cell. The DNA male specific phages, whose diameters are about the same as F pili, must also inject their DNA through their tubular protein coats as the DNA alone penetrates the cell (Tzagoloff and Pratt, 1964).

(11) In electron micrographs of E. coli K12 strains the only surface structures large enough and distinct enough to be detectable as possible candidates for nucleic-acid conduction are F pili, Type I pili, Type V pili, flagella, the spheroidal pieces of cell-wall-related material produced by some strains (Brinton, 1959), and the "conjugation bridges" described by Anderson, Wollman, and Jacob (1957). Type I pili and flagella can be eliminated for genetic reasons. Type V pili do not occur in sufficient numbers. The cell-wall fragments and "conjugation bridges" exist also in pure female cultures. Furthermore, the formation of a conjugation bridge in which the cell wall and membrane are not intact but are fused together to form an intercytoplasmic connection is unlikely, since mechanical disruption of mating pairs does not lead to cell death and a high rate of spontaneous separation would not be expected.

The last alternative mechanism is direct transfer of DNA through the medium. The insensitivity of the mating process to DNAase and the very low transformation frequency of gram-negative bacteria by free DNA makes this possibility unlikely.

2. Transfer of colicinogenic factor and drug resistance transfer factor DNA.
The three known kinds of conjugally transmissible genetic elements of
bacteria — the fertility factors (F), the transmissible colicinogenic factors
(col), and drug resistance transfer factors (RTF) — have many features in
common:

(1) They are self-replicating molecules of DNA, which include a variety
of functional genes in addition to those controlling fertility.
(2) They occur only in gram-negative strains and are widely transmissible
among the various genera and species (Baron, 1965).
(3) They are autotransmissible to recipient cells by conjugation (Watanabe,
1963; Fredericq, 1963).
(4) They can promote the conjugal transmission of other DNA, both
chromosomal and extrachromosomal (Watanabe, 1963; Sugino and
Hirota, 1962; Kahn and Helinski, 1964; 1965; Clowes, 1961; Smith
and Stocker, 1962).
(5) They can genetically recombine with each other (Kahn and Helinski,
1965; Harada *et al.*, 1964).
(6) They can repress or interfere with their own and each other's phenotypic expression (Hirota *et al.*, 1964; Kahn and Helinski, 1964;
Watanabe and Fukasawa, 1962; Watanabe *et al.*, 1962; Nagel de
Zwaig and Anton, 1965).
(7) In the extrachromosomal state they can be eliminated from the cell
by treatment with acridine orange (Hirota, 1960; Watanabe, 1963;
Sugino and Hirota, 1962; Kahn and Helinski, 1964; 1965).
(8) They confer sensitivity to the same class of RNA male specific phages
that requires F pili for attachment and injection. (Meynell and Datta,
1965; Kahn and Helinski, 1965).

Although one can suppose that the DNA of the F, col, and R factors are
all transferred by different mechanisms or by different types of pili, the striking similarities just listed strongly suggest a common mechanism. A simple
and unifying hypothesis is that all conjugal DNA transfer occurs through F
pili. This hypothesis implies that the transmissible F, col, and R factors all
possess the same set of genes determining F piliation and therefore contain
at least these regions of homology in their DNA. The possession of common
fertility genes would permit their recombination with each other and the
repression of each other's phenotypic expression of fertility. Such homology
should be detectable by the technique of physical hybrid formation between
homologous DNA molecules (Falkow and Citarella, 1965).

Not only can male phage sensitivity be conferred upon bacteria by the
presence of one of the transmissible genetic factors; the levels of fertility
and male phage sensitivity also are quantitatively related, as shown later.

This is perhaps the strongest evidence that the phenotypic presence of F pili is required for the fertility of all three factors. As has been pointed out in Section IV-H, a negative test for RNA male phage sensitivity must be interpreted cautiously, since all cells of the culture may not be F piliated and RNA phage can be released from some host cells without lysis. Thus, cultures of bacteria thought to be resistant to male phages by plaque formation, cross-streaking, or adsorption tests may be shown to be phage susceptible by the more sensitive method of titer increase (Brinton *et al.*, 1964). Meynell and Datta (1965) used an improved titer increase technique to show that the presence of the RTF factor conferred RNA male phage sensitivity and that fertility and phage sensitivity varied phenotypically in a coordinate manner.

Kahn and Helinski (1964; 1965) tested colicine V strains for sensitivity to male phage μ by spreading the culture to be tested on nutrient agar with a drop of phage suspension in the center. A positive test was indicated by a clear zone after several hours of incubation. Col V strains, which could transfer both the col V factor and chromosomal markers to recipient cells, were phage sensitive by this test. Col V strains that had impaired fertility lost their phage sensitivity. Reinfection of some of the strains with the col V factor restored fertility and phage sensitivity to the same extent.

Brinton and Carnahan (unpublished [a]) surveyed a series of colicinogenic strains of *Salmonella typhimurium* for F piliation by electron microscopy and found F pili on two of three transmissible strains (col I and col B), but not on strains that were nontransmissible or transmissible at low frequency (col E_1, col E_2, and col K). Although one exceptional col B culture had no F pili by the electron microscope test, its level of fertility had not been determined, and a more sensitive test might have detected F piliation. Clowes (1963) found that col I strains were not sensitive to RNA male phage μ but did not use a sufficiently sensitive test.

Thus, the finding that the structure conducting chromosomal DNA is also necessary for RNA male phage sensitivity permits the extension of the F pili conduction model to include col factors and RTF. The F pili hypothesis of infectious heredity implies that the infectious genetic elements originated by recombination of their functional genes with the F factor, a virus-like molecule of DNA having the capacity to infect recipient cells through its own protein coat without detaching from its host cell. According to this view, the several classes of genetic factors are differentiated only by the kind of noninfectious genes which have become attached to the fertility DNA.

3. Transfer of male phage DNA. The rod-shaped DNA male-specific phages are similar to F pili in having approximately the same diameter and the ability to exit from the cell without lysing it (Hofschneider and Preuss, 1963). Currently available evidence indicating that F pili may serve as the receptors for the DNA male phages may be summarized briefly:

(1) The number of adsorption sites for M13 DNA male phage has been estimated from the rate and extent of phage adsorption to be 3 or 4 (Tzagoloff and Pratt, 1964).
(2) DNA male phages infect only cells containing the F factor.
(3) Bacterial mutants resistant to RNA male phages are usually resistant to DNA male phages (Bradley, 1964); this resistance is due to inability to attach the phage.
(4) The presence of certain strains of resistance transfer factor suppresses RNA and DNA male phage sensitivity coordinately. (Watanabe et al., 1962; Hirota et al., 1964).

The correspondence between number of adsorption sites and maximum number of F pili per cell suggests that only a single adsorption site exists on a given F pilus. The only unique part of an F pilus composed of helically polymerized subunits would be its end. The rod-shaped structure of the DNA phages also suggests that an end-to-end interaction would efficiently discharge their DNA into the cell; however, no definite adsorption of DNA phage could be detected in electron micrographs of phage mixed with F-piliated bacteria (Brinton and Carnahan, unpublished [b]). Since penetration can occur in less than 20 sec (Tzagoloff and Pratt, 1964), the association of the DNA particle with the F pilus during penetration might be very transient and, therefore, microscopically undetectable. The slow adsorption rate of DNA phage (Tzagoloff and Pratt, 1964) could be accounted for by the low probability of collision between the F pilus end and the phage rod end and the small number of F pili per cell at any given time (about one).

4. Transfer of male phage RNA. Electron microscopic observation of mixtures of RNA male phage and male bacteria suggest attachment to the F pilus as the first step in phage infection (Brinton, 1965; Crawford and Gesteland, 1964). A working model of the F pilus–RNA phage interaction will be presented now along with currently available evidence concerning attachment and injection of phage RNA. In this model, the events involved in infection may be divided into three periods: precontact, attachment and penetration, and postpenetration.

Precontact period
(1) Replication of the DNA of the fertility factor and synthesis of F pili protein.
(2) Assembly of F pili protein and fertility factor DNA.
(3) Exit of F pilus–DNA complex from the donor cell. (Spontaneous detachment of the F pilus can eventually occur.)

Attachment and penetration period
(1) Collision of phage particle with attached F pilus.

(2) Attachment of RNA phage particle at any of a large number of sites along the length of the F pilus. A temperature-insensitive reaction which can occur at 0°C.
(3) Release of phage RNA from protein coat.   ⎫   Temperature-sensitive
(4) Conduction of phage RNA via the F pilus ⎬   reactions which occur
    into the cell.   ⎭   at 37°C but not at 0°C.
(5) Attachment of phage to *free* F pili may also occur but no phage RNA is released from the protein coat.

Postpenetration period

(1) Intracellular replication of phage.
(2) Release of mature phage particles with or without cell lysis.

The model assumes that F pili are required for RNA phage adsorption and infection. The following evidence is consistent with this hypothesis:

(1) RNA phages infect only cells containing the F factor, genetically controlling F pili (Brinton, 1965; Brinton et al., 1964; Loeb. 1960; Dettori et al., 1961).
(2) The inability of RNA phages to infect bacteria lacking the F factor results from their failure to attach to these bacteria (Loeb and Zinder, 1961; Crawford and Gesteland, 1964; Dettori et al., 1961; 1963).
(3) The inability of RNA phages to infect bacteria lacking the F factor does not result from their failure to replicate, since spheroplasts of non-F-piliated cells are as susceptible as spheroplasts of F-piliated cells to infection by phage RNA (Paranchych, 1963).
(4) Cells containing the F factor must be phenotypically F piliated to be RNA phage sensitive (Brinton, 1965; Novotny and Brinton, unpublished; Fisher, 1965).
(5) RNA phages can be seen adsorbed along the entire length of either free or attached F pili in the electron microscope (Brinton, 1965; Brinton et al., 1964).
(6) Infection of F-piliated bacteria with certain strains (f_i^+) of the drug resistance transfer factor, RTF, simultaneously suppresses DNA donor ability, agglutinability by male specific antisera, and sensitivity to RNA phages (Hirota et al., 1964; Watanabe et al., 1962). The suppression is phenotypic since all four properties reappear when fi^+ RTF factor is lost or mutates to f_i^-.
(7) Mechanical removal of F pili removes RNA phage adsorption capacity (Brinton, 1965).
(8) Regeneration of F pili restores RNA phage adsorption capacity in proportion to the amount of F pili regenerated (Brinton, 1965).
(9) Mechanical removal of F pili removes the ability to be infected by RNA phage (Brinton, 1965).

(10) RNA phage preattached to male bacteria at 0°C are removed completely by mechanical removal of F pili. Upon warming to 37°C, the amount of phage RNA removable by blending decreases with time until, after about 10 min, approximately 70% can no longer be removed (Brinton, 1965).

(11) The presence of extracellular RNAase or streptomycin can prevent infection of F-piliated bacteria by RNA phage (Zinder *et al.*, 1963; Brock, 1962; Brock and Wooley, 1963).

(12) Extracellular RNAase releases RNA from the phage–bacterium complex *after* phage adsorption if the temperature is high enough to permit penetration (Brinton, 1965).

(13) The rapidity of RNA phage adsorption (K = 2.2×10^{-3} ml/min for R17) (Paranchych and Graham, 1962) shows that attachment is efficient and implies the existence of many receptor sites on sensitive cells (presumably the sides of the F pili).

The F pili conduction model of phage RNA transport helps to explain some puzzling features of RNA phage infection.

The existence of a fraction of bacteria in an F-piliated population which transiently have no F pili (Brinton *et al.*, 1964) implies the existence of a transiently phage resistant fraction of cells in even the most susceptible cultures. Such a fraction has been detected experimentally (Knolle, 1964).

The existence of a large proportion of free F pili in cultures of F-piliated bacteria (Brinton *et al.*, 1964) and the ability of RNA phage to adsorb to them prevents many of the added phage from infecting susceptible cells. This could explain the observation that the viability of RNA phage preparations varies from 10–50% although viable and nonviable particles cannot be separated (Zinder, 1965). Perhaps in the best phage preparations all phage particles are viable but 50% do not form plaques because of adsorption to free F pili.

The inhibition of RNA phage infection by RNAase or streptomycin implies a stage of infection accessible to hydrolysis by RNAase or direct binding by streptomycin. Phage RNA could become accessible during passage from the phage particle into the F pilus or during passage along the F pilus. It is conceivable that the phage RNA could be conducted along the outside surface of the F pilus where it would be more accessible. This might occur if the inside of the F pilus were filled with DNA as is assumed by the F pili conduction model of DNA transfer. The difference between attached and detached F pili responsible for their different phage RNA releasing activities might be that detached F pili have no DNA. More experiments will be required to unravel the numerous possibilities.

VII. Summary and Conclusions

Pili are a large class of bacterial surface filaments, each type with a characteristic structure, whose common property is the ability to pass through the cell wall-membrane barrier without altering its integrity. They are, if one can generalize from Type I and F pili, hollow tubes assembled by polymerization of presynthesized protein molecules. For reasons of topology and the specificity of proteins, pili seem ideally suited for specific transport. One type of pilus can, in fact, transport high molecular weight nucleic acid into or out of the cell.

The kinetics and cytology of the transfer process, as well as the numerical correspondence of F pili with F factors, suggest that the F factor–F pilus complex is a virus-like nucleoprotein. Since detached F pili appear to lose both their DNA and their infectivity, the F factor "virus" must infect a second cell before it leaves the first one.

In analogy to virus transduction, the F factor DNA can transfer not only itself but other DNA to which it has become attached by genetic recombination. An essential difference is that F transfer does not require that the transferred DNA fit into an extracellular nucleoprotein particle. The imposition of this constraint in virus transduction causes transducing viruses to be defective, since virus DNA must be displaced to make room for other DNA. The close association of the F "virus" with the cell removes this constraint and allows the transfer of large amounts of genetic material at high efficiency.

Since F DNA can recombine with DNA whose functions give the cell a selective advantage, the occurrence of transmissible genetic elements is widespread. The abilities to resist drug killing (RTF), to kill other related cells competing for the same ecological niche (colicine factors), and to synthesize new enzymes (F' factors) have become transferable by association with F DNA. Thus, the high transmission efficiency and recombining power of F DNA provide populations of gram-negative bacteria with the ability to rapidly acquire useful new mutations.

The functions of the other, far more numerous kinds of pili remain undetermined. Some possibilities are transport of metabolites or informational macromolecules, colicine-like killing of other cells, or simply adhesion to surfaces. Another possibility is that some of the structures presently called pili are actually rod-shaped viruses being released from cells without noticeably affecting cell growth and division.

NOTES ADDED IN PROOF

Since this article was written, additional evidence consistent with a role of pili in nucleic acid conduction has appeared.

1. The prediction (Section VI-D-3) that the filamentous DNA male phages might adsorb to the distal end of the F pilus has been confirmed by electron microscope observation of negatively stained preparations (Caro and Schnös, 1966).

2. The F pili presumed to exist on col V strains by virtue of their sensitivity to male phage (Section VI-D-2) have actually been observed (Caro and Schnös, 1966).

3. Hirota, Fujii, and Nishimura (1966) have obtained evidence suggesting that R factors contain genes controlling F piliation. A series of non-transmissible, infertile, non-pili-producing R factor mutants were isolated from a pili-producing wild type R factor. The defective R factors could be transmitted independently of the chromosome when present in Hfr or F^+ cells (F-piliated) but were not transmissible if the F factor was removed. Conversely, non-piliated sterile strains containing mutant F factors were restored to piliation and F type fertility by the presence of R factors.

It now seems likely that F pili are involved in the conjugal transfer of chromosome, F factors, col V factor, and f_i^+ R factors. However, it should be noted that the conjugal genetic transfer of col I factors and f_i^- R factors may be mediated by structures other than F pili, or by F pili whose formation is only transiently expressed. Cultures transferring col I at high frequency have been observed to have no F pili (Gemski, 1966; Clowes, 1966). Col I strains of *Salmonella typhimurium* had no pili and were insensitive to male phage by the titer increase test (Gemski, 1966). Strains having f_i^- R factors are as fertile as those containing f_i^+ R factors but have no F pili and are insensitive to male phages (Meynell and Datta, 1966a, b; Watanabe, 1966).

ACKNOWLEDGMENT

This work was supported by a Research Career Development Award and a Research Grant from the National Institute of Allergy and Infectious Diseases of the National Institute of Health.

REFERENCES

Adelberg, E. A., and J. Pittard. 1965. *Bacteriol Rev.* 29: 161.

Anderson, T. F., E. L. Wollman, and F. Jacob. 1957. *Ann. Inst. Pasteur* 93: 450.

Baron, L. S. 1965. *Trans. N. Y. Acad. Sci.* 27: 999.

Beer, H., J. Carnahan, and C. C. Brinton, Jr. Unpublished data.

Bradley, D. E. 1964. *J. Gen. Microbiol.* 35: 471.

Brinton, C. C., Jr. 1959. *Nature* 183: 782.

Brinton, C. C., Jr., 1965. *Trans. N. Y. Acad. Sci.* 27: 1003.

Brinton, C. C., Jr., and L. S. Baron. 1960. *Biochim. Biophys. Acta* 42: 298.

Brinton, C. C., Jr., A. Buzzell, and M. A. Lauffer. 1954. *Biochim. Biophys. Acta* 15: 533.

Brinton, C. C., Jr., and J. Carnahan. Unpublished observations [a].

Brinton, C. C., Jr., and J. Carnahan. Unpublished observations [b].

Brinton, C. C., Jr., and J. Carnahan. Unpublished observations [c].

Brinton, C. C., Jr., P. Gemski, Jr., S. Falkow, and L. S. Baron. 1961. *Biophys. Biochem. Res. Commun.* 5: 293.

Brinton, C. C., Jr., P. Gemski, Jr., and J. Carnahan. 1964. *Proc. Natl. Acad. Sci. U. S.* 776.

Brinton, C. C., Jr., and S. L. Huang. 1962. *Bacteriol. Proc.* G103.

Brinton, C. C., Jr., and M. A. Lauffer. 1959. In *Electrophoresis, Theory, Methods, and Applications*, ed. M. Bier. New York: Academic Press, Inc.

Brinton, C. C., Jr., and M. J. Stone. 1961. *Bact. Proc.* G96.

Brock, T. D. 1962. *Biochem. Biophys. Res. Commun.* 9: 184.

Brock, T. D., and S. O. Wooley, 1963. *Science* 131: 1065.

Campbell, I. 1961. Ph.D. dissertation. Univ. of Edinburgh, Scotland.

Caro, L. G. 1966. *Bact. Proc.* V19.

Caro, L. G., and M. Schnös, *Proc. Natl. Acad. Sci. U. S.* Submitted for publication.

Clowes, R. 1966. Personal Communication.

Clowes, R. C. 1961. *Nature* 190: 988.

Clowes, R. C. 1963. *Biochem. Biophys. Res. Commun.* 13: 449.

Constable, F. L. 1956. *J. Pathol. Bacteriol.* 72: 133.

Crawford, E. M., and R. F. Gesteland. 1964. *Virol.* 22: 165.

Dettori, R., G. A. Maccacaro, and G. L. Piccinin. 1961. *Giorn. Microbiol.* 9: 141.

Dettori, R., G. A. Maccacaro, and M. Turri. 1963. *Giorn. Microbiol.* 11: 15.

Duguid, J. P. 1959. *J. Gen. Microbiol.* 21: 271.

Duguid, J. P., and R. R. Gillies. 1957. *J. Pathol. Bacteriol.* 74: 397.

Duguid, J. P., and R. R. Gillies. 1958. *J. Pathol. Bacteriol.* 75: 519.

Duguid, J. P., I. W. Smith, G. Dempster, and P. N. Edmunds. 1955. *J. Pathol. Bacteriol.* 70: 335.

Falkow, S., and R. V. Citarella. 1965. *J. Mol. Biol.* In press.

Fisher, K. W. 1957a. *J. Gen. Microbiol.* 16: 120.

Fisher, K. W. 1957b. *J. Gen. Microbiol.* 16: 136.

Fisher, K. W. 1965. *J. Gen. Microbiol.* 41: xvii.

Fredericq, P., 1963. *J. Theoret. Biol.* 4: 159.

Gemski, P., Jr., 1964. Ph.D. dissertation. Univ. of Pittsburgh, Pa.

Gemski, P. 1966. Personal Communication.

Gillies, R. R., and J. P. Duguid. 1958. *J. Hyg., Cambridge* 56: 303.

de Haan, P. G., and J. D. Gross. 1962. *Genet. Res., Cambridge* 3: 188.

Harada, K., M. Kameda, M. Suzuki, and S. Mitsuhashi. 1964. *J. Bacteriol.* 88: 1257.

Heumann, W., and R. Marx. 1962. *Archiv Mikrobiol.* 43: 245.

Heumann, W., and R. Marx. 1964. *Archiv Mikrobiol.* 47: 325.

Hirota, Y., Y. Nishimura, F. Ørskov, and I. Ørskov. 1964. *J. Bacteriol.* 87: 341.

Hirota, Fujii, and Nishimura. 1966. *J. Bact.* 91: 1298

Hoeniger, J. F. M. 1965. *J. Gen. Microbiol.* 40: 29.

Hofschneider, P. H., and A. Preuss. 1963. *J. Molec. Biol.* 7: 450.

Houwink, A. L., and W. van Iterson. 1950. *Biochim. Biophys. Acta* 5: 10.

Jacob, F., S. Brenner, and F. Cuzin. 1963. *Cold Spring Harbor Symp. Quant. Biol.* 28: 329.

Kahn, P. L., and D. Helinski. 1964. *J. Bacteriol.* 88: 1573.

Kahn, P. L., and D. Helinski. 1965. *J. Bacteriol.* 90: 1276.

Kellenberger, E., and W. Arber. 1957. *Virol.* 3: 245.

Knolle, P. 1964. *Virol.* 23: 271.

Lodish, H. F., and N. D. Zinder. 1965. *Biochem. Biophys. Res. Commun.* 19: 269.

Loeb. T. 1960. *Science* 131: 932.

Loeb, T., and N. D. Zinder. 1961. *Proc. Natl. Acad. Sci. U. S.* 47: 282.

Meynell, E., and N. Datta. 1965. *Nature* 207: 884.

Meynell, E., and N. Datta. 1966a. *Genet. Res. Cambridge* 7, 134.

Meynell E., and N. Datta, 1966b. *Genet, Res. Cambridge* 7, 141.

Nagel de Zwaig, R., and D. N. Anton. 1965. *Biochem. Biophys. Res. Commun.* 17: 358.

Novotny, C., and C. C. Brinton, Jr. Unpublished data.

Old, D. C. 1963. Ph.D. dissertation. Univ. of Edinburgh, Scotland.

Ørskov, I., and F. Ørskov. 1960. *Acta Pathol. Microbiol. Scand.* 48: 37.

Paranchych, W. 1963. *Biochem. Biophys. Res. Commun.* 11: 28.

Paranchych, W., and A. F. Graham. 1962. *J. Cell. Comp. Physiol.* 60: 199.

Smith, S. M., and B. A. D. Stocker. 1962. *Brit. Med. Bull.* 18: 46.

Sugino, Y., and Y. Hirota. 1962. *J. Bacteriol.* 84: 902.

Tzagoloff H., and D. Pratt. 1964. *Virol.* 24: 372.

Valentine, R. C., and M. Strand. 1965. *Science* 148: 511.

Watanabe, T. 1963. *Bacteriol. Rev.* 27: 87.

Watanabe, T. 1966. Personal Communication.

Watanabe, T., and T. Fukasawa. 1962. *J. Bacteriol.* 83: 727.

Watanabe, T., T. Fukasawa, and T. Takano. 1962. *Virol.* 17: 217.

Weibull, C., and J. Hedvall. 1953. *Biochim. Biophys. Acta* 10: 35.

Wohlhieter, J. H., C. C. Brinton, Jr., and L. S. Baron. 1962. *J. Bacteriol.* 84: 416.

Zinder, N. D. 1965. *Ann. Rev. Microbiol.* 19: 455.

Zinder, N. D., R. C. Valentine, M. Roger, and W. Stoeckenius. 1963. *Virol.* 20: 638.

Bacterial Membranes[1]

M. R. J. Salton

Department of Microbiology
New York University School of Medicine
New York, New York

One of the fascinating discoveries to emerge from the interest in the anatomy and function of the surface structures of the bacterial cell is that not all of the layers normally present are essential for the continued existence of the cell. The rigid cell wall, which accounts for the whole or much of the surface structure of gram-positive bacteria, may be dispensed with, and the resultant protoplast may be capable of further growth or may even under the appropriate conditions enter the L-phase pathway of survival. Organisms of the gram-negative group may also dispense with much, if not all, of the rigid glycopeptide (mucopeptide, glycosaminopeptide), structure and grow as a "spheroplast" form. Whether the gram-negative bacteria can lose other components of their complex envelope structure and continue to survive cannot be said with any degree of certainty at the present time. There is, however, increasing evidence to suggest that gram-negative bacteria may possess two barriers separated by the rigid layer. The release of certain enzymes after treatment with EDTA and lysozyme from a "surface location" (Malamy and Horecker, 1961; Neu and Heppel, 1964) and the nonspecific increase in permeability induced in *Escherichia coli* by treatment with EDTA (Leive, 1965) would be in accord with the existence of a double membrane type of envelope. Indeed, it was suggested that the presence of two such components in gram-negative bacteria could be responsible for their greater resistance to antibacterial agents such as the ionized detergents (Schulman *et al.*, 1955).

[1] Part of the work reviewed was supported by grant GB 2877 from the National Science Foundation.

71

Owing to the greater complexity of the envelope structure of the gram-negative organisms (Salton, 1964) together with the absence of a suitable enzyme system for the selective removal of the outer components, it is not possible to make any definite conclusions about the specific functions and nature of the layers on either side of the glycopeptide wall. In some gram-negative species it is likely that wall and membrane functions are condensed in the form of a single unit membrane type of structure as in the PPLO (pleuropneumonia like organisms) or a more complex "membrane" as in the halophilic bacteria.

Membranes of the gram-positive organisms have been much more amenable to direct investigation, for the walls of many species can be completely removed by digestion with lysozymes or other wall-degrading enzymes. Weibull (1953) was the first to show that bacterial protoplasts and their "ghost" structures could be isolated from *Bacillus megaterium*. These investigations stimulated considerable interest in bacterial membranes, and it has been generally assumed that the membranes isolated after dissolution of the walls represented the plasma membrane structures.

With the development of suitable fixation and sectioning techniques for the examination of thin sections in the electron microscope, it has become evident that, in addition to the limiting plasma membrane, many bacteria possess intracellular membrane systems (Ryter and Kellenberger, 1958; Shinohara *et al.*, 1957). These have been referred to as "mesosomes" (Fitz-James, 1960) and "chondrioids" (van Iterson, 1962). The intracytoplasmic membranes or mesosomes are obviously identical to the "peripheral bodies" seen in the early sections of Chapman and Hillier (1953). The mesosome structure is apparently formed by an invagination of the plasma membrane. Although the internal mesosome membrane systems are most conspicuous in the gram-positive bacteria, they are by no means unique to this class, for membranous organelles have also been seen in sections of various gram-negative species (Murray and Watson, 1965; van Iterson, 1965).

The mesosome membranes appear, in the bacteria studied, in two forms: as a lamellar type of structure resulting from the coiled up membranes, as seen in *Micrococcus lysodeikticus*; or the vesicular type of mesosome, as found in many of the *Bacillus* spp. In the latter organisms, the mesosome is usually seen as a "sac" of membrane vesicles surrounded by the invaginated plasma membrane. Thus, the mesosome membrane vesicles are really external to the bacterial protoplast, and there is now abundant evidence that they are released on dissolution of the wall during protoplast formation (Ryter and Landman, 1964; Fitz-James, 1964). In *Micrococcus lysodeikticus* and other organisms possessing lamellar-like mesosomes, it appears likely that the structures uncoil and become part of the membrane surface during protoplast formation.

There are no obvious differences in chemical composition of bacterial membranes that can be correlated with these two forms, which are most frequently observed in the mesosome structure. Although the lamellar types appear regularly in some organisms and the vesicular types in others, it seems quite feasible that growth conditions, such as temperature or nutritional factors affecting the rates of wall and membrane synthesis, may well influence the anatomical disposition of the final structure.

The presence of intracytoplasmic mesosome membrane structures has, for the time being, introduced an added complication in considerations of bacterial membrane systems. No experimental facts are available at present to show that the mesosome membranes are functionally and structurally distinct from the plasma or protoplast membrane. Indeed, it seems quite possible that the only difference between a mesosome membrane and the plasma membrane may be in its anatomical location in fixed sections of whole bacteria, although a special role in wall synthesis first suggested by Salton (1956) has also been raised again more recently by Fitz-James (1964) and Landman and Halle (1963). It has been suggested by van Iterson (1965) that the greater intensity of tellurite reduction in the mesosome area, compared with that in the plasma membrane region (as seen in thin sections), can be taken as an index of functional difference. While this may appear to be convincing evidence, it should be emphasized that the results based on tellurite reduction are inevitably biased in favor of the mesosome, for there is a greater surface area of membrane for tellurium deposition. This does not, however, constitute proof of intrinsic differences in the ability of mesosome and plasma membranes to reduce tellurite or other indicators, such as tetrazolium compounds. It is the opinion of this author that the differences between membranes derived from plasma and mesosome membrane structures still remain to be defined in precise chemical and biochemical terms. With the realization that this question is still unresolved, it is important to point out that the membrane fractions isolated from bacteria undoubtedly represent the whole plasma and mesosome membrane system of the cell (Salton and Chapman, 1962). Until ways of proving or disproving differences in function and structure have been found, or methods developed for isolating one from the other, bacterial membrane preparations should be referred to as plasma membrane — mesosome membrane fractions. Unless otherwise specified, all subsequent references to "membranes" of gram-positive bacteria can be taken to mean the total mesosome — plasma membrane system.

Anatomy and isolation of membranes from gram-positive bacteria. Micrococcus lysodeikticus was selected as a suitable organism for an investigation of the isolated membrane structures. Thin sections of the membranes isolated from *Micrococcus lysodeikticus* either by direct lysis with lysozyme or by osmotic lysis of protoplasts were examined by Salton and Chapman (1962), and the typical appearance of such preparations is shown in Fig. 1. No differences in the appearance of the membranes as seen in thin sections could be detected when the two methods of isolation were compared. At the time of these studies (Salton and Chapman, 1962), it was suggested that the concentric membrane shells probably represented the unfolded mesosome membranes. As the lamellar-like mesosomes in *Micrococcus lysodeikticus* disappear on conversion to protoplasts, however, it now appears more likely that these concentric membranes may be attributed to the natural propensity for vesicle formation that most membranes exhibit. It is perhaps relevant to add that our attempts to isolate the mesosome structures, by forming protoplasts and lysing them in the presence of agents (e.g. ATP, DNP, Mg^{2+}) known to inhibit the swelling of mitochondria, failed to give fractions differing from those prepared by either of the procedures just mentioned.

The isolated bacterial membranes show the typical profile widely associated with "unit membrane" structures (Robertson, 1959). As is shown in Fig. 1, the membranes from *Micrococcus lysodeikticus* possess the alternate electron dense, transparent, dense layering with an over-all thickness of about 75 Å. The anatomical features of the plasma–mesosome membrane systems of gram-positive bacteria are in marked contrast with the profiles obtained with the envelopes of gram-negative bacteria so elegantly resolved in the studies of Murray, Steed and Elson (1965).

In addition to the general similarity in size and profile, membranes of gram-positive bacteria also possess another property in common with mitochondrial membranes. Recent studies with membranes stained negatively with phosphotungstic acid (PTA) showed that those of both *Bacillus stearothermophilus* (Abram, 1965) and *Micrococcus lysodeikticus* (Biryuzova, *et al.* (1964) possessed the stalked particles so characteristic of mitochondrial cristae membranes. Abram (1965) also mentioned that similar structural units were detected in mesophilic organisms of the gram-negative group. From the information available thus far, the stalked particles appear to be studded over the inner membrane surfaces and do not seem to be localized in the mesosome membranes. The functions of these membrane associated particles have not yet been defined in the bacterial systems, but it is perhaps more than a coincidence that such structural units are generally found in association with respiratory organelles. Other membrane-bound cellular components reported include ribosomes (Nielsen and Abrams, 1964) and bacterial DNA (Ryter and Jacob, 1963; Ganesan and Lederberg, 1965), although the mode of attachment has not been specifically determined.

Isolation of membranes from gram-positive bacteria sensitive to lysozyme can be readily achieved, and the localization of characteristic components such as the cytochromes, carotenoids, phospholipids, and vitamin K_2 compounds in the membranes provides useful 'marker' molecules for investigations of membrane fractionation. Under appropriate conditions a very clear distribution of these components between membrane and cell "sap" or protoplasmic fractions can be achieved. Figures 2 and 3 illustrate the localization of carotenoids and cytochromes in the membranes isolated from *Sarcina lutea*,

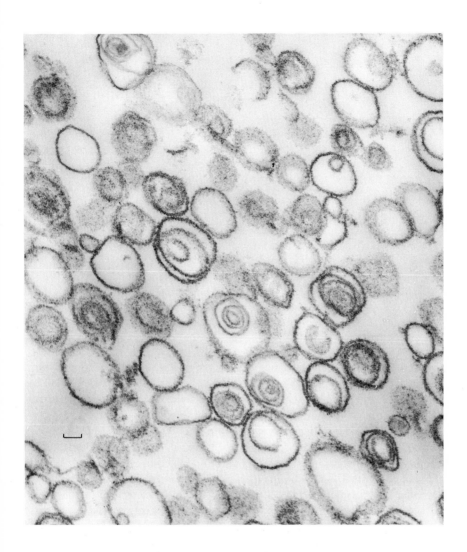

Fig. 1. Typical appearance of the isolated membrane fraction from *Micrococcus lysodeikticus*. The fraction is made up almost entirely of membranous structures; in many cases these consist of a series of concentric shells. Diffuse membranes are due to oblique sectioning. Membrane is stained with uranyl acetate. (From Salton and Chapman, 1962. *J. Ultrastructure Res. 6*:489.)

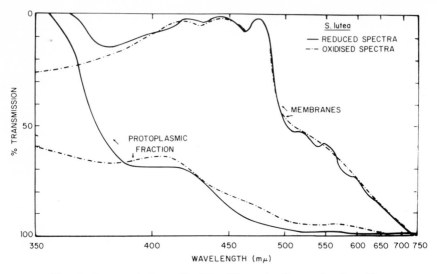

Fig. 2. Spectra before ("oxidized") and after reduction ("reduced") with $Na_2S_2O_4$ of the isolated membranes of *Sarcina lutea* (4.4 mg dry weight/ml.) and of the corresponding protoplasmic fraction as described by Salton and Ehtasham-ud-din. 1965. *Aust. J. Exptl. Biol. and Med. Sci. 43*:255.

and the cytochromes in the membranes from *Bacillus stearothermophilus.* Thus, by digestion of the walls with lysozyme in tris buffer at pH 7.5 and by treatment of the cell lysate with deoxyribonuclease, membrane fractions can be obtained from a number of gram-positive organisms (Salton and Ehtasham-ud-din, 1965); under these conditions the cytochromes and the carotenoids, when present, are completely localized in the membranes. The stability of the membrane structures can be followed by determining the fate of these components on subsequent handling. Any breakdown of the membranes is accompanied by release of nonsedimentable material containing the cytochromes and carotenoids. Isolation of the membranes in tris buffer, with or without $10^{-2} - 10^{-3}$ M Mg^{2+}, has given fractions which have been washed, in the cold, on the centrifuge as many as six or more times without any evidence of release of nonsedimentable carotenoids or cytochromes. Membranes from cells grown in the presence of diphenylamine (DPA) were frequently less stable and the "spontaneous" disaggregation was accompanied by a loss of the bacterial cytochromes (Salton and Ehtasham-ud-din, 1965).

By using suitable conditions for isolating the membranes, it was felt that close to quantitative recovery of these structures would be achieved. The definition of the homogeneity of cellular fractions such as the membranes presents many problems, as pointed out by Shockman *et al.* (1963). More criteria are obviously needed to determine the extent of contamination of bacterial membrane preparations with intracellular components. With these

M. R. J. Salton 77

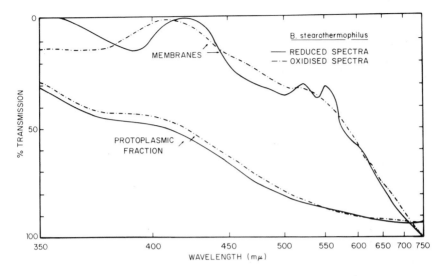

Fig. 3. Spectra before ("oxidized") and after reduction ("reduced") with $Na_2S_2O_4$ of the isolated membranes of *Bacillus stearothermophilus* (2.7 mg dry weight/ml. suspension) and of the corresponding protoplasmic fraction as described by Salton and Ehtisham-ud-din. 1965. *Aust. J. Exptl. Biol. and Med. Sci. 43*:255.

reservations in mind, however, we have been able to obtain consistent values for the amount of membrane isolated from several gram-positive bacteria (Salton and Freer, 1965); these results are presented in Table 1. The extent to which varying the growth conditions may influence the amount of membrane synthesized by *Micrococcus lysodeikticus* has been studied; the data obtained are presented in Table 2. No really dramatic effects on the yields of membranes were observed when complex or defined media were used. The

TABLE 1

YIELDS OF MEMBRANES ISOLATED QUANTITATIVELY
FROM SEVERAL GRAM-POSITIVE BACTERIA

Membranes from:	Age of culture (h)	% Membrane*
Bacillus licheniformis	24	10.6
Bacillus stearothermophilus	9	16.2
Micrococcus lysodeikticus	24	25.2
Sarcina lutea	24	25.0
	48	31.0

* The "% Membrane" is defined as the percentage of the dry weight of cells from which the membranes were isolated; values represent the means of at least two determinations.

inclusion of DPA in the medium results in the inhibition of the formation of
unsaturated carotenoids (Goodwin, 1959), and owing to the instability of the
membranes so formed, variable yields of membrane were observed. As
shown in Table 2 there was some suggestion of higher membrane yields from
older cells.

TABLE 2

INFLUENCE OF GROWTH CONDITIONS ON THE AMOUNTS OF
MEMBRANE ISOLATED FROM *Micrococcus lysodeikticus*

Growth medium	% Membrane*	
	24-hour cells (30°)	48-hour cells (30°)
(A)†		
Synthetic	23.6	29.0
PWYE	25.2	23.1
PWYE + diphenylamine	7.4, 11.8, 25.5	22.3
(B)‡		
PWYE	23.4	29.4
PWYE + diphenylamine	18.7	19.2

* "% Membrane" expressed as a percentage of the dry weight of cells from which the
membranes were isolated; individual values for % membranes given for diphenylamine-
grown cells, all other determinations are mean values of at least two estimates.

† Cells grown with continuous agitation on the New Brunswick Shaker.

‡ Cells grown by aeration with compressed air.

Chemical composition of bacterial membranes. Since the isolation of
Bacillus megaterium membranes by Weibull (1953) a number of investigations
of the composition of bacterial membranes has been reported and these have
been reviewed by Kodicek (1962). These earlier and subsequent studies
(Freimer, 1963; Shockman *et al.*, 1963; Salton and Freer, 1965) have established that in over-all composition bacterial membranes are not dissimilar
to those isolated from other sources, i.e., they are made up largely of protein
and lipid. Protein contents generally range between 55–75% and lipids
account for about 20–30% of the weight of the membrane. Despite extensive
washing during preparation, most bacterial membrane fractions contain
RNA, usually ranging between 1–3%, although higher values have been reported in several instances.

The composition of membranes isolated from several gram-positive
bacteria grown under different conditions is illustrated in Table 3 by some
of the data from recent studies of Salton and Freer (1965). Apart from the
low lipid contents of membranes isolated from *Micrococcus lysodeikticus*
grown on a defined medium, no marked effects of growth conditions on composition were apparent. Shockman *et al.*, (1963) found that on growth in
media permitting threonine and valine depletion, however, a significant in-

TABLE 3

PROTEIN, RNA, AND P CONTENTS OF MEMBRANES ISOLATED FROM
M. lysodeikticus, *S. lutea*, AND *B. licheniformis*

Medium	Membranes from 24-hr cells		
	% Protein	% RNA	% P
M. lysodeikticus			
Synthetic	64	1.4	0.5
PWYE (A)*	63	1.7	0.8
(B)†	66	2.7	0.9
PWYE + diphenylamine‡	75	2.4	0.7
S. lutea			
PWYE	53	3.3	0.6
PWYE + diphenylamine‡	61	7.5	——
B. licheniformis			
PWYE + Glu**	75	0.8	——

* = cultures grown on New Brunswick Shaker.
† = cultures aerated with compressed air.
‡ = 25 μg diphenylamine/ml medium.
** = PWYE + 1% monosodium glutamate.

fluence on the lipid contents and other constituents of the membranes of *Streptococcus faecalis* could be observed. It will thus be of considerable interest to determine to what extent the composition of the membrane can be varied without impairing its functions.

That membranes can accomodate some alteration in their constituents is illustrated by the growth of cells in the presence of DPA. Thus the unsaturated carotenoids do not appear to be obligatory constituents of the cell membranes of organisms such as *Micrococcus lysodeikticus* and *Sarcina lutea*. Whether the membrane instability, resulting frequently from growth in the presence of DPA can be ascribed to a stabilizing role for carotenoids in bacterial membranes cannot be said at present. The most conspicuous effect of this compound is undoubtedly on the formation of the unsaturated carotenoids, but Cho, Corpe, and Salton (1964) also found changes in the fatty-acid composition of the membrane lipids, shown in Table 4. It is not known whether these changes in fatty-acid composition are because of direct effects on the enzymes synthesizing these membrane constituents or result indirectly from other effects on the membrane structure.

Some bacteria can apparently tolerate the presence of a foreign compound such as DPA in the membrane. DPA was detected in the membrane lipid fraction obtained from *Bacillus megaterium* by examination of the ultraviolet absorption spectra of the lipids in iso-octane and by thin-layer chromatography. Figure 4 shows the ultraviolet absorption spectra of the lipid fractions extracted from the membranes isolated from "normal" and DPA-

TABLE 4

INFLUENCE OF GROWING BACTERIA IN THE PRESENCE OF DIPHENYLAMINE
ON THE FATTY-ACID COMPOSITION OF LIPIDS EXTRACTED FROM
ISOLATED MEMBRANES

Methyl esters	Fatty acid composition of lipids (%)			
	Isolated membranes			
	M. lysodeikticus		Sarcina lutea	
	without DPA	with DPA	without DPA	with DPA
$C_{12:0}$	0.4	trace	——	——
$C_{13:0\ br.}$	1.2	0.2	——	——
$C_{14:0}$	4.4	0.2	1.8	0.3
$C_{14:0\ br.}$	——	0.2	6.0	0.3
$C_{14:1}$	——	——	——	——
$C_{15:0\ iso}$	0.4	——	——	——
$C_{15:0\ anteiso}$	85.4	56.4	80.2	74.2
$C_{16:0}$	0.2	4.4	1.5	8.0
$C_{16:0\ br.}$	5.0	4.0	1.8	6.1
$C_{16:1}$	——	——	1.3	——
$C_{17:0\ iso}$	0.4	——	——	——
$C_{17:0\ anteiso}$	2.6	34.6	1.3	9.8
$C_{18:0}$	trace	trace	2.5	0.3
$C_{18:0\ neo}$	——	——	——	——
$C_{18:1}$	——	——	3.6	1.0
$C_{20:1}$	——	——	——	——

The values for the percentage fatty-acid composition of the lipids represent the percentage of the total recovered methyl esters separated on the gas-liquid chromatograph columns and have been calculated from the peak areas. The fatty acids are designated by their carbon number with the number of double bonds.

grown cells of *Bacillus megaterium*. As shown in Figure 4 the most characteristic constituent of the normal membrane lipid detectable in the ultraviolet is the vitamin K_2 compound, which has been shown by Bishop and King (1962) to be localized in the bacterial membrane. In the membrane lipid fraction from *Bacillus megaterium* grown in the presence of DPA, both vitamin K_2 (C_{35} compound) and DPA were detected, and the presence of the latter and an additional unknown compound was confirmed by thin-layer chromatography. The membrane lipid fractions extracted from *Micrococcus lysodeikticus* also showed some differences on ultraviolet spectroscopy (Fig. 5), but as could be anticipated from these spectra much smaller amounts of DPA were found by thin-layer chromatography. In both instances there is an apparent reduction in the amounts of the vitamin K_2 compounds in the membrane lipid. The reduction in membrane vitamin K_2 contents becomes more pronounced when the concentration of DPA in the growth medium is increased above the level of $25\mu g/ml$.

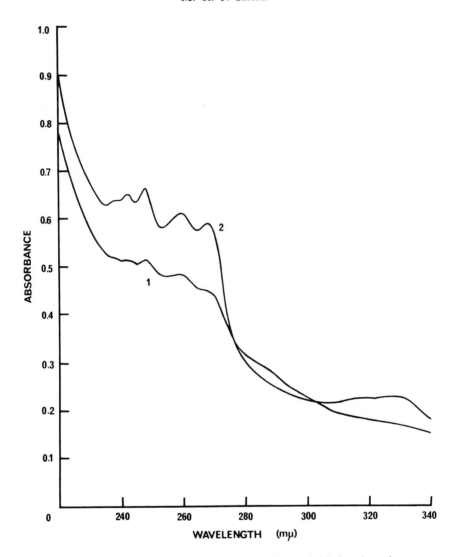

Fig. 4. Ultraviolet absorption spectra of the lipid fractions in isooctane, extracted from the isolated membranes of *Bacillus megaterium* grown in the presence of 25 μg diphenylamine/ml. medium (curve '1') and in the absence of DPA (i.e., 'normal' membranes) as shown in curve '2.' The amounts of lipid dissolved in isooctane were 0.23 mg/ml. (curve 1) and 0.53 mg/ml. (curve 2) for the membranes from DPA—grown and normal cells respectively. (Unpublished observations, Salton).

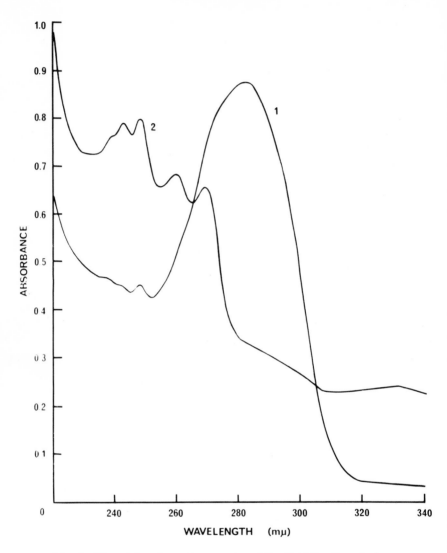

Fig. 5. Ultraviolet absorption spectra of the lipid fractions in iso-octane, extracted from the isolated membranes of *Micrococcus lysodeikticus* grown in the presence of 25 μg diphenylamine/ml. medium (curve '1') and in the absence of DPA (i.e. 'normal' membranes) as shown in curve '2.' The amount of membrane lipid dissolved in isooctane were 1 mg/ml. for both normal and DPA-grown preparations. (Unpublished observations, Salton).

M. R. J. Salton 83

Subunits of bacterial membranes. The bacterial plasma-mesosome membrane system obviously performs a number of biochemical functions. The electron transport system is localized in the membranes, permeation mechanisms for transporting substances into and out of the cell must reside in the membrane, and it is likely that some steps in wall biosynthesis would be located in the membrane structure. In addition, it would seem probable that certain enzymes involved in the biosynthesis of membrane constituents may also be found specifically in the membrane. Thus it would be expected that the membranes contain a wide variety of enzymatically active proteins or enzyme complexes.

To obtain some information about the nature of membrane "subunits," investigations of the products of disaggregation of the bacterial membranes were undertaken. Nonionic and ionized detergents were effective in solubilizing or disaggregating the membranes. Treatment with a nonionic detergent, "Nonidet P. 40," the active constituent of which is a polyoxyethylated alkyl phenol, disaggregated the membranes to the extent of 96% (as determined by amounts of nonsedimentable material and sedimentable residues). Sedimentation patterns obtained in the ultracentrifuge showed a major component with a sedimentation coefficient of 3.1S. The products obtained after disaggregation with other detergents were examined in the ultracentrifuge, and the resulting data compared with those obtained by sonic vibration in Table 5 (Salton and Netschey, 1965). The formation of 5S components by sonication of a bacterial membrane has also been reported by Brown (1965).

TABLE 5

DISAGGREGATION OF MEMBRANES BY VARIOUS TREATMENTS AND
SEDIMENTATION COEFFICIENTS OF PRODUCTS

Membranes	Treatment	Buffer	% Disaggregation (as % nonsedimentable material)	Sedimentation coefficients (at 1% conc.) (Svedberg units)
M. lysodeikticus	Nonidet P.40*	PO₄	96	3.1
	Nonidet P.40	Tris	>95	3.1
	SDS	PO₄	75	1.7
	DTAB	PO₄	40	0.7
	Sonic vibration	PO₄	>95	4.2
S. lutea	Nonidet P.40	PO₄	>95	3.3 (3.56†)
	Nonidet P.40	Tris	>95	3.4 (1.88†)

* Polyoxyethylated alkyl phenol.
† Sedimentation coefficients extrapolated to zero concentration.

Considering the variety of activities associated with membrane structures, it is surprising that treatment by ultrasound has produced components ("subunits"?) of such apparent uniformity. Attempts to resolve the 4.2S material from the sonicated membranes by electrophoresis under a variety of conditions have thus far proved unsuccessful. However, the "subunit" material does migrate as a single major component both on sucrose-gradient electrophoresis and on thin-layer plates of G100 Sephadex. Other fractionation procedures have been used, and prior removal of lipids by treatment with *n*-butanol gave soluble and insoluble protein fractions from the membranes.

At the present time we have no precise information about the variety of protein or lipoprotein subunits in membrane systems. With specific transporting mechanisms localized in the membrane together with electron transport systems in the bacterial membranes it is evident that they must contain a variety of "functional" proteins. The presence of "structural" protein or proteins that account for a substantial fraction of the membrane is believed to be a common feature of several membrane systems, but it is not yet clear how universal this property may be. Thus, the characterization of the "functional" and "structural" proteins of membranes is of considerable interest and such studies will permit us to build up a more complete picture of the molecular anatomy of living membrane systems.

Indeed, the recent exciting work on a "functional" membrane protein in the β-galactoside transport system of *Escherichia coli* reported by Fox and Kennedy (1965) has pointed the way to a new approach in the localization and specific labeling of important membrane components. Such studies will undoubtedly reveal new knowledge of the mechanism of transportation of substances across membranes and lead to an understanding of the basic functioning of a structure common to all cellular systems.

REFERENCES

Abram, D. 1965. *J. Bacteriol*. 89: 855.

Biryuzova, V. I., M. A. Lukoyanova, N. S. Gelman and A. I. Oparin. 1964. *Dokel Akad. Nauk. SSSR* 156: 198.

Bishop, D. H. L., and H. K. King. 1962. *Biochem. J.* 85: 550.

Brown, J. W. 1965. *Biochim. Biophys. Acta* 94: 97.

Chapman, G. B., and J. Hillier. 1953. *J. Bacteriol.* 66: 362.

Cho, K. Y., W. A. C. Corpe, and M. R. J. Salton. 1964. *Biochem. J.* 93: 26c.

Fitz-James, P. C. 1960. *J. Biophys. Biochem. Cytol.* 8: 507.

Fox, C. F., and E. P. Kennedy. 1965 *Proc. Nat. Acad. Sci.* 54: 891.

Freimer, E. H. 1963. *J. Exptl. Med.* 117: 377.

Ganesan, A. T., and J. Lederberg. 1965. *Biochem. Biophys. Res. Commun.* 18: 824.

Goodwin, T. W. 1959. *Advan. Enzymol.* 21: 295.

Kodicek, E. 1962. In *Recent Progress in Microbiology*, *Proc. 8th Intern. Congr. Microbiol.*, Montreal: University of Toronto Press. P. 23.

Landman, O. E., and S. Halle. 1963. *J. Mol. Biol.* 7: 721.

Leive, L. 1965. *Proc. Natl. Acad. Sci.* 53: 745.

Malamy, M., and B. L. Horecker. 1961. *Biochem. Biophys. Res. Commun.* 5: 104.

Murray, R. G. E., P. Steed, and H. E. Elson. 1965. *Canad. J. Microbiol.* 11: 547.

Murray, R. G. E., and S. W. Watson. 1965. *J. Bacteriol.* 89: 1594.

Neu, H. C., and L. A. Heppel. 1964. *Biochem. Biophys. Res. Commun.* 17: 215.

Nielsen, L., and A. Abrams. 1964. *Biochem. Biophys. Res. Commun.* 17: 680.

Robertson, J. D. 1959. *Biochem. Soc. Symp.* (Cambridge, Eng.) 16: 3.

Ryter, A., and F. Jacob. 1963. *Compt. Rend.* 257: 3060.

Ryter, A., and E. Kellenberger. 1958. *Z. Naturforsch.* 13b: 597.

Ryter, A., and Landman, O. E. 1964. *J. Bacteriol.* 88: 457.

Salton, M. R. J. 1956. In *Proc. Soc. Gen. Microbiol. Symp.* 6: 81.

Salton, M. R. J. 1964. *The Bacterial Cell Wall.* Amsterdam: Elsevier Publishing Co·

Salton, M. R. J., and J. A. Chapman. 1962. *J. Ultrastruct. Res.* 6: 489.

Salton, M. R. J., and A. F. M. Ehtasham-ud-din. 1965. *Austr. J. Exptl. Biol. Med. Sci.* 43: 255.

Salton, M. R. J., and J. H. Freer. 1965. *Biochim. Biophys. Acta* 107: 531.

Salton, M. R. J., and A. Netschey. 1965. *Biochim. Biophys. Acta* 107: 539.

Schulman, J. H., B. A. Pethica, A. V. Few, and M. R. J. Salton. 1955. In *Prog. Biophysics and Biophysical Chem.* 5: 41.

Shinohara, C., K. Fukushi, and J. Suzuki. 1957. *J. Bacteriol.* 74: 413.

Shockman, G. D., J. J. Kolb, B. Bakay, M. J. Conover, and G. Toennies. 1963. *J. Bacteriol.* 85: 168.

van Iterson, W. 1962. In *Recent Progress in Microbiology. Proc. 8th Intern. Congr. Microbiol.*, *Montreal:* University of Toronto Press. p. 14.

van Iterson, W. 1965. *Bacteriol. Rev.* 29: 299.

Weibull, C. 1953. *J. Bacteriol.* 66: 688 and 696.

Bacterial Lipids

John H. Law

Department of Biochemistry
University of Chicago
Chicago, Illinois

The flexible permeability barrier that bounds the cellular cytoplasm is composed of lipids and proteins and, in some cases, other materials as well. While there are proponents of the idea that either the lipids alone or the proteins alone determine the properties of the membrane, most prefer to believe that it is the interaction of these two components which gives the membrane its characteristic and vital properties. The first task is, of course, to define in chemical and physical terms the individual components of the membrane. Since the lipids are smaller and less sensitive molecules than the proteins, they have received more attention, and for many membranes accurate inventories of lipids are available. The protein components have received attention only quite recently, as we have heard from Dr. Salton, so that much work lies between our present vantage point and a complete understanding of how membranes work.

In considering the relationship between the biochemistry of lipid metabolism and the structure and function of a membrane it is desirable to choose a system offering the simplest case in terms of the component lipids. In bacterial membranes the number and structural variety of lipids seems to be less than in other organisms. In the *E scherichia coli* membrane, for example, one finds that the lipid complement consists of about 90–95% of a mixture of two phospholipids, small amounts of quinones, and traces of neutral lipids and free fatty acids (Kaneshiro and Marr, 1962; Kates, 1964). The phospholipids have a very simple fatty-acid composition consisting of saturated, monounsaturated, and cyclopropane fatty acids (Kaneshiro and Marr, 1962). Of course, this relative simplicity is no proof that the *E. coli* membrane is less complicated than the membrane in other organisms, for we may find that the protein component of the membrane is unusually complex when we finally learn something of it.

For consideration of the lipids in membranes, then, it seems that bacteria offer the most simplified situation; I shall therefore limit this discussion to bacterial lipids. This subject has been expertly reviewed in considerable detail by Kates (1964) and Lennarz (1966), and so I shall summarize only briefly the differences between the lipid composition of bacteria and other organisms, and then proceed to discuss in fuller detail the biosynthesis and metabolism of bacterial lipids.

I. Lipid Composition of Bacteria

The major types of lipids found in bacterial membranes are glycerol-3-phosphate derivatives (I), particularly those where R_3 is ethanolamine (phosphatidylethanolamine); glycerol (phosphatidylglycerol); or a substituted glycerol (aminoacyl phosphatidylglycerol or diphosphatidylglycerol). Phosphatidylcholine, the major phospholipid of most plant and animal tissues, is a rare phospholipid in bacteria. It occurs abundantly only in members of the genus *Agrobacterium* (Kaneshiro and Marr, 1962; Goldfine and Ellis, 1964). Variations of this structure are possible. One may find, especially in anaerobes (Allison *et al.*, 1962; Wegner and Foster, 1963; Baumann *et al.*, 1965), vinyl ether linkages rather than ester linkages (II), and in one case, an unusual phosphatidylglycerol phosphate derivative from *Halobacterium cutirubrum* (Kates *et al.*, 1965) contains terpenoid ether groups (III). In addition, many gram-positive organisms have glycosylglycerols (IV) where the sugars may be mannose, galactose, or glucose (Lennarz, 1966). The fatty acids (R_1 and R_2) found in these compounds are usually 12–18 carbon chains, sometimes with methyl branches or cyclopropane rings, but never with more than one double bond. The relative simplicity of the bacterial lipid mixtures is indicated in Table 1.

It is amusing to reflect that ten years ago, when very little was known of the nature of bacterial lipids, the tendency was to suspect that many complex and unusual compounds would be found here. Hofmann and his coworkers (see Hofmann, 1962) had found the cyclopropane fatty acid, lactobacillic acid, in the lipids of *Lactobacillus arabinosus*. However, this proved to be one of the few examples of the unusual in the lipids of the true bacteria, although the mycobacteria have continued to provide complex surprises (Asselineau, 1962; Lederer, 1964).

TABLE 1

DISTRIBUTION OF LIPIDS IN NATURE

Lipid type	Bacteria	Fungi	Green plants	Animals
Phosphatidylethanolamine	+	+	+	+
Phosphatidylserine	+	+	+	+
Phosphatidylcholine	rare	+	+	+
Phosphatidylglycerol	+	?	+	?
Diphosphatidylglycerol	+	+	+	+
Aminoacylphosphatidylglycerol	+	−	−	−
Phosphatidylinositol	rare	+	+	+
Phosphatidic acid	+	+	+	+
Plasmalogens	rare	?	+	+
Glycolipids	+	+	+	+
Quinones	+	+	+	+
Triglycerides	−	+	+	+
Sterols	−	+	+	+
Sphingolipids	−	+	+	+
Polyunsaturated fatty acids	−	+	+	+
Fatty acids of chain greater than 20	rare	+	+	+
Cyclopropane fatty acids	+	−	rare	−

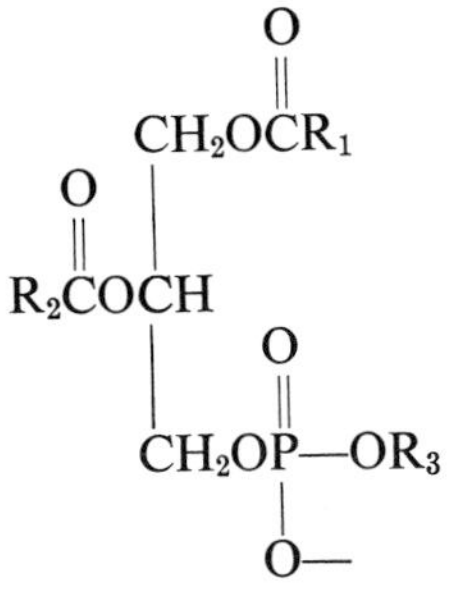

$$CH_2OCR_1$$ (O)

$$R_2COCH$$ (O)

$$CH_2OP{-}OR_3$$ (O), $O-$

I

$$CH_2OCH{=}CHR_1$$

$$R_2CO{-}CH$$ (O)

$$CH_2O{-}P{-}OR_3$$ (O), $O-$

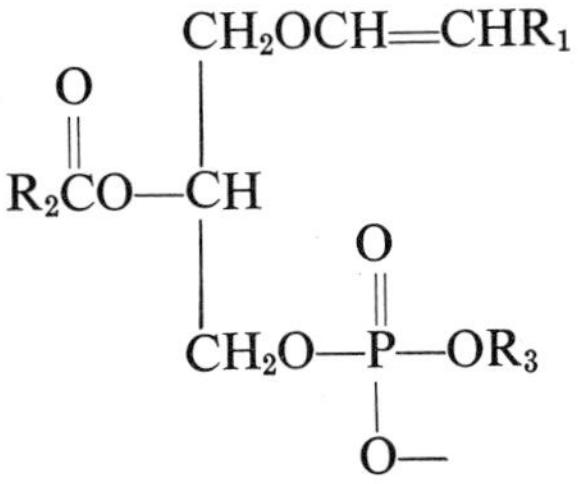

II

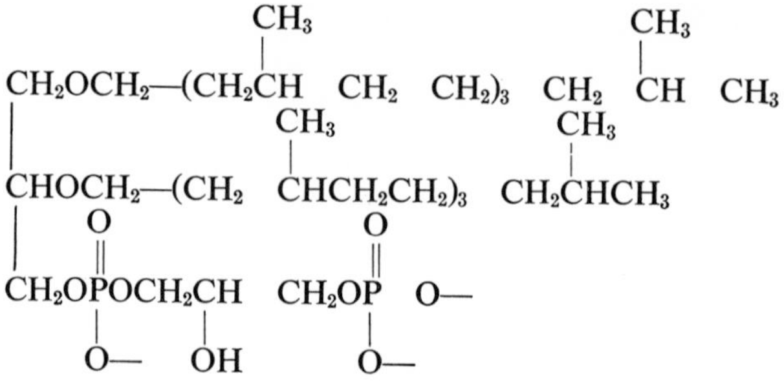

$$
\begin{array}{ccccccc}
& & CH_3 & & & CH_3 & \\
& & | & & & | & \\
CH_2OCH_2 & \!\!-\!\!(CH_2CH & CH_2 & CH_2)_3 & CH_2 & CH & CH_3 \\
| & & CH_3 & & CH_3 & & \\
& & | & & | & & \\
CHOCH_2 & \!\!-\!\!(CH_2 & CHCH_2CH_2)_3 & & CH_2CHCH_3 & & \\
| & O & & O & & & \\
& \| & & \| & & & \\
CH_2OPOCH_2CH & & CH_2OP & O\!\!- & & & \\
| & | & & | & & & \\
O\!\!- & OH & & O\!\!- & & &
\end{array}
$$

III

$$
\begin{array}{cc}
& O \\
& \| \\
& CH_2OCR_1 \\
O & | \\
\| & \\
R_2COCH & \\
& | \\
& CH_2O\!\!-\!\!\text{mono or disaccharide}
\end{array}
$$

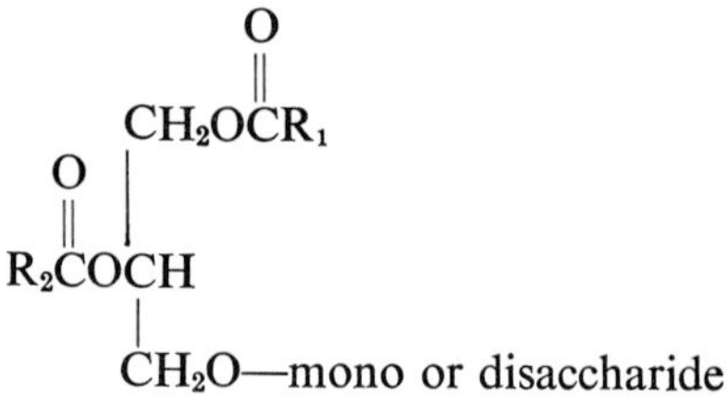

IV

Bacterial membranes are similar to mitochondrial membranes, since both contain principally phospholipids, although in mitochondria long-chain poly-unsaturated fatty acids as well as small amounts of sterols are present (Marinetti *et al.*, 1958; Fleischer *et al.*, 1961). It is likely that the functional role of lipids in mitochondria can be filled by a combination of phospholipids and the quinone coenzymes alone (Fleischer *et al.*, 1962).

II. Biosynthesis of Bacterial Lipids

How are the two main types of bacterial lipids, the phospholipids and the glycolipids, made? First, let us consider briefly the synthesis of the aliphatic chains, the fatty acids. The recent work of Vagelos, Wakil, and Bloch has provided a fairly complete outline of this process as it occurs in *E. coli* (Vagelos, 1964; Wakil *et al.*, 1964; Sauer *et al.*, 1964; Majerus *et al.*, 1964, 1965; Lennarz *et al.*, 1962; Norris *et al.*, 1964). It has become considerably more intricate and exciting than could have been predicted 10 years ago, when most workers were still thinking in terms of the reversal of β-oxidation of fatty acids.

Acetyl coenzyme A, which arises from either the decarboxylation of pyruvate or the activation of acetic acid by ATP, provides the carbon atoms of the chain. For the formation of the bonds of the chain, however, this molecule requires further activation to the carboxylated derivative, malonyl

CoA (Reaction 1). Acetyl groups and malonyl groups are then transferred by specific transacylases to a small protein, the acyl carrier protein (ACP), which bears a 4′ phosphopantetheine prosthetic group, similar to that at the carrier end of coenzyme A (Reactions 2 and 3). The acetyl and malonyl groups are then caused to undergo decarboxylative coupling to form the β-keto acyl ACP (Reaction 4). Reduction, dehydration, and a second reduction of this compound (Reactions 5, 6, and 7) lead to the 4-carbon acyl chain. Repetition of these steps with additional molecules of malonyl ACP eventually leads to the formation of saturated fatty acids, primarily hexadecanoic acid.

$$
CH_3\underset{SCoA}{\overset{O}{\parallel}{C}} + CO_2 + ATP \rightleftharpoons CH_2\underset{CO_2^-}{\underset{\mid}{\overset{O}{\parallel}{C}}}{SCoA} + ADP + Pi \quad (1)
$$

$$
CH_3\underset{SCoA}{\overset{O}{\parallel}{C}} + ACPSH \rightleftharpoons CH_3\overset{O}{\overset{\parallel}{C}}{-}SACP + CoASH \quad (2)
$$

$$
\underset{\underset{CO_2^-}{\mid}}{CH_2}{-}\underset{SCoA}{\overset{O}{\diagup\!\!\diagdown}{C}} + ACPSH \rightleftharpoons \underset{\underset{CO_2^-}{\mid}}{CH_2}{-}\overset{O}{\overset{\parallel}{C}}{-}SACP + CoASH \quad (3)
$$

$$
CH_3\overset{O}{\overset{\parallel}{C}}{-}SACP + \underset{\underset{CO_2^-}{\mid}}{CH_2}{-}\overset{O}{\overset{\parallel}{C}}{-}SACP
$$
$$
\rightleftharpoons CH_3\overset{O}{\overset{\parallel}{C}}{-}CH_2\overset{O}{\overset{\parallel}{C}}{-}SACP + CO_2 + ACPSH \quad (4)
$$

$$
CH_3\overset{O}{\overset{\parallel}{C}}{-}CH_2\overset{O}{\overset{\parallel}{C}}SACP + NADPH + H^+ \rightleftharpoons CH_3\overset{OH}{\overset{\mid}{C}}HCH_2\overset{O}{\overset{\parallel}{C}}{-}SACP + NADP^+ \quad (5)
$$

$$
CH_3\overset{OH}{\overset{\mid}{C}}HCH_2\overset{O}{\overset{\parallel}{C}}{-}SACP \rightleftharpoons CH_3CH{=}CH\overset{O}{\overset{\parallel}{C}}{-}SACP + H_2O \quad (6)
$$

$$CH_3CH{=}CH{-}\overset{\overset{\displaystyle O}{\|}}{C}SACP + NADPH + H^+$$

$$\rightleftharpoons CH_3CH_2CH_2\overset{\overset{\displaystyle O}{\|}}{C}{-}SACP + NADP^+ \quad (7)$$

Mono-olefinic acids are produced by the operation of a chain-length specific enzyme which circumvents Reaction 6 and leads to a *cis* unconjugated olefinic intermediate with the double bond lying between atoms 3 and 4 (scheme 1, Reaction 6′).

Scheme 1

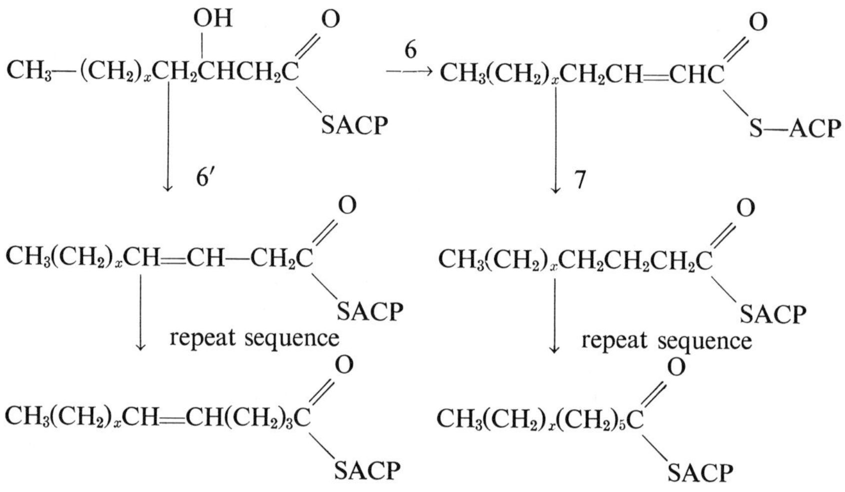

Elongation of this nonconjugated olefinic acid leads ultimately to the hexadecenoic and octadecenoic acids. It can be seen that the specificity of the 3,4 dehydrase enzyme for different values of x can lead to different products, and indeed, the octadecenoic acids with double bonds at 11, 12 (*cis*-vaccenic) and 9, 10 (oleic) are both observed in the bacterial fatty acids.

Branched chain acids may arise by using a branched chain starter in place of acetyl ACP. These branched acids can arise from amino acid catabolism, as has been shown by Lennarz (1961). Other methods of introducing branches by alteration of straight chain compounds will be discussed later.

Pathways by which fatty acids are esterified to glycerol by microbial enzymes are not yet fully investigated. Pieringer (1965) and Pieringer and Kunnes (1965) have reported two reactions in extracts of *E. coli* that lead to phosphatidic acid. One involves the esterification of glycerol phosphate by acyl CoA derivatives.

$$\text{glycerol-3-phosphate} + 2\,\text{RC}\underset{\text{SCoA}}{\overset{\text{O}}{\diagup}} \rightarrow \text{phosphatidic acid} + 2\,\text{CoASH} \qquad (8)$$

and the second is a phosphorylation of a diglyceride:

$$\text{1,2-diglyceride} + \text{ATP} \rightarrow \text{phosphatidic acid} + \text{ADP}. \qquad (9)$$

The role of ACP derivatives in Reaction 8 has not yet been investigated. Furthermore, it appears that the products of fatty acid synthesis by bacterial enzymes are the free acids, rather than thiol esters. Massaro and Lennarz (1965) have shown that in *Bacillus megaterium* free fatty acids can be activated to coenzyme A derivative using energy from ATP. It seems uneconomical, however, to release the group transfer energy of the thiol ester of the ACP derivative and then to expend additional energy to raise the carboxylic acid to a high group-transfer potential for ester synthesis—unless some other more important, and at present not understood, advantage is realized concurrently.

Phosphatidic acid is the parent compound from which the other bacterial phospholipids are formed. Several bacterial phospholipids have the 1,2-diacyl-3-phosphoglycerol stereochemistry (Hildebrand and Law, 1964), in conformity with phospholipids from nearly all natural sources. The investigations of Kanfer and Kennedy (1964) have charted the pathway to the other phospholipids in *E. coli*. As shown in Reaction 10, the presumed first step is the conversion of phosphatidic acid to a nucleotide derivative:

$$\text{phosphatidic acid} + \text{CTP} \rightleftharpoons \text{CDP-diglyceride} + \text{PPi}. \qquad (10)$$

This lipid-nucleotide then reacts with serine:

$$\text{CDP-diglyceride} + \text{serine} \rightleftharpoons \text{phosphatidylserine}. \qquad (11)$$

Reaction 11 is catalyzed by a soluble enzyme that acts *in vitro* only in a medium of very high ionic strength and in the presence of a medium chain length alcohol such as *n*-octanol. This stimulatory effect of a surfactant is an example of a phenomenon commonly encountered in lipid enzymology, and it will be discussed again later. Very little phosphatidylserine is found in *E. coli* cells, probably because a potent decarboxylase for this compound can be found in particulate preparations of the cell extracts.

$$\text{phosphatidylserine} \rightarrow \text{phosphatidylethanolamine} + CO_2. \qquad (12)$$

Thus we arrive at the major lipid product in the *E. coli* cells, phosphatidylethanolamine (Kanfer and Kennedy, 1963). Cytidine diphosphodiglyceride

also undergoes another reaction in the presence of enzymes from *E. coli*:
CDP diglyceride + glycerol-3-phosphate

$$\rightleftharpoons \text{phosphatidylglycerol-3'-phosphate} + \text{CMP} \quad (13)$$

$$\text{phosphatidylglycerol-3'-phosphate} \rightarrow \text{phosphatidylglycerol} + \text{Pi.} \quad (14)$$

While in the *E. coli* cell, phosphatidylglycerol is a minor component, in some gram-positive organisms it is a major component. It may occur as an aminoacyl derivative, with an ester of glycine, alanine, lysine, glutamic acid, or aspartic acid occupying the 2' or 3' position (McFarlane, 1964; Houtsmiller and Van Deenen, 1964).

These biosynthetic investigations of Kennedy and his colleagues with *E. coli* give us nearly our only information on phospholipid biosynthesis in bacteria. Since the variety of compounds in bacteria is very limited, however, these reactions will probably be sufficient, if they prove general, to explain the synthesis of most of the bacterial lipids.

The synthesis of mannosyldiglycerides in *Micrococcus lysodeikticus* has been studied by Lennarz (1964) and Lennarz and Talamo (1966). This organism contains mannosylmannosyl $(1 \rightarrow \alpha)$ diglyceride. Extracts of the organism catalyze the reaction of 1,2-diglyceride with GDP-D-mannose to give a monomannoside, which then adds a second mannose from the nucleotide.

Kaufman *et al.*, (1965) have demonstrated an analogous formation of a galactosylglucosyl diglyceride by extracts of *Pneumococcus*. In this case the sugars are added sequentially from the uridine nucleotides to an endogenous lipid acceptor, presumably a diglyceride.

III. The Dynamic State of Bacterial Lipids and Control of Lipid Synthesis

In logarithmic cultures of *E. coli* cells it appears that most of the phospholipids are stable and do not turn over (Kanfer and Kennedy, 1963). This can be understood in terms of a growing lipoprotein membrane that must be continually synthesized to permit cell expansion and division. Kanfer and Kennedy (1963) also reported that phosphatidylglycerol, a minor component of *E. coli* lipids, did turn over during logarithmic growth. This may indicate a special role for phosphatidylglycerol in bacterial physiology. Two recent reports (Jones and Benson, 1965; Bishop and Work, 1965) indicate, however, that under certain conditions phospholipids can be excreted from the bacterial cell. This process of excretion, if occurring in cultures such as those studied by Kanfer and Kennedy, would be difficult to differentiate from turnover.

The control of lipid synthesis in bacteria is an important problem about which we know very little. While animal fatty-acid synthesis is probably controlled in part by the effect of citrate on acetyl CoA carboxylase (Martin and Vagelos, 1962), the bacterial enzyme does not seem to respond similarly. Various parameters, for example, growth temperature, can alter the proportion of saturated and unsaturated fatty acids. The control point for this should be the β-hydroxydecanoyl coenzyme A dehydrase (Norris *et al.*, 1964), but nothing is known of how control is exerted.

The experiments of Yudkin (1963) indicate that lipid synthesis in protoplasts is inhibited by streptomycin, but not to the same degree as protein synthesis. However, Shockman *et al.*, (1962) have shown that *Streptococcus faecalis* cells accumulate lipid materials in membranes when they are starved for certain amino acids. Bacterial cells in the stationary phase of growth do not continue to accumulate lipid (Law *et al.*, 1963). It seems likely that the availability of an appropriate protein for forming the proper lipoprotein structure plays a role in the control of lipid synthesis.

IV. Phospholipid Transformations

The biosynthetic reactions discovered by Kanfer and Kennedy are examples of phospholipid transformations. They may serve as models for systems of enzyme-membrane reactions, since certainly there are reactions that occur with phospholipids already deposited in the membrane. An example was discovered in our laboratory a few years ago during an investigation of cyclopropane ring formation. As indicated earlier, cyclopropane fatty acids occur in a number of bacterial species, and we thought it would be amusing to discover how this unusual strained ring is formed. The work of Hofmann had indicated that the essence of the process was the addition of a one-carbon unit to the double bond of an olefinic fatty acid, and we looked in bacterial extracts for a reaction of a free acid or a coenzyme A derivative with S-adenosylmethionine. Through the efforts of Zalkin and Chung, and with very useful advice from Goldfine, the reaction on page 96 was found to be catalyzed by a soluble enzyme system from *Clostridium butyricum* (Zalkin *et al.*, 1963; Chung and Law, 1964a, b).

Reaction was shown to occur at either of the fatty acid chains (Hildebrand and Law, 1964).

There are many interesting features of this reaction, but I will concentrate on those related to the structural requirements of the phospholipid substrate and its physical state during the reaction, an area where we have some preliminary information, and not on the mechanistic aspects of the reaction, where our information is sparse.

$$
\begin{array}{l}
\text{CH}_2\text{O}\overset{\text{O}}{\overset{\|}{\text{C}}}(\text{CH}_2)_x\text{CH}{=}\text{CH}(\text{CH}_2)_y\text{CH}_3 \\
\text{CHO}\overset{\text{O}}{\overset{\|}{\text{C}}}(\text{CH}_2)_x\text{CH}{=}\text{CH}(\text{CH}_2)_y\text{CH}_3 \\
\text{CH}_2\text{O}\overset{\text{O}}{\overset{\|}{\text{P}}}\text{OCH}_2\text{CH}_2\overset{+}{\text{NH}}_3 \\
\quad\;\; |\\
\quad\;\; \text{O}{-}
\end{array}
+ \;
\underset{\overset{+}{\text{NH}_3}}{\overset{\text{CO}_2^-}{\text{CH}}}{-}\text{CH}_2\text{CH}_2{-}\overset{\overset{\text{CH}_3}{|}}{\underset{+}{\text{S}}}{-}\text{CH}_2
$$

$$
\begin{array}{l}
\text{CH}_2\text{O}\overset{\text{O}}{\overset{\|}{\text{C}}}(\text{CH}_2)_x\overset{\overset{\displaystyle\text{CH}_2}{\diagup\;\diagdown}}{\text{CH}{-}\text{CH}}(\text{CH}_2)_y\text{CH}_3 \\
\text{CHO}\overset{\text{O}}{\overset{\|}{\text{C}}}(\text{CH}_2)_x\text{CH}{=}\text{CH}(\text{CH}_2)_y\text{CH}_3 \\
\text{CH}_2\text{O}\overset{\text{O}}{\overset{\|}{\text{P}}}\text{OCH}_2\text{CH}_2\overset{+}{\text{NH}}_3 \\
\quad\;\; |\\
\quad\;\; \text{O}{-}
\end{array}
+ \;
\underset{\overset{+}{\text{NH}_3}}{\overset{\text{CO}_2^-}{\text{CH}}}{-}\text{CH}_2\text{CH}_2{-}\text{S}{-}\text{CH}_2
\qquad (15)
$$

That cyclopropane fatty acid formation occurs at the phospholipid level was not a great surprise, for *in vivo* studies with bacterial cell cultures had indicated that the process took place to a considerable extent in late logarithmic growth or even in the stationary phase—long after the olefinic acids had been deposited in the form of phosphatidylethanolamine. The process then continued until all olefinic acids were converted to cyclopropane acids (Croom and McNeill, 1961; Law *et al.*, 1963). Figure 1 illustrates this situation for a growing culture of *Serratia marcescens*; the lag of cyclopropane acid synthesis compared to growth can be seen. In some organisms, e.g., *Agrobacterium tumefaciens*, the synthesis of cyclopropane acids can continue over a long period of time after growth has ceased (Law *et al.*, 1963).

There is no obvious reason why this process is not coupled to the growth rate, while the net synthesis of the phosphatides is so coupled. Indeed, why bacteria make cyclopropane acids at all has not been explained, and no advantage in carrying out this energetically expensive reaction has been recognized.

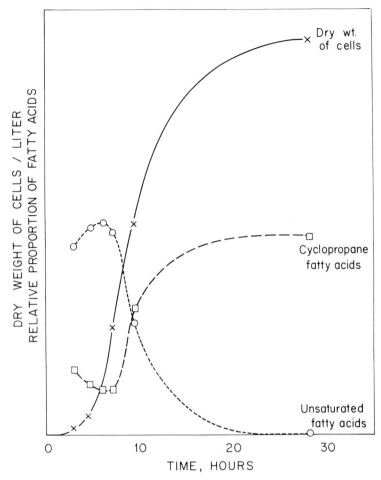

Fig. 1. Content of unsaturated and cyclopropane fatty acids in the lipids of *Serratia marcescens* during growth of a batch culture. The data are taken from Law, *et al.,* (1963).

We discovered early in our enzymatic studies that the state of dispersion of the phospholipid substrate was of considerable importance in the cyclopropane fatty acid synthetase reaction. Reproducible reaction rates could only be obtained when the phospholipids were dispersed by the dialysis technique of Fleischer and Klouwen (1961). This method is tedious, since it involves solution of the lipids in a butanol-bile salt mixture and then prolonged dialysis against many changes of buffer; however, it yields water-clear dispersions that give higher reaction rates than dispersions produced by sonication or other techniques.

Horne and Rothfield have recently produced some electron micrographs of this sort of dispersion of *E. coli* phosphatidylethanolamine. Shown in Fig. 2 are sheets of bimolecular leaflets that the phospholipid molecules have formed by pairing their nonpolar aliphatic chains and exposing the polar phosphoryl-ethanolamine ends to the medium. These pictures resemble very closely the electron micrographs of similar dispersions of phosphatidylcholine made by Fernandez-Moran and published by Green and Fleischer (1963). While there is some scepticism whether these pictures, made by the negative staining technique, represent the actual situation in the aqueous dispersion, it seems clear that we can conclude that such dispersions consist of very large aggregates of phospholipid molecules in an ordered array. The cyclopropane fatty acid synthetase molecule is faced with the difficult task of transferring a small group from a highly polar and hydrophilic molecule, S-adenosylmethionine, to a hydrophobic aliphatic chain lying within a packed bimolecular layer.

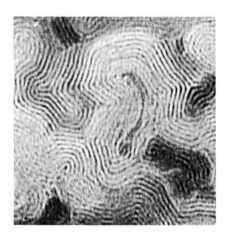

Fig. 2. Electron micrograph of an aqueous dispersion of *E. coli* phosphatidylethanolamine. The sample was stained with ammonium molybdate. This micrograph was prepared and provided by Dr. R. W. Horne and Dr. L. Rothfield.

A second problem in the use of a phospholipid substrate is concerned with the charge on the surface of the lipid aggregate. This area has been explored by Bangham and Dawson (1958; 1959; 1960; 1962), whose experiments are just beginning to receive the attention they deserve. Bangham (1963) has recently reviewed this field.

In barest essence, these workers have evolved the idea that if an enzyme, which is a large charged structure, is to react with a large lipid aggregate — also a charged structure — some complementarity of charges will be needed to bring the two structures together. At a given *p*H and ionic strength the surface charge (zeta potential) of the protein is fixed, but that of the lipid aggregate may be altered by the penetration into the bimolecular leaflet of other charged or uncharged molecules. With an enzyme acting upon a lipid aggregate, this change in surface potential may be reflected in the rate of reaction. A bad matching of charges between enzyme and substrate would give relatively few reactive collisions, while a good matching will permit the enzyme and substrate to come together at the maximum rate.

As a practical example, we found that a crude phospholipid mixture consisting of about 85% phosphatidylethanolamine, 10% phosphatidylglycerol, and 5% neutral lipids gave high rates when used as a substrate for the cyclopropane fatty acid synthetase reaction, whereas purified phosphatidylethanolamine gave initial velocities only 30% as great. Contamination of the pure phosphatidylethanolamine with a variety of anionic surfactants, e.g., sodium dodecylsulfate, gave initial velocities greater than those obtained with crude phospholipids. Apparently the phosphatidlyglycerol in the crude mixture served the same function as the anionic surfactant and endowed the aqueous lipid substrate aggregates with an appropriate surface potential for maximal enzyme-substrate complex formation (Chung and Law, 1964a).

A corollary to the idea that the enzyme recognizes a vast wall of bimolecular leaflet with an appropriate surface potential, rather than the structural details of the phospholipid molecule, is that compounds other than phosphatidylethanolamine should serve as substrates under appropriate conditions. Experiments to test this idea were started by Chung and are being carried on by Thomas in our laboratory. Table 2 shows that anionic lipids such as

TABLE 2

EFFECTIVENESS OF LIPID SUBSTRATES DISPERSED IN BUFFER

Lipid	Additions necessary	Maximum rate mμmoles/hr/mg protein
Phosphatidylethanolamine 10^{-3}M	Na lauryl sulfate, 5 × 10^{-4}M	25
Diether phosphatidylethanolamine	Na lauryl sulfate, 5 × 10^{-4}M	7
Phosphatidylglycerol 10^{-3}M	Ca^{++}, 10^{-3}M	16
Phosphatidylserine 0.2 × 10^{-3}M	None	11
Phosphatidylserine 1.6 × 10^{-3}M	None	7
Phosphatidic acid 10^{-3}M	Ca^{++}, 10^{-3}M	6
None		1

phosphatidic acid and phosphatidylglycerol are effective substrates when calcium ion is added. Phosphatidylserine is a fair substrate when it is present in low concentrations, but not at high concentrations. Chung and Goldfine (1965) recently showed that a mono-N-methylphosphatidylethanolamine with an unsaturated vinyl ether chain can undergo reaction on the vinyl ether chain.

$$\begin{array}{l} \text{CH}_2\text{OCH}{=}\text{CH(CH}_2)_x\text{CH}{=}\text{CH(CH}_2)_y\text{CH}_3 \\ \overset{\text{O}}{\underset{\parallel}{}} | \\ \text{RCOCH} \\ | \text{O} \\ \overset{}{\underset{\parallel}{}} + \\ \text{CH}_2\text{OP}{-}\text{OCH}_2\text{CH}_2\text{NH}_2\text{CH}_3 \\ | \downarrow \\ \text{O}{-} \end{array}$$

$$\begin{array}{l} \text{CH}_2\text{OCH}{=}\text{CH(CH}_2)_x\text{CH}{-}\text{CH(CH}_2)_y\text{CH}_3 \\ \overset{\text{O}}{\underset{\parallel}{}} | \diagdown\diagup \\ \text{RCOCH} \text{CH}_2 \\ | \text{O} \\ \overset{}{\underset{\parallel}{}} + \\ \text{CH}_2\text{OP}{-}\text{OCH}_2\text{CH}_2\text{NH}_2\text{CH}_3. (16) \\ | \\ \text{O}{-} \end{array}$$

Paul Thomas (1965) has carried this one step further and shown that a phosphatidylethanolamine analog, which has two octadec-9-enyl ethers (V), is a substrate for the reaction. These experiments rule out a reaction mechanism that involves removal and replacement by the enzyme of the acyl groups esterified to glycerol. Such a mechanism, similar to the one proposed by Glomset (1962) for the transfer of acyl groups from phospholipids to sterols, would be attractive for explaining how the enzyme can reach the center of the fatty acid chain to carry out the reaction. Unless a totally different mechanism operates in the case of the ether compounds, however, a transacylation step is not involved in the reaction.

$$\begin{array}{l} \text{CH}_2\text{OCH}_2(\text{CH}_2)_7\text{CH}{=}\text{CH(CH}_2)_7\text{CH}_3 \\ | \\ \text{CHOCH}_2(\text{CH}_2)_7\text{CH}{=}\text{CH(CH}_2)_7\text{CH}_3 \\ | \text{O} \\ | \overset{}{\underset{\parallel}{}} + \\ \text{CH}_2\text{OP}{-}\text{OCH}_2\text{CH}_2{-}\text{NH}_3 \\ | \\ \text{O}{-} \\ \text{V} \end{array}$$

The specific conditions which give the best rates with each phospholipid are probably those providing the most nearly optimal surface potential values for the lipid aggregates. The method of dispersal, however, is also of great importance. Thomas (1965) has recently found that phospholipids impregnated on filter paper disks serve as substrates for the reaction. The disks are treated with solutions of phospholipids in organic solvents. The solvents are dried off and the disks are placed in the bottom of scintillator counting bottles. Just enough enzyme and radioactive substrate solution is added to saturate the disk, and the bottles are then incubated at the appropriate temperature. The reactions are stopped by adding trichloroacetic acid and washing thoroughly with dilute acid and water. The phospholipid substrates and products remain impregnated into the fibers of the paper, while all water-soluble materials are washed away. This technique is a variation on a very useful and general assay for the conversion of water-soluble radioactive substrates into lipids developed by Goldfine (1966). The thought behind these experiments owes a debt to the work of Meadow et al., (1964), who showed that filter paper is a suitable matrix for bacterial cell wall synthesis.

With the lipid substrate impregnated in paper, phosphatidylglycerol is a superior substrate. The rate with phosphatidylethanolamine is not enhanced by the addition of anionic surfactants in this case (Table 3). It is likely that

TABLE 3

EFFECTIVENESS OF LIPID SUBSTRATES IMPREGNATED ON PAPER

Lipid (conc. = 10 μg/cm^2)	Maximum rate mμmoles/hr/mg protein
Phosphatidylethanolamine	5
Diether Phosphatidylethanolamine	3
Phosphatidylglycerol	11
Phosphatidylserine	1
Phosphatidic acid	3
Neutral lipids	1
None	1

the cellulose chains play a role in organizing the lipid bilayer and thus aid in establishing the surface potential. In much the same way, the protein of the membrane probably acts to aid in the organization and charge distribution of the membrane phospholipid. If this is true, then studies with this or similar enzymatic systems may be useful for probing the nature of membranes and for testing model membrane systems.

Undoubtedly a great number of other enzymes bring about transformation of phospholipid molecules deposited in a membrane. Several phospholipases have been studied by Bangham and Dawson (1958, 1959, 1960, 1962), by Dawson (1962), and by van Deenen and de Haas (1963). These enzymes, like cyclopropane fatty acid synthetase, have broad specificities for phospholipid structures,[2] but they act with maximal rates only upon phospholipid

[2] See, however, van Deenen and de Haas (1963), who demonstrated that glycerol-3-phosphate compounds are substrates for phospholipase A, while the enantiomorphic glycerol-1-phosphates are not. Thomas (1965) has shown that cyclopropane fatty acid synthetase also has a stereospecific requirement for the glycerol-3-phosphate isomer of phosphatidylethanolamine.

aggregates bearing a specific electrokinetic potential. Phospholipase A is capable of disrupting membrane structures, and its lytic action on erythrocytes may account in part for the action of snake venom as a hemotoxic agent.

V. Phospholipid Function

While a role for phospholipids in the vital functioning of membranes remains obscure, two recent discoveries have demonstrated the involvement of phosphatides in the synthesis of cell surface structures. It is still too early to speculate on the rationale of how and why membrane components facilitate the formation of cell walls and lipopolysaccharides, but a clear relationship is evolving.

Rothfield and Horecker (1964) found that to demonstrate the addition of glucose or galactose units to purified *Salmonella* lipopolysaccharide preparations, the addition of a phospholipid to the enzyme incubation mixture was essential. The lipopolysaccharide and the phospholipid were first combined by means of a heating and cooling treatment, and then the transfer enzyme and sugar nucleotides were added. Rothfield and Takeshita (1965) propose that a lipid-lipopolysaccharide complex is formed, which then adds enzyme to form a lipid-lipopolysaccharide-enzyme complex. The latter can be isolated by centrifugation and reacted with the nucleotide sugar. Neither reaction nor complex formation was observed in the absence of the phospholipid. Phosphatidylethanolamine, which is the predominant phospholipid of *Salmonella*, was most effective as a lipid cofactor. The presence of unsaturated or cyclopropane fatty acids in the molecule was important, for fully saturated phospholipid preparations were ineffective.

Another finding of great importance was made by Anderson *et al.* (1965) in studies of cell wall synthesis in *Staphylococcus aureus* and *Micrococcus lysodeikticus*. These workers found that when labeled UDP-N-acetylmuramyl pentapeptide was incubated with particulate enzyme preparations of these cells, UMP was released, and labeled muramyl pentapeptide derivatives were found in a solvent extract. The lipophilic muramyl pentapeptide derivative could add an N-acetylglucosamine unit and glycine (Matsuhashi *et al.*, 1965) when incubated again with particulate enzymes and appropriate cofactors. After each addition a new lipid intermediate can be isolated, indicating that the repeating unit of the cell wall structure is built up on a lipid carrier and then transferred to the growing cell-wall matrix with the elimination of the lipid carrier. The structure of the lipid is unknown, but evidence indicates that the lipid and sugar portions are linked by a phosphodiester.

We have already heard about the work performed in the laboratory of Dr. Robbins (Wright *et al.*, 1965) and that performed in the laboratory of Horecker (Weiner *et al.*, 1965) demonstrating that similar lipid intermediates are involved in the synthesis of the peripheral chains of *Salmonella* lipopoly-saccharides. It seems that a general feature of the assembly of heteropolysac-charides may be the involvement of lipid intermediates.

VI. Summary

We have considered briefly the occurrence, formation, transformation, and function of lipids in bacteria. Hopefully, the results of these studies from many laboratories will help in an ultimate understanding of more complex membrane systems and of the vital functions of membranes, especially the problem of active transport of ions and nutrients.

ACKNOWLEDGMENT

Experiments in the author's laboratory have been supported by grants from the National Science Foundation.

REFERENCES

Allison, M. J., M. P. Bryant, I. Katz, and M. Keeney. 1962. *J. Bacteriol.* 83: 1084.

Anderson, J. S., M. Matsuhashi, M. A. Haskin, and J. L. Strominger. 1965. *Proc. Natl. Acad. Sci. U. S.* 53: 881.

Asselineau, J. 1962. *Les Lipides Bacteriens*. Paris: Hermann.

Bangham, A. D. 1963. In *Advances in Lipid Research*, Vol. 1, ed. R. Paoletti and D. Kritchevsky. New York: Adademic Press, Inc. Pp. 65–104.

Bangham, A. D., and R. M. C. Dawson. 1958. *Nature* 182: 1292.

Bangham, A. D., and R. M. C. Dawson. 1959. *Biochem. J.* 72: 486.

Bangham, A. D., and R. M. C. Dawson. 1960. *Biochem. J.* 75: 133.

Bangham, A. D., and R. M. C. Dawson. 1962. *Biochim. Biophys. Acta* 59: 103.

Baumann, N. A., P. O. Hagen, and H. Goldfine. 1965. *J. Biol. Chem.* 240: 1559.

Bishop, D. G., and E. Work. 1965. *Biochem. J.* 96: 567.

Chung, A. E., and H. Goldfine. 1965. *Nature* 206: 1253.

Chung, A. E., and J. H. Law. 1964a. *Biochem.* 3: 967.

Chung, A. E., and J. H. Law. 1964b. *Biochem.* 3: 1989.

Croom, J. A., and J. J. McNeill. 1961. *Bacteriol. Proc.* P. 170.

Dawson, R. M. C. 1962. *Nature* 196: 67.

Fleischer, S., G. Brierley, H. Klouwen, and D. B. Slautterback. 1962. *J. Biol. Chem.* 237: 3264.

Fleischer, S., and H. Klouwen. 1961. *Biochem. Biophys. Res. Commun.* 5: 378.

Fleischer, S., H. Klouwen, and G. Brierley. 1961. *J. Biol. Chem.* 236: 2936.

Glomset, J. A. 1962. *Biochim. Biophys. Acta* 65: 128.

Goldfine, H. 1966. *J. Lipid Res.* 7: 146.

Goldfine, H., and M. E. Ellis, 1964. *J. Bacteriol.* 87: 8.

Green, D. E., and S. Fleischer. 1963. *Biochim. Biophys. Acta* 70: 554.

Hildebrand, J. G., and J. H. Law. 1964. *Biochem.* 3: 1304.

Hofmann, K. 1962. *Fatty Acid Metabolism in Microorganisms.* New York: John Wiley & Sons.

Houtsmuller, U. M. T., and L. L. M. van Deenen. 1964. *Biochim. Biophys. Acta* 84: 96.

Kaneshiro, T., and A. G. Marr. 1962. *J. Lipid Res.* 3: 184.

Kanfer, J., and E. P. Kennedy. 1963. *J. Biol. Chem.* 238: 2919.

Kanfer, J., and E. P. Kennedy. 1964. *J. Biol. Chem.* 239: 1720.

Kates, M. 1964. In *Advances in Lipid Research*, Vol. 2, ed. R. Paoletti and D. Kritchevsky. New York: Academic Press, Inc. Pp. 17–90.

Kates, M., L. S. Yengoyan, and P. S. Sastry. 1965. *Biochim. Biophys. Acta* 98: 252.

Kaufman, B., F. D. Kundig, J. Distler, and S. Roseman. 1965. *Biochem. Biophys. Res. Communun.* 18: 312.

Law, J. H., H. Zalkin, and T. Kaneshiro. 1963. *Biochim. Biophys. Acta* 70: 143.

Lederer, E. 1964. *Proc. Plenary Sessions, 6th Internatl. Cong. Biochem.*

Lennarz, W. J. 1961. *Biochem. Biophys. Res. Commun.* 6: 112.

Lennarz, W. J. 1964. *J. Biol. Chem.* 239: 3110.

Lennarz, W. J. 1966. In *Advances in Lipid Research*, ed. R. Paoletti and D. Kritchevsky. New York: Academic Press, Inc. Vol. 4.

Lennarz, W. J., R. J. Light, and K. Bloch. 1962. *Proc. Natl. Acad. Sci. U. S.* 48: 840.

Lennarz, W. J., and Talamo, B. 1966. *J. Biol. Chem. in press.*

Macfarlane, M. G. 1964. In *Advances in Lipid Research*, Vol. 2, ed. R. Paoletti and D. Kritchevsky. New York: Academic Press, Inc. Pp. 91–125.

Majerus, P. W., A. W. Alberts, and P. R. Vagelos. 1964. *Proc. Natl. Acad. Sci. U. S.* 51: 1231.

Majerus, P. W., A. W. Alberts, and P. R. Vagelos. 1965. *Proc. Natl. Acad. Sci. U. S.* 53: 410.

Marinetti, G. V., J. Erbland, and E. Stotz. 1958. *J. Biol. Chem.* 233: 562.

Martin, D. B., and P. R. Vagelos. 1962. *J. Biol. Chem.* 237: 1787.

Massaro, E. J., and W. J. Lennarz. 1965. *Biochem.* 4: 85.

Matsuhashi, M., C. P. Dietrich, and J. M. Gilbert. 1965. *Federation Proc.* 24: 607.

Meadow, P. M., J. S. Anderson, and J. L. Strominger. 1964. *Biochem. Biophys. Res. Commun.* 14: 382.

Norris, A. T., S. Matsumura, and K. Bloch. 1964. *J. Biol. Chem.* 239: 3653.

Pieringer, R. A. 1965. *Federation Proc.* 24: 476.

Pieringer, R. A., and R. S. Kunnes. 1965. *J. Biol. Chem.* 240: 2833.

Rothfield, L., and B. L. Horecker. 1964. *Proc. Natl. Acad. Sci. U. S.* 52: 939.

Rothfield, L., and M. Takeshita. 1965. *Federation Proc.* 24: 479.

Sauer, F., E. L. Pugh, S. J. Wakil, R. Delaney, and R. L. Hill. 1964. *Proc. Natl. Acad. Sci. U. S.* 52: 1360.

Shockman, G. D., J. J. Kolb, B. Bakay, M. J. Conover, and G. Toennies. 1962. *J. Bacteriol.* 85: 168.

Thomas, P. J. 1965. Ph.D. dissertation, Harvard Univ., Cambridge, Mass.

Vagelos, P. R. 1964. *Ann. Rev. Biochem.* 33: 139.

van Deenen, L. L. M., and G. H. de Haas. 1963. *Biochim. Biophys. Acta* 70: 538.

Wakil, S. J., E. L. Pugh, and F. Sauer. 1964. *Proc. Natl. Acad. Sci. U. S.* 52: 106.

Wegner, G. H., and E. M. Foster. 1963. *J. Bacteriol.* 85: 53.

Weiner, I. M., T. Higuchi, L. Rothfield, M. Saltmarsh-Andrew, M. J. Osborn, and B. L. Horecker. 1965. *Proc. Natl. Acad. Sci. U. S.* 54: 228.

Wright, A., M. Dankert, and P. W. Robbins. 1965. *Proc. Natl. Acad. Sci. U. S.* 54: 235.

Yudkin, M. D. 1963. *Biochem. J.* 89: 290.

Zalkin, H., J. H. Law, and H. Goldfine. 1963. *J. Biol. Chem.* 238: 1242.

Animal
Cell Membranes

The Isolation of Animal Cell Membranes[1]

L. Warren, M. C. Glick, and **M. K. Nass**

Department of Therapeutic Research
School of Medicine
University of Pennsylvania
Philadelphia, Pennsylvania

It is well known that there are few studies on the structure and composition of the surface membranes of animal cells. This is because few methods have been developed for the isolation of these membranes, and the methods that are available can only be applied to a very limited range of cells. There is also some skepticism concerning the identity and purity of the final product of isolation.

Most of the work done on surface membranes has employed the red-cell stroma, as it is relatively easy to obtain in large quantity. The red cell, however, is a special anucleate cell whose surface structure is strong enough to remain intact during isolation. Unfortunately the surface membranes of most other kinds of nucleated animal cells under similar treatment are not stable enough to remain intact while the nucleus and other contents are being flushed out.

Neville (1960) has developed a method for isolating liver-cell membranes which was employed by Emmelot *et al.* (1964), Skipski *et al.* (1965), Lansing *et al.* (1965), and by Herzenberg and Herzenberg (1961). This method was also applied to thyroid cells, although no criteria of purity were given (Turkington, 1962). The membranes of muscle cells have been isolated by Kono and Colowick (1961) and by Koketsu *et al.* (1964). O'Neill (1964) has

[1] The research described in this chapter was supported by United States Public Health grant 1-RO1-HD-00052-01 and The American Cancer Society grant T-333.

reported on the isolation of the surface membranes of an amoeba, *Amoeba proteus*. However, this method could not be used with another protozoan *Amoeba dubia* nor with tissue culture cells. Intestinal brush border membrane has been isolated (Miller and Crane, 1961). Wallach and his coworkers (1964); (Kamat and Wallach, 1965), working with Ehrlich ascites carcinoma cells, have developed a method for the isolation of surface membranes. They have established in some detail, criteria for their identity.

In this paper some new reproducible methods for the isolation of the surface membranes of animal cells will be presented. Before the individual methods are discussed, it might be useful to summarize what could be the underlying principles of these isolation methods. The problem is to rid a cell of its nucleus and cytoplasm without demolishing its surrounding membrane. Most animal cell membranes, however, are delicate and cannot stand the procedures required to free them of underlying cell material.

Accordingly, one of the first steps in the isolation methods is to fix, or harden, the surface membrane. We found that this could be accomplished in various ways. 1) The surface membrane is treated at a pH below 6.0. Cells placed in dilute acetic acid, or acetate buffer below pH 6.0, develop what appears to be a thickened tough membrane that can be readily observed by phase-contrast microscopy. 2) Sulphydryl groups are blocked. This can be accomplished with 5, 5′-dithiobis (2-nitrobenzoic acid) (DTNB), fluorescein-mercuric acetate (FMA), or with heavy metal ions such as zinc, mercury, or lead. It is thought the heavy metal ions may act by combining with sulphydryl groups.

The second effect we try to achieve in our methods is to have the cell membrane harden in a hypotonic medium so that the cell swells. The membrane rises and becomes more resistant to disintegrative forces, as it pulls away from the underlying cytoplasm. In some of the methods to be described, an unexpected benefit is that the cytoplasm becomes nondispersible and is anchored to the nucleus. Thus when the cell is broken by homogenizing most of the cytoplasm stays in place, while the surface membrane is removed from the cell.

Although most of our work has been with the L cell, a mouse fibroblastic cell, we now have enough experience to know that by using these principles we can obtain the surface membranes of several kinds of cells. Methods can now be devised and tailored for a particular type of cell by varying the pH, sulphydryl blocking reagent, the metal ion, or other factors.

There is little question that we are dealing with the surface membranes. They can be seen coming off the cells and by simple inspection of the final product under the phase-contrast microscope or the electron microscope, their identity is readily established. In some cases, whole ghosts are obtained. There is some attached underlying material, but no nuclei, nuclear membranes, or mitochondria appear to be present.

Before the methods are discussed more fully, it should be emphasized that preparations were constantly monitored with the phase-contrast microscope. In addition, electron micrographs were made of some of the preparations.

For our studies we used L cells grown in suspended culture, in Eagle's medium with 10% fetal calf serum. The cells were harvested in log phase and washed twice with a solution of 0.16 M NaCl. The cell concentration was then adjusted to $5 \times 10^7/\text{ml}$.

In the first method of cell membrane isolation to be described, 9 volumes of 0.001 M $ZnCl_2$ are added to 1 volume of cells. After 10 min at room temperature, one-half volume of 1% Tween-20 is added, and then after 2 min, one-half volume of 0.01 M $ZnCl_2$ is added. The suspension is then cooled to 3°. After this treatment, the cells appear in the phase contrast microscope as in Fig. 1. The cells are enlarged and the surface membranes appear thickened. Frequently a clear area can be seen, where the surface membrane has pulled away from the underlying cytoplasm. The cytoplasm is attached to the nucleus.

The cells are then broken in the Dounce homogenizer fitted with a loose pestle. In the homogenate one can see free surface membranes as well as

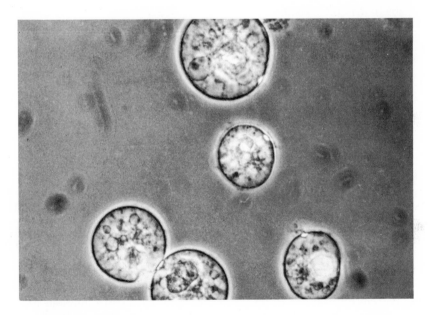

Fig. 1. L cells after zinc ion treatment. The cells are swollen and the surface membranes appear as dark rings. The region immediately beneath the surface membrane is quite clear. The granular cytoplasm surrounds the nuclei. A phase contrast positive area can be seen within the membrane. Phase contrast × 500.

cells which have lost their surface membrane but otherwise seem to be intact. There is relatively little debris present. The nuclei remain intact (Fig. 2).

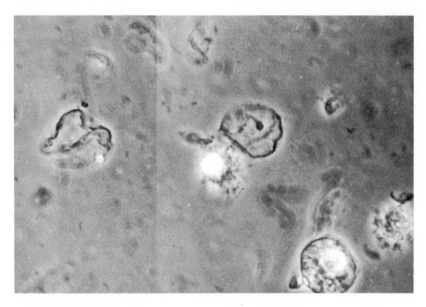

Fig. 2. Homogenate of L cells after zinc ion treatment. The entire membranes of two cells and some fragments of membrane are seen. Two cells appear intact except for the absence of their surface membranes. One cell is unaltered by the homogenization. Note that little debris is present. Phase contrast $\times$ 500.

For the partial purification of the membranes, the entire homogenate is placed on a column of fine glass beads. Almost all cells, with or without a surface coat, are retained by the column; and, as far as we can ascertain, most of the membrane passes through as the column is washed with distilled water at room temperature. The interactions of the various components of the homogenate with the glass beads are complex although there appears to be some filtering action. The column eluate is then centrifuged at 5000 g for 15 min and the supernatant solution is discarded.

Further purification is attained by mixing the pellet with 65% sucrose at the bottom of a centrifuge tube and then layering sucrose solutions above, from 60% to 45% sucrose. After 3 hr at 100,000 g in the SW 25.2 rotor of the Spinco centrifuge the membranes are isolated as a band at approximately 55% sucrose concentration that has a density of 1.258. The density of the membranes depends upon the method of isolation. The membranes obtained by this method are heavier than those obtained by some other procedures. The gradient centrifugation is repeated.

A thin section of the membranes examined under the electron microscope is seen in Fig. 3. The bimolecular leaflet pattern is still intact. The outside of the membrane can be distinguished from the inside, which has some endoplasmic reticulum still attached. In some sections (Fig. 4), what appears to be a cluster of ribosomes can be seen attached to the surface membrane.

With this method as few as 1.5×10^7 cells and as many as 1.5×10^9 cells can be processed at one time. From 1.5×10^9 cells we get a membrane preparation containing about 7 mg of protein. Membranes are stored in distilled water or in sucrose solution at 4°C, since salts cause them to agglutinate and to deteriorate.

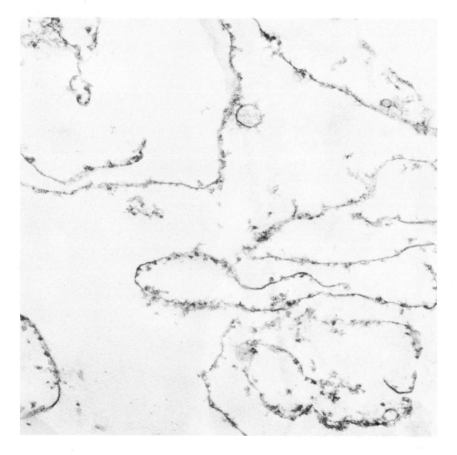

Fig. 3. Electron micrograph of isolated surface membranes of L cells. Zinc ion method. The outer surface of the membrane is distinguishable from the inner which has some adhering material. Fixed in buffered OsO4; sections stained with uranyl acetate and lead hydroxide. × 35,000.

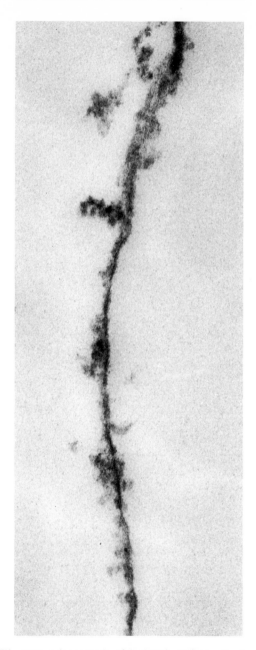

Fig. 4. Electron micrograph of isolated surface membrane of L cell. Zinc ion method. A bimolecular leaflet structure can be seen in some areas. Note the structure on the membrane that resembles a cluster of ribosomes. Fixed in buffered OsO4; sections stained with lead hydroxide. × 106,000.

Zinc ions are not the only ions that can be used for isolation of membranes. Mercuric, uranyl, cupric, and lead ions appear to be effective. Preliminary experiments indicate that lead ions are best for the isolation of surface membranes of the KB cell.

We found that if we suspend in water the glass beads of the column containing the nuclei and cells of the homogenate and shake vigorously, we can elute the nuclei and cells quantitatively. If dilute acetic acid is added and these nuclei and cells are homogenized, the resulting nuclei are free of cytoplasm, as seen under the phase contrast microscope. They are quite dense, and can be isolated in a sucrose or glycerol gradient. We are attempting to obtain the membranes from these nuclei, and if this can be done, we will be able to study the nuclear and plasma membranes from the same cells.

In the course of developing the zinc method we found that after the addition of zinc ions to L cells a small, highly phase-contrast, positive area appeared in the wall of the cell (Fig. 1). Under the phase-contrast microscope it appears to be within the outer membrane and does not seem to have any particular connection with either the underlying cytoplasm or the nucleus. For some unknown reason most cells come to rest under a coverslip with the body seen in profile. When the cell is turned the refractile area cannot be seen in face view in the whole cell unless it is stained with Janus green, whereupon it becomes amber. At least 95% of L cells have only one such area visible, and in a count of 142 cells only two had more than one body. They do not appear to be more frequent in cells grown into the stationary phase. During homogenization they apparently can tear away from the main body of surface membrane, so that in their final form they have only a small amount of jagged-edged membrane around them. Some look like the yolk of a fried egg surrounded by the white — the membrane. In the isolated form they appear, in face view, as dark round dots, approximately $1\text{-}2\mu$ in diameter. These "dots" can be isolated in a sucrose gradient, because they are more dense than the surface membrane (Fig. 5). The function and composition of these bodies is under investigation at the present time.

A second method for the isolation of membranes is to add 3 volumes of 0.1 M acetic acid to 1 volume of cells. After 5 min at room temperature the cells are cooled and broken in a Dounce homogenizer with a tight pestle. After addition of acetic acid, the cells are swollen, and their surface membranes become prominent (Fig. 6). After homogenization, dimethyl sulfoxide is added. The membranes shrink to their former size and appear to be stable during the isolation procedure. Purification is effected on a gradient of glycerol and then of sucrose (Fig. 7).

A third method for the isolation of membranes is to combine 1 volume of cells with 3 volumes of a dilute solution of the sulfhydryl blocking reagent DTNB (Ellman, 1959). Once again the cells become distended and the membrane is very prominent. The cells are then broken in a Dounce homogenizer with a tight pestle. Surface membranes can be seen in the homogenate after

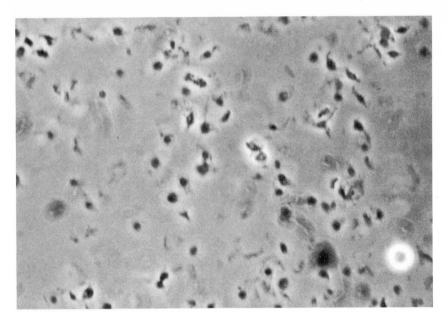

Fig. 5. "Dots" isolated by centrifugation on a sucrose gradient. A small amount of membrane surrounds some bodies. The isolated structures appear dark in face view, in contrast to those still on the cell which are invisible. Phase contrast × 500.

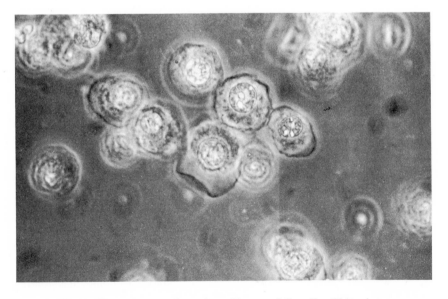

Fig. 6. Homogenate of acetic acid-treated L cells. This picture was taken early in the homogenizing process. The membrane is seen coming off the cell in the center. Note the prominent surface structure of some of the surrounding cells. Phase contrast × 500.

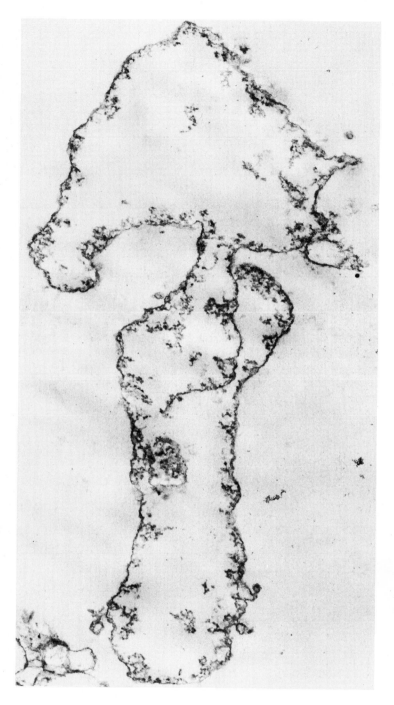

Fig. 7. Electron micrograph of the surface membrane of an L cell—acetic acid method. Fixed in buffered OsO4; sections stained with uranyl acetate and lead hydroxide. × 35,000.

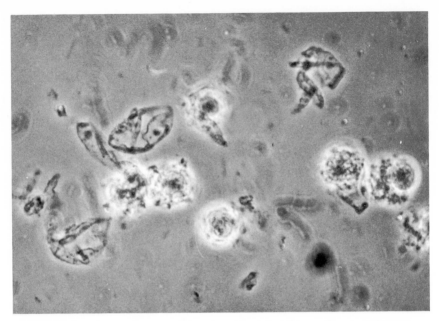

Fig. 8. Homogenate of DTNB-treated L cells. The surface membranes of several cells are seen. The dot structure can be seen in some of the cell ghosts. The cells appear intact except for the absence of surface membrane. There is relatively little cellular debris. Phase contrast × 500.

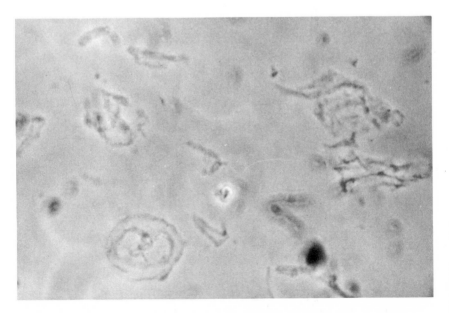

Fig. 9. Isolated surface membranes of DTNB-treated L cells. The hole through which the nucleus and cytoplasm escaped can be seen in one of the ghosts. Phase contrast × 500.

separation from the cells. The cells appear to be more or less intact except for the absence of membranes. There is relatively little cytoplasmic debris (Fig. 8). The membranes are purified by centrifugation on sucrose and glycerol gradients (Fig. 9).

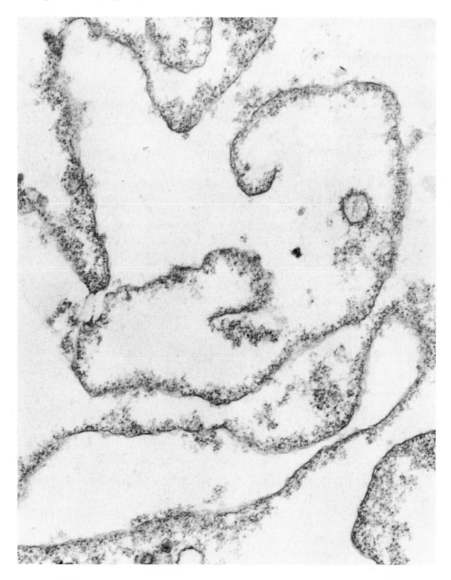

Fig. 10. Electron micrograph of isolated surface structure of DTNB-treated L cells. The outer 500 to 1000 Å of cytoplasm is attached to the surface membrane. Fixed in buffered OsO4; sections stained with uranyl acetate and lead hydroxide.

Under the phase-contrast microscope these membranes appeared pale grey, and almost transparent. In thin section under the electron microscope, however, the membranes contained a fairly uniform rind of underlying material (Fig. 10). Roughly, the outer 500Å to 1000Å of the cytoplasm has been removed with the surface membrane by means of a physico-chemical dissection of the cell. The isolated surface membrane still retains the bimolecular leaflet structure, and appears to be stable for at least two months in sucrose solution at 4°C.

Another reagent that has been used for the isolation of surface membranes is fluorocein mercuric acetate, or FMA (Karush *et al.*, 1964). This reagent can combine with free sulphydryl groups, but it is also possible that it acts by solution of the fluorocein moiety in the lipid portion of the membrane. It should be most enlightening to compare the effects on surface membrane of methyl mercurichloride with its ethyl, propyl, and higher homologues.

In this method, 1 volume of cells is treated with 3 volumes of FMA $(2 \times 10^{-3}M)$ in Tris-Cl buffer, *p*H 8.0. The cells become swollen but the membrane does not appear to be very prominent. Many cells show clear

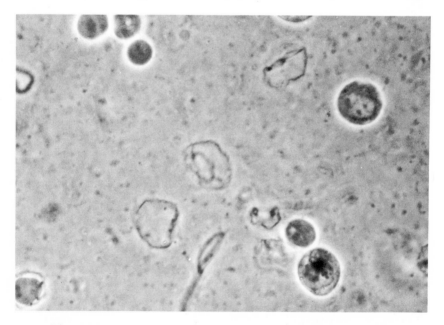

Fig. 11. Homogenate of FMA-treated L cells. Several whole membranes can be seen. An opening is present in the ghost in the center of the picture. As homogenization proceeds the membranes roll up evenly around the opening in the cell ghost until it forms a ring structure, which in side views looks like a scroll. Whole cells, nuclei and cytoplasmic debris are present. Phase contrast × 500.

areas under the surface membrane. After breaking the cells in the Dounce homogenizer, large clear ghosts are seen. (Fig. 11.) In this method the cytoplasm disperses and free nuclei are commonly seen in the homogenate. A fine underlying material is found on the inner surface of these membranes. The membrane itself, in thin section, displays a bimolecular leaflet structure (Fig. 12). The membranes are purified by centrifugation on sucrose gradient. Membranes obtained by this method have not, as yet, been analyzed.

Still another method of obtaining membranes is to wash the L cells with Tris-Cl buffer, pH 7.4, instead of with physiological saline. The cells are homogenized in 0.1 M Tris at pH 7.4 in a Dounce homogenizer in the presence of $MgCl_2$. The membranes obtained are purified on gradients of Ficoll and sucrose. The yield in this method is increased many fold by the addition of dimethylsulfoxide during the isolation. The membranes thus obtained are lighter in density than those obtained with the other procedures. Figure 13 shows an electron micrograph of these membranes.

We have described several methods for the isolation of surface membranes. Our strategy has been to try to isolate a cellular organelle by several approaches. If the final products of all the approaches resemble one another, then our confidence increases that we are dealing with a cellular entity.

Thus far we have analyzed membranes obtained by these various methods for protein (Lowry *et al.*, 1951), Bial-reactive pentose (Mejbaum, 1939), which we call RNA, and for sialic acid (Warren, 1959). In the immediate future however, we plan to analyze for hexose, fucose, and hexosamine. Dr. Julian Marsh and David Weinstein of the University of Pennsylvania are in the process of analyzing the lipids in the membrane preparations. As shown in Table 1, our results suggest that the product we obtain by all of the methods

TABLE 1

ANALYSES OF MEMBRANES: L CELLS (5×10^8)

Method of preparation	Protein mg	RNA* mg/mg of protein	NAN† mμmoles/mg of protein
0.001 M zinc chloride	2.3	0.05	14
0.01 M acetic acid	3.3	0.04	7
0.04% DTNB‡	1.4	0.03	6
0.1 M Tris, pH 7.4	2.6	0.04	5
Whole cells	100	0.05	5

* Bial reactive pentose calculated as RNA.

† Calculated as N-acetylneuraminic acid.

‡ 5,5′-dithiobis-(2-nitrobenzoic acid).

resemble one another, at least in gross composition. The yield of membranes obtained from 5×10^8 cells is approximately the same by the four methods examined. This represents 1.5-3% of the total cell protein. The amount of RNA — measured as Bial-reactive pentose — represents 1-2% of the total

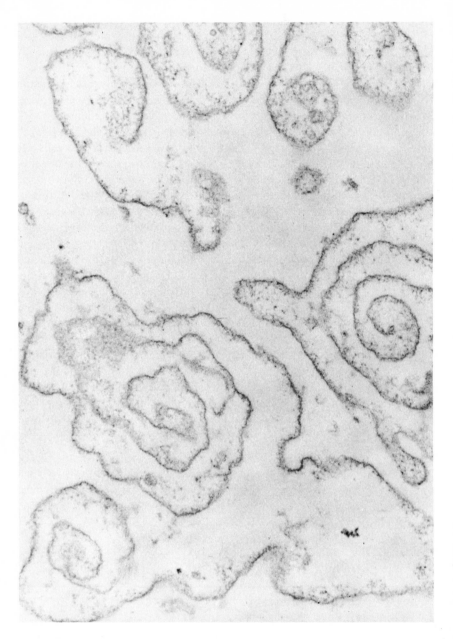

Fig. 12. Electron micrograph of isolated surface membranes of FMA-treated L cells. Fixed in buffered OsO4; sections stained with uranyl acetate and lead hydroxide. × 35,000.

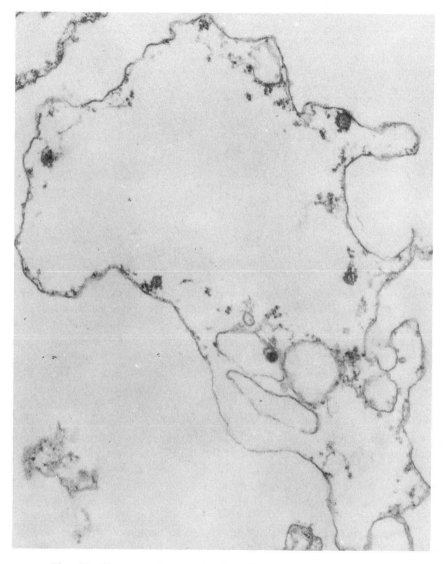

Fig. 13. Electron micrograph of surface membrane of a Tris-treated L cell. There are relatively large sections in which there is no underlying adherent material. Fixed in buffered OsO4; sections stained with uranyl acetate and lead hydroxide. × 35,000.

cell RNA. This again is approximately the same in all the membrane preparations. We have tried to reduce this amount and have succeded to some extent but have never obtained membranes free of Bial-reactive pentose. The ultraviolet light-absorption spectrum of the hot perchloric acid extract of the membranes appear the same regardless of the method of preparation, the maximum light absorption occurs at 260-261 mμ.

With the exception of the zinc ion method, the sialic acid contents of the membranes are quite similar. The sialic acid represents 2-5% of the total cell sialic acid. Because much of the sialic acid of a cell is on the surface (Wallach and Eylar, 1961; Cook et al., 1962; Eylar et al., 1962), it is possible that this sialic acid is on an adventitious surface glycoprotein, which is removed during isolation. The rather constant values of sialic acid, shown in Table 1, may reflect the presence of a more firmly attached surface glycoprotein, which remains after purification of the membranes.

We spoke earlier of the phase-contrast positive body in the membrane that was isolated as an entity separate from the membrane by centrifugation in sucrose density gradients. We found that the amount of RNA in the refractile bodies appears similar per mg of protein to the membrane fraction. No sialic acid, however, was detected in this fraction.

Na$^+$, K$^+$ dependent ATPase activity was shown by Post et al. (1960) to be associated with the erythrocyte stroma. Investigators have shown the activity associated with microsomal or membrane fractions from brain (Skou, 1962), kidney (Post et al., 1964), and salivary gland (Schwartz et al., 1963). Emmelot et al. (1964) have shown that membrane fractions from rat liver have this activity. Wallach and Kamat (1964) have demonstrated the activity in membrane preparations from Ehrlich ascites tumor cells. Preliminary experiments show that the L cell grown in tissue culture contains Mg^{++} - ATPase as well as the Na$^+$, K$^+$ dependent type (Table 2). It can be seen that the membrane fractions also contain these activities although they are somewhat variable. Maximum activity of Na$^+$, K$^+$ dependent ATPase was obtained by the addition of egg lecithin (Tanaka and Abood, 1964). The activity of the membrane preparations represents about 2-3% of the original amount of enzyme in the cell. The specific activities of both ATPases are somewhat increased in the membrane fractions although not always to the same extent. Obviously, additional studies are required to determine whether the enzymes are inhibited, destroyed or released from the membrane during their isolation.

As was stated before, most of our work has been done with the L cell, a mouse fibroblastic cell. From time to time, however, we have applied our methods to other types of cells. Our criterion of success was the appearance of cell membranes or large fragments of membranes in the cell homogenate. Rarely was an attempt made to isolate the membrane fraction.

We have found that the DTNB method gives good results with KB cells as well as with rat and rabbit lymphocytes and thymocytes. The FMA method appears to have the broadest range. Good-looking membranes were obtained from the KB cell, mouse ascites tumor cells MT890 (a lymphoma),[2] 70-F

[2] Kindly supplied by Drs. J. S. Roszel and I. Kaprowska, Hahnemann Medical College, Philadelphia, Pennsylvania.

TABLE 2

ATPASE ACTIVITY OF MEMBRANES
L CELLS (5×10^8)

Method of preparation	Total activity μmoles Pi/hr at 37°			Specific activity μmoles Pi/hr/mg membrane protein	
	Mg^{++}–ATPase	Na^+, K^+, Mg^{++}–ATPase	Mg^{++}–ATPase	Na^+, K^+, Mg^{++}–ATPase	
0.001 M zinc chloride	2.9	3.8	1.1	1.4	
0.001 M zinc chloride	6.0	1.7	2.6	0.7	
0.1 M Tris, *p*H 7.4	2.4	2.4	3.0	3.0	
0.1 M Tris, *p*H 7.4	4.2	2.4	2.3	1.4	
Whole cells	189	106	1.9	1.1	

(a squamous cell carcinoma),[2] and a fast-growing form of Ehrlich ascites tumor cell.[3] In addition, surface membranes of the mouse lymphoblastic cell L-5178Y[4] have been obtained. These are the only free cells that have been investigated. In all cases we obtained surface membranes as judged under the phase-contrast microscope. A few experiments have indicated that it should be possible to obtain the surface membranes of L cells which have been allowed to settle on a glass surface.

Very little work has been done with the cells of solid tissues. In a few preliminary experiments we were not successful with rat liver or kidney. It is probable that with solid tissues it will be essential to disperse the cells before treating them with reagents. This was not done in our experiments. Rat intestinal epithelium and lung, however, appeared to yield some surface membranes. Many membranes were obtained from lymphocytes of the rat spleen.

After succeeding in the stabilization and removal of surface membranes of animal cells one would think that their purification from cells and cytoplasmic debris would be simple. This has not proved so. Theoretically, this task should present no difficulty but in practice this has not been easy to accomplish. Other separation techniques must still be tried, such as electrophoresis in thin vertical liquid films, filtration through layers of material with holes of 3–15μ in diameter, and gradient centrifugation on materials other than salts, sucrose, and glycerol.

Summary

Some new methods for the isolation of surface membranes of animal cells have been presented. These methods, in their present state, are standardized and reproducible for the L cell. They enable us to isolate sufficient membrane material for chemical analysis. The rationale of the methods is to strengthen the membrane in a hypotonic medium. As the cell swells the prominent surface membrane appears to rise from the underlying cytoplasm. The altered membranes can be removed readily from the cell. These changes can be brought about at a pH below 6, by heavy metal ions, or by reagents that combine with free sulphydryl groups. The organometallic compound, fluorescein mercuric acetate (FMA), displays an unusually broad activity; perhaps because it not only combines with sulphydryl groups but may also have important lipophilic properties. By varying the metal component or the structure of the organic chemical moiety of the organometal, a whole array of reagents may be developed that may enable us to stabilize and isolate the

[3] Kindly supplied by Dr. Elizabeth Miller, University of Pennsylvania, Philadelphia, Pennsylvania.

[4] Kindly supplied by Dr. L. A. Manson, Wistar Institute, Philadelphia, Pennsylvania.

surface membranes and perhaps other cell organelles of many kinds of cells. The action of Tris base, a cation, at a neutral pH in stabilizing the membranes is not known.

REFERENCES

Cook, G. M. W., D. H. Heard, and G. V. F. Seaman. 1962. *Exptl. Cell Res.* 28: 27.

Ellman, G. L. 1959. *Arch Biochem. Biophys.* 82: 70.

Emmelot, P., C. J. Bos, E. L. Benedetti, and P. Rümke. 1964. *Biochim. Biophys. Acta* 90: 126.

Eylar, E. H., M. A. Madoff, O. V. Brody, and J. L. Oncley. 1962. *J. Biol. Chem.* 237: 1992.

Herzenberg, L. A., and L. A. Herzenberg. 1961. *Proc. Natl. Acad.* 47: 762.

Kamat, V. B., and D. F. H. Wallach. 1965. *Science* 148: 1343.

Karush, F., N. R. Klinman, and R. Marks. 1964. *Anal. Biochem.* 9: 100.

Koketsu, K., R. Kitamura, and R. Tanaka. 1964. *Am. J. Physiol.* 207: 509.

Kono, T., and S. P. Colowick. 1961. *Arch. Biochem. Biophys.* 93: 520.

Lansing, A. 1965. Personal communication.

Lowry, O. H., N. J. Rosebrough, A. L. Farr, and R. J. Randall. 1951. *J. Biol. Chem.* 193: 265.

Mejbaum, W. 1939. *Z. Physiol. Chem.* 258: 117.

Miller, D., and R. V. Crane. 1961. *Biochim. Biophys. Acta* 52: 293.

Neville, D. M., Jr. 1960. *J. Biophys. Biochem. Cytol.* 8: 413.

O'Neill, C. H. 1964. *Exptl. Cell Res.* 35: 477.

Post, R. L., C. R. Merritt, C. R. Kinsolning, and C. D. Albright. 1960. *J. Biol. Chem.* 235: 1796.

Post, R. L., A. K. Sen, and A. S. Rosenthal. 1964. *J. Biol. Chem.* 240: 1437.

Schwartz, A., A. H. Laseter, and L. Kraintz. 1963. *J. Cell. Comp. Physiol.* 62: 193.

Skipski, V. P., M. Barclay, F. M. Archibald, O. Terebus-Kekish, E. S. Reichman, and J. J. Good. 1965. *Life Sciences* 4: 1673.

Skou, J. C. 1962. *Biochim. Biophys. Acta* 58: 314.

Tanaka, R., and L. G. Abood. 1964. *Arch. Biochem. Biophys.* 108: 47.

Tria, E., and O. Barnabei. 1963. *Nature* 197: 598.

Turkington, R. W. 1962. *Biochim. Biophys. Acta* 65: 386.

Wallach, D. F. H., and E. H. Eylar. 1961. *Biochim. Biophys. Acta* 52: 594.

Wallach, D. F. H., and V. B. Kamat. 1964. *Proc. Natl. Acad. Sci. U. S.* 52: 721.

Warren, L. 1959. *J. Biol. Chem.* 234: 1971.

Isolation of Plasma
Membranes of Animal Cells

Donald F. Hoelzl Wallach

Biochemistry Department
Harvard Medical School
Boston, Massachusetts

Although our conception of the plasma membrane is undergoing rapid and dramatic growth, two complex questions remain unsolved: 1) whether this structure is a single entity, or a mosaic of separate organelles, arranged in the form of a limiting envelope, and 2) whether some of these may also be a part of intracellular membrane elements. These questions bear heavily on the development and evaluation of plasma membrane isolation procedures, and will serve as major points of reference in the ensuing discussion.

I. Evaluation of Relevant Literature

The major aim of this review is to determine whether it is possible to arrive at any useful general conclusions concerning the fate of the plasma membranes after the disruption of animal cells. The discussion will include reports bearing on the isolation of plasma membranes from mammalian erythrocytes, intestinal mucosa, liver, and skeletal muscle.

A. Erythrocytes. Because of their relative simplicity and their lack of intracellular membrane systems, adult mammalian erythrocytes have been widely used as source material for the study of plasma membranes. Examination of the techniques used for the preparation of erythrocyte membranes shows that both electrostatic repulsion between negatively charged components and exposure to sufficiently high mechanical stress, can fragment these into small subunits.

The membranes of erythrocytes can be completely freed of hemoglobin by lysis of the cells in hypotonic solutions under controlled conditions. Methods for the preparation of erythrocyte membranes, or "ghosts," have been detailed by Dodge et al. (1962). During hemolysis the membranes become transiently permeable to large molecules, and then reseal to recover the low permeability to cations typical of intact erythrocytes (Teorell, 1952; Hoffman, 1958; Hoffman et al., 1962, Hoffman, 1962; Whittam, 1962; Whittam, 1964; Whittam and Ager, 1964).

The size of the membrane fragments depends upon the ionic strength ($\Gamma/2$) and the pH of the medium. Thus, lysis in 0.020 M phosphate buffer at pH 7.4 produces ghosts of uniform appearance with about the same diameter as intact erythrocytes. At very low $\Gamma/2$ and at high pH, however, large ghosts fragment into smaller particles (Post et al., 1960; Anderson and Turner, 1960; Dodge et al., 1962). This is presumably a result of electrostatic disaggregation of membrane subunits, an extremely prominent process in experiments with the membranes of halophilic bacteria (Brown, 1963, 1965).

Low $\Gamma/2$ and/or high pH are not the only factors that cause fragmentation of erythrocyte membranes. Fragmentations also occur when these membranes are exposed to shearing stresses that exceed those usually employed in the preparation of ghosts (Anderson and Turner, 1960; Tosteson et al., 1965). Indeed, even under ionic conditions not conducive to electrostatic disaggregation (0.108 M NaCl; pH 6.1), vesiculation of the erythrocyte surface occurs when it is exposed to sufficiently high mechanical strain (Rand, 1964).

B. Intestinal Brush Border. The luminal surfaces of the cells lining the mammalian small intestine are specialized into brush borders, consisting of numerous microvilli about 1.5μ in length and 0.15μ in diameter. This region has been shown by histochemical means to be the locus of intestinal alkaline phosphatase (Deane and Dempsey, 1945; Burgos, et al., 1955; Fredericsson, 1956; Feigin and Wolf, 1957).

When intestinal mucosa is homogenized under appropriate conditions of shear, in media containing 0.005 M EDTA (pH 7.4), the brush borders break off as large sheets in which the microvilli retain their orderly array. Because of their large size, these fragments of brush border are readily sedimented by low-speed centrifugation (Miller and Crane, 1961; Porteous and Clark, 1965).

When epithelial cells are homogenized in iso-osmotic media, e.g., 0.3 M sucrose, 0.005 M EDTA, the nuclei remain intact and sediment with the brush borders (Porteous and Clark, 1965). When homogenization is performed in

0.005 M EDTA alone, however, the nuclei are disrupted, and the washed low-speed sediment (1500 rpm, 10 min) is free of membrane components other than the brush borders although it contains most of the alkaline phosphatase and invertase of the cells (Miller and Crane, 1961).

The enzymatic finding of Miller and Crane is consistent with the histochemical demonstration of intestinal alkaline phosphatase in the brush borders. The apparently inconsistent localization of this enzyme in "microsomal" fractions obtained from homogenates of intestinal mucosa (Hers *et al.*, 1951; Morton, 1954; Allard *et al.*, 1957; Triantaphyllopoulos and Tuba, 1959; Ailhaud *et al.*, 1963; Robinson, 1963) is because exposure of brush borders to excessive shear and/or an unsuitable ionic environment leads to their disintegration into small particles that sediment only at high centrifugal force fields. This has been shown by Carnie and Porteous (1962) in a study of the effects of homogenization conditions on the subcellular distribution of invertase activity (Table 1). Their data indicate that the invertase-bearing

TABLE 1

EFFECT OF HOMOGENIZATION CONDITIONS UPON SUBCELLULAR
DISTRIBUTION OF INTESTINAL INVERTASE*

Fractions	Centrifuged at	Invertase activity %		
		(a)	(b)	(c)
Homogenate	——	100	100	100
Nuclei	1.0×10^4 g·min	60	36	10
Heavy mitochondria	3.2×10^4 g·min	6	9	36
Light mitochondria	15.0×10^4 g·min	3	14	
Microsomes	4.5×10^6 g·min	17	30	55
Cell sap	——	5	4	2
Total	——	91	93	103

* Intestinal mucosal cells were disrupted in 0.25 M sucrose at 2°C using a) a piston homogenizer with a loose Teflon pestle for 1 min, and b) a homogenizer with a tight pestle for 1 min, and c) a blender for 5 min (Carnie and Porteous, 1962).

portions of the plasma membrane break off in fragments whose size depends upon shear. Subsequently, Clark and Porteous (1965) demonstrated that the deliberate disintegration of brush borders (by "blending" in distilled water) shifts their alkaline-phosphatase and invertase activities to particles requiring high force fields (2.4×10^6 g · min) for sedimentation.

Isolated brush borders are stable in a variety of electrolyte solutions such as 2.5-10 mM EDTA, 0.001 M $CaCl_2$, and isotonic saline (Miller and Crane,

1961; Harrison and Webster, 1964; Porteous and Clark, 1965; Isselbacher, 1965), but transfer to media of very low ionic strength produces rapid disintegration into submicroscopic particles. The action of ions is presumably that of stabilization against electrostatic disaggregation just as in the case of erythrocytes.

The isolation of intestinal brush borders clearly depends upon the relatively high mechanical strength of these reinforced surface regions. The unspecialized areas of the plasma membrane are evidently more fragile and fragment into submicroscopic particles even under the relatively mild homogenization conditions used for the isolation of the brush borders. It should, therefore, be possible to isolate separately the specialized and unspecialized regions of the epithelial plasma membrane for comparative study.

C. Liver. The isolation of plasma membranes from liver is complicated by the intricate structure of this tissue. In the first place, liver is composed of two major cell types, namely, hepatocytes (69%) and littoral macrophages (26%) (Daoust, 1958). Second, the surfaces of hepatocytes exist in two major arrangements depending upon the location on the cell, as follows: 1) The plasma membrane facing toward the hepatic sinusoids is convoluted into microvilli up to 0.9μ in length and 0.2μ in diameter (Aterman, 1963). 2) The adjacent membranes of bordering hepatocytes are about 200 Å apart except in the regions of the bile canaliculi. The canaliculi are formed by opposing grooves in the cell surfaces. They have no walls other than the membranes of the adjacent hepatocytes, which within the canaliculi are characterized by microvilli of variable number, size, and shape (Rouiller and Jezequel, 1963). The tubules are held in place by terminal bars lying on each side. The opposing surfaces of adjacent hepatocytes are also held together by desmosomes and by stud-like projections fitting into concavities in the adjacent cell and vice versa.

A method for the isolation of the bile-canalicular regions of hepatocyte cell surfaces was devised by Neville in 1960 and has also been employed by other workers (Herzenberg and Herzenberg, 1961; Emmelot and Bos, 1962; Tria and Barnabei, 1963; Emmelot *et al.*, 1964a, b; Skipski *et al.*, 1965; Herberman and Stetson, 1965). The procedure is as follows:

Exsanguinated rat livers are homogenized in 5 volumes of cold 0.001 M $NaHCO_3$ (*p*H 7.2). The homogenates are diluted five-fold and stirred. All cells are disrupted as are 90% of the nuclei. Much of the resulting nucleoprotein gel and most of the connective tissue debris are removed by filtration. Large particles (intact nuclei, erythrocytes, white cells, and membrane fragments) are sedimented and purified by two cycles of low-speed differential layering of the pellet (1200-1500g, 10 min). The purified sediment is then homogenized in sucrose of density *d* 1.22 and overlayered with *d* 1.16 sucrose. After centrifugation at 100,000 g for 75 min the membranes have collected at the d 1.16/d 1.20 interface. Emmelot and coworkers (Emmelot and Bos, 1962; Emmelot *et al.*, 1964a, b) introduce sucrose layers of d 1.20 or d 1.18 between the layers used by Neville, and collect the membranes from the d 1.16/d 1.20 or d 1.16/d 1.18 interface.) After withdrawal the membrane fraction is diluted and the particles washed in water or 0.25 M sucrose by low-speed sedimentation.

Although designed for the isolation of "hepatic bile fronts," the Neville method has been employed without modification for the preparation of "plasma membrane" fractions from thyroid (Turkington, 1962) and from Hela cells (Holland, 1962; Holland and Hoyer, 1962). Moreover, the procedure has been taken to yield a considerable and representative fraction of the plasma-membrane material of liver in relatively pure form. However, careful scrutiny of the method and the results obtained with it by Neville (1960) and Emmelot, *et al.* (1964a, b) shows that such cannot be the case. On the contrary, the published data indicate that homogenization of liver breaks most of the cell surfaces into small fragments that require high force fields for sedimentation.

1. Purity. Both Neville (1960) and Emmelot, *et al.* (1964a, b) have published electron micrographs of thin sections of their membrane fractions. These show two major components.

The first of these is *sheets of membranes* still connected by desmosomes, expanded at intervals into spaces, on each side of which the contiguous membranes are still connected by terminal bars. These spaces are clearly remnants of bile canaliculi. The residual bile spaces are said to show microvilli *in situ* (Emmelot *et al.*, 1964a, b). However, the published pictures do not show any real continuity between the smooth membranes lining the residual bile spaces and the 1000 Å membrane profiles contained therein. The most plausible interpretation of the appearance of these sections is that the microvilli have pinched off to form vesicles about 1000 Å in diameter. Indeed, two photographs (Emmelot *et al.*, 1964a, Fig. 4; 1964b, Fig. 2) actually show the pinching-off process.

The second membrane component consists of *smooth spherical vesicles*, 1000-2000 Å in diameter, either adhering to the large membrane sheets or located at some distance from them. Membrane vesicles of 1000-2000 Å diameter ordinarily require force fields of $2\text{-}5 \times 10^6 \mathrm{g} \cdot \mathrm{min}$ for sedimentation. Therefore, their presence in the low-speed plasma-membrane fraction of Neville raises serious doubts about the purity of this preparation. These doubts are strengthened by the fact that there are many enzymes which are found in both the plasma-membrane fraction and in liver microsomes (Emmelot *et al.*, 1964b), and the observation that antisera against the plasma-membrane preparations also contain antibodies against intracellular components (Emmelot *et al.*, 1964a, Fig. 7).

Two possibilities exist concerning the presence of these vesicles: 1) They are formed by fragmentation of the large membrane sheets after the final sedimentation step, as is suggested by the pinching off seen in some sections (Emmelot et al., 1964b). 2) They are fragments of diverse origins — cell surface, lysosomes, smooth endoplasmic reticulum — contaminating the plasma-membrane fraction. There are at least two reasons to expect such contamination, both related to nuclear disruption caused by homogenization in 0.001 M NaHCO₃; first, trapping by DNP gel that is not removed by. the washing steps and, second, adsorption of basic nuclear proteins to various membrane components, leading to co-aggregation of large and small fragments. This mechanism is quite likely operative in the Neville procedure because 1) even morphologically intact nuclei are permeable to protamines and histones (Philpot and Stanier, 1956; Wolfe and McIlwain, 1961); 2) these substances bind readily to negatively charged macromolecules (McIlwain, 1961) and subcellular fragments, especially microsomes, producing flocculation (Wolfe and McIlwain, 1961); and 3) membranes prepared by the Neville procedure contain considerable amounts of basic protein (Emmelot et al., 1964b), which is readily extracted by 0.9% NaCl.

Arguing against this considerable evidence for contamination is the observation that all the components of the plasma-membrane fraction stain with phosphotungstic acid after bleaching, whereas in sections of intact liver this staining occurs only at cell surfaces (Emmelot et al., 1964a). This argument is not convincing, however, since no data are given concerning the staining reactions of isolated intracellular membranes.

2. Yield. It is already evident that plasma membranes often tend to fragment into very small particles during homogenization. This appears to be true in the case of liver as well as in that of intestinal brush border. These small fragments might arise from the budding off of microvilli in the bile canalicular region, or by fragmentation of other surface regions of hepatocytes and also of macrophages. This process could be quantitatively significant, and if so, one would expect the recovery of plasma membrane material to be quite small.

I have computed estimates for the maximum recovery of cell surface material in plasma-membrane fractions prepared by the Neville method, using the lipid analyses and protein recoveries reported by Emmelot et al., (1964b). This requires (1) an estimate of the total cellular surface area in 1 gm of liver and (2) the surface area that can be covered by the membrane material from 1 gm of liver.

(1) There are 1.2×10^8 hepatocytes per gm of fresh liver (Daoust, 1958). Their mean radius is about 1.5×10^5 Å (15μ). A minimum surface area is computed by treating the hepatocytes as smooth spheres. The surface area of 1.2×10^8 spheres of 1.5×10^5 Å radius is 34×10^{18} Å².

(2) From the data of Emmelot *et al.* (1964b) one can calculate that the "plasma membrane" from 1 gm of fresh liver yields at most 13×10^{16} molecules of phospholipid and 6×10^{16} molecules of cholesterol. Phospholipid and cholesterol are the preponderant lipid components of rat liver membrane organelles (Getz *et al.*, 1962). The low surface tensions found in living cells (Ackerman, 1962) imply rather high surface pressures, and under these conditions phospholipid-cholesterol mixtures of the proportions found by Emmelot *et al.* (1964b) pack with an area of about 50 Å^2 per lipid molecule (de Bernard, 1958; Vandenheuvel, 1963). The 19×10^{16} molecules from 1 gm of liver will therefore cover $9.5 \times 10^{18} \text{ Å}^2$ if spread into a monolayer. As a *bimolecular* layer they can cover $4.75 \times 10^{18} \text{ Å}^2$, i.e., only about 14% of the expected minimum surface area.

These calculations are considered to give an excessive upper limit of recovery for the following reasons. 1) It has been assumed that all the lipid is in a continuous bimolecular layer. If some is in micellar form (Kavanau, 1965), the cell surface area per lipid molecule would decrease. 2) It has been assumed that the hepatocyte surface is smooth, when, in fact the considerable proportion of plasmalemma facing the sinusoids and canaliculi is in the form of microvilli. It can readily be calculated that if $\frac{1}{6}$ of the total surface is convoluted into cylinders 5000 Å in length and 500 Å in diameter, the surface area per cell would be 2.6 times that computed for a smooth sphere. 3) The calculations assume a spherical shape, when in fact hepatocytes are polygons, which have a greater surface area per cell for the same maximal dimensions. 4) The calculations assume that only hepatocytes contribute to the plasma-membrane fraction. But 26% of the cells in liver are macrophages with large surface areas. It would thus appear that the membrane preparations obtained by the Neville procedure account for only a small proportion of the plasma-membrane material in rat-liver homogenates.*

D. Muscle. The sarcolemma, or surface coat, of skeletal muscle is rather complex and consists of four layers (Mauro and Adams, 1961): 1) an outer region of variable thickness, containing unidentified filaments less than 100 Å in diameter; 2) a braid-like layer of variable thickness consisting of collagen fibers 300 Å in diameter; 3) an amorphous layer, 300-400 Å in width, containing some filaments 100 Å in diameter (Draper and Hodge, 1949); and 4) the plasmalemma, which is closely apposed to the amorphous layer. Presumably because of its reinforced structure, the sarcolemma has very high mechanical strength (Casella, 1951; Mauro and Sten-Knudsen, 1952).

Two detailed procedures for the isolation of muscle cell membranes have been published. In the method of Kono and Colowick (1961) the muscle

---

* The electron microscopic studies of Berry and Simpson (*J. Cell Biology* **15**, 9, 1962) quite clearly demonstrates the easy disruption of the plasma membranes of hepatocytes into minute vesicles, even under conditions primarily designed for isolation of intact liver cells.

is minced in 0.01 M Tris (*p*H 8.2) and connective tissue debris filtered out. Broken up muscle fibers are sedimented at 12,000 g for 10 min and then extracted extensively, first with 0.4 M LiBr and then with 1.0 M KCl. Small granules and loose collagen fibers are then removed by several steps of ultra-centrifugation in KBr solutions of appropriate density. Phase microscopy shows the membrane fraction to consist of empty transparent tubules — 300 × 50μ — with some attached cord-like fibers and some loose fibers. The fraction contains 3% carbohydrate and 15% lipid. The protein is high in hydroxyproline, proline, and glycine. The tubules disintegrate upon treatment with collagenases. The tubular structure is destroyed by stirring in distilled water. The preparation contains several enzymes usually considered to be membrane associated.

The approach of McCollester (1962) differs from that of Kono and Colowick in several important respects. In his approach, the muscles are homogenized in 0.05 M CaCl$_2$ and the resulting muscle fibers extracted repeatedly, first in 0.025 M NaCl, both in the cold and at 37°C, and then repeatedly by neutralized distilled water. The final preparation consists of large membrane tubules in which capillaries are retained and believed to account for about half of the dry weight.

The data indicate that both preparations are composed of fragments of the outer coat of muscle fibers, only a small proportion of which consists of plasmalemma. The preparation of Kono and Colowick clearly contains lipoprotein membrane, although the severe conditions of extraction do not permit any conclusions about whether this comes only from the plasma membrane. It seems quite feasible that the plasma membrane of muscle, protected from shear by the heavy outer coats, remains intact in large sheets lining the inside of the tubules. This would be analogous to the situation observed with A. proteus (O'Neill, 1964) and intestinal brush border. Removal of the outer layers by collagenase might then lead to fragmentation of the plasma membrane into small vesicles sedimentable only at high force fields. This possibility, unfortunately not explored by Kono and Colowick, might provide the means for isolation of pieces of pure plasma membrane from muscle.

The data provided by McCollester do not allow conclusions about the fate of the muscle plasmalemma. Since lipoprotein membranes tend to fragment into small vesicles at the low $\Gamma/2$ used in this procedure, one must seriously consider that this component is lost in the repeated washings and low-speed centrifugations.

E. Conclusions. The data reviewed in the foregoing indicate that when cell surfaces are sheared sufficiently to disrupt them, the plasma membranes rearrange into fragments whose size can vary over at least two orders of magnitude. Certain generalizations are suggested.

(1) *Large fragments* tend to form in the following situations:
   a. low shearing stress.
   b. presence of surface specializations with high resistance to shear deformation e.g., intestinal brush border.
   c. presence of surface coats which shield all or part of the cell from shearing forces, e.g., skeletal muscle.
(2) *Small fragments* tend to appear in the following situations:
   a. high shear, e.g., intestinal brush border, erythrocytes.
   b. under conditions favoring electrostatic disaggregation of membrane subunits, i.e., low $\Gamma/2$, low levels of divalent cations, high pH, e.g., erythrocytes, brush border.
   c. lack of surface coats or mechanical surface specializations.

The conditions favoring the fragmentation of the plasma membrane into *small* pieces apply wholly, or in part, to most tissue fractionations. There is thus very good reason to expect fragments of plasma membrane among small subcellular particles. This possibility has been raised repeatedly on various grounds of evidence (Novikoff, 1958, 1960; Goldberg and Green, 1960; Holland and McLaren, 1961; Wallach and Eylar, 1961; and others), but has not received the needed quantitative scrutiny.

At the present stage of sophistication in cell fractionation, this must be considered the major cause for the presence in microsomal fractions of substances known or suspected to be cell surface components, e.g., 1) *Histocompatibility antigens* (Basch and Stetson, 1962; Manson *et al.*, 1962; Basch and Stetson, 1963; Dumonde, *et al.*, 1963; Manson *et al.*, 1963; Al-Askari *et al.*, 1965; Davies, 1965; Herberman and Stetson, 1965; Manson *et al.*, 1965; 2) *Virus receptor sites* (Holland and McLaren, 1961; Holland, 1962; Holland and Hoyer, 1962); and 3) *Alkali-ion-activated ATPases* (Skou, 1957; Deul and McIlwain, 1961; Aldridge, 1962; Schwartz *et al.*, 1962; Skou, 1962; Landon and Norris, 1963; Schwartz, 1963; Emmelot *et al.*, 1964; Wallach and Ullrey, 1964).

There are, of course, additional possibilities. It may well be that these components are common to both surface and cytoplasmic membranes, or that these membrane systems are continuous in a functional as well as a structural sense. Much telling evidence is needed, however, to bring these frequent suggestions out of the realm of speculation.

II. Membrane Disruption

Any procedure for the isolation of plasma membranes must include at least transient interruption of the integrity of these structures. With erythrocytes this is easily achieved by osmotic lysis, but this simple approach is clearly not effective with solid tissues, nor is it desirable with cells which have osmot-ically fragile intracellular compartments. Other generally disruptive methods, such as "sonication" and freeze thawing are also hazardous because of almost inevitable nuclear disruption. These are the reasons for the widespread use of mechanical devices of many kinds, all designed to apply enough shearing stress to disrupt the cell surface while sparing nuclei, mitochondria and lysosomes. While the gross mechanical action of these devices plays an obvious role in the destruction of tissue organization, disruption of the plasma membrane is probably produced by liquid shear. Although the exact mechan-isms by which this occurs are not known, two processes must be considered, namely: 1) *deformation of the membrane structure at the supramolecular level:* 2) *alteration of the molecular organization of membrane components changing its viscous and other properties.*

The action of liquid shear on the molecular organization of biological membranes has not been widely investigated, but it is known that the mechan-ical properties of cell surfaces change as the forces acting on them alter, ie.., they have non-Newtonian viscous properties (Curtis, 1960). Indeed, the sur-faces of some cells show a remarkable fall in viscosity in the first few seconds after exposure to shear (Curtis, 1961). This thixotropic behavior indicates that exposure to shearing stress can decrease the molecular packing of cell surfaces. The extent and direction of viscosity alteration with shear, however, depends very much on the shearing force and the rate of change of shear (Joly, 1956). Short periods of low shear may decrease molecular packing in surfaces and lower surface viscosity, while long periods of strong shear can produce increased molecular packing and increased surface viscosity (rheo-pexy). Finally the effects of shear will depend upon the molecular organiza-tion and the homo- or heterogeneity of the surface.

If exposure to liquid shear can produce thixotropic expansion of part of the plasma membrane, this would be most prominent under conditions favoring electrostatic disaggregation of membrane components. It would be most likely to occur in those regions where the protein layers are discontinuous, and where the integrity of the membrane depends primarily upon the cohesive forces within the lipid phase. The effects of shear and of electrostatic repul-sions may thus act in concert to produce membrane disruption at specific molecular "fracture lines" rather than by random mechanical tearing.

Regardless of which mechanism predominates in the disruption of plasma membranes, the nature of the shearing stress is clearly an important variable and one that is not readily controlled in conventional homogenization pro-cedures. For this reason we employ a somewhat different method — the rapid decompression of an inert gas — for disruption of plasma membranes (Hunter and Commerford, 1961). The procedure is rather simple. Suspensions of cells in suitably buffered, iso-osmotic media are equilibrated at 1-4°C with an inert gas (usually nitrogen), under 50-75 atmospheres pressure. This is done

in a modified hydrogenation "bomb". The actual pressure used depends
on the dimensions of the cells to be ruptured. After equilibration the cell
suspension is expelled from the bomb. Disruption of the plasma membrane
occurs after release from the apparatus and is believed to come about as a
result of the localized shearing action of the small gas bubbles that form
near the cell surface. The method provides quantitative disruption of cells
under iso-osmotic conditions, in an inert atmosphere, without danger of local
heating and without nuclear rupture. Furthermore, large volumes of cell
suspension can be handled.

No matter what method is employed for the disruption of the plasma
membrane, the same questions arise concerning its subsequent topology,
i.e., 1) Do the membranes break up into open "sheets?" 2) Do they reseal
to form closed shells? 3) If they do reseal, do they retain their original
asymmetric orientation?

Electron micrographs of isolated intestinal brush borders or the isolated
bile canalicular regions of liver might be interpreted to show that these membrane regions break off as sheets, i.e., that they have free edges. Disrupted
erythrocyte membranes, however, certainly reseal to recover very low permeability to small molecules. The same is true for the plasma membrane of
"nerve ending particles," isolated from nervous tissue homogenized in 0.32
M sucrose (Johnson and Whittaker, 1963). As far as small membrane fragments are concerned, Novikoff (1958; 1960) has shown by electron microscopy of liver homogenates that the plasma membrane 'pinches off' closed
vesicles during cell disruption. Similar pinching off of surface vesicles has
been observed during immune cytolysis of Krebs ascites tumor cells (Goldberg
and Green, 1960), although in this instance the membranes appear to have
become more permeable than normal. Finally, it has been shown that small
plasma membrane fragments from Ehrlich ascites carcinoma cells are in the
form of vesicles, with very restricted permeability to small molecules (Wallach
and Kamat, 1964; Wallach et al., 1965). The preponderance of available
evidence thus indicates that plasma membranes disrupted by physical means
reseal to form vesicles with restricted permeability.

There is less information about the topologic orientation of the components of the membrane shells. Erythrocyte ghosts appear to keep the asymmetrical orientation of intact cells, with the inside and outside surfaces re-
taining their differential sensitivities to Na^+ and K^+, respectively (Whittam
and Ager, 1964). A certain proportion, at least of the plasma membrane
vesicles from ascites carcinoma cells are believed, on immunologic grounds,
to retain their original orientation (Wallach and Kamat, 1964).

Previously mentioned electron-microscopic evidence also suggests that in
the pinching-off process resealing occurs at the internal surfaces, but this
information does not exclude eversion of membrane components at the
molecular level. The same considerations apply to the 'budding off' of virus

particles from cell surfaces. Finally, it must be kept in mind that there are at least two special situations where membrane fusion occurs at external surfaces, namely, pinocytosis and phagoctyosis, Little is known, however, about the functional topology of the membrane regions involved in these processes.

III. Membrane "Markers"

Essential to any rational approach to the isolation of plasma membrane is the use of specific markers that trace the fate of the membrane and its component parts during cell rupture and various fractionation procedures. This concept has been too little explored and, while many workers have examined the subcellular distribution of substances known or suspected to be part of the plasma membrane, few studies have been carried out with the primary aim of following the fate of the disrupted membrane. Indeed, many of these experiments, particularly those concerning the plasma membrane, have been carried out without full realization of the limitations of conventional cell fractionation procedures.

This discussion of membrane markers is intended to be illustrative of relevant principles and will be limited to approaches which utilize already existing membrane components rather than experimental membrane modifications. Within these limitations the topic of markers divides into two categories, namely, *morphologic criteria* and *"ectobiologic indices,"* i.e., naturally occurring membrane components, in some way involved in the interaction of the cell with its external environment.

A. Morphologic Criteria. The use of electron microscopic criteria to monitor the fate of the plasma membrane after cell rupture still has several shortcomings. 1) While it permits localization of those plasma-membrane fragments having distinct and permanent morphologic properties, e.g., brush borders, bile canaliculi, it does not, at present, allow one to follow the prevalent regions of plasma membrane which lack such specializations. 2) Except where a given fraction contains only one type of membrane fragment, clearly recognizable as plasma membrane, there is no criteria for purity. 3) The approach is not quantitative.

B. "Ectobiologic Indices". The ectobiologic markers to be discussed can be grouped into three categories:

(1) *Specific ionizable groups.*
(2) *Membrane-associated enzymes.*
(3) *Receptors for macromolecules such as viruses and antibodies.*

Interpretation of data obtained with the aid of such markers must include an awareness that 1) plasma membranes are not static structures; their components must at some time be synthesized, assembled, and replaced. Some of these processes, especially those involving membrane proteins, are likely to occur within the cell interior. Thus a small proportion, even of truly surface-specific components, may be intercepted on their way to and from the plasma membrane. 2) the occurrence of a given marker on the surface of an intact cell does not exclude its presence also within the cell. 3) In addition, a given marker may be present on certain regions of the membrane but not on others. Disruption of the membrane may then produce two types of particles, those that bear the marker and those which do not. These may behave differently in fractionation procedures. 4) Disruption of the plasma membrane into small fragments is likely to alter the kinetic reactivity of membrane-associated groups. This is likely to complicate comparisons between whole cells and disrupted cells of subcellular fragments and, moreover, disruption of the plasma membrane may lead to the formation of vesicles in which some regions of the originally external surface are now inaccessible. For these reasons it would appear imperative to utilize multiple criteria to monitor the plasma membrane.

The three categories of ectobiologic indices will now be discussed in detail.

1. Specific ionizable groups. The only substance in this category that can, at present, qualify as surface indicator is sialic acid, a 9-carbon sugar with a strongly acid carboxyl group ($pK \sim 2.6$). Sialic acid is present on the external surfaces of many cells. This has been shown by the reduction in the anodic electrophoretic mobility of some cells after the enzymatic removal of sialic acid from the cell surface by sialidase (neuraminidase) (Cook et al., 1961; Wallach and Eylar, 1961; Cook et al., 1962; Eylar et al., 1962; Forrester et al., 1962; Fuhrmann et al., 1962; Cook et al., 1963; Forrester et al., 1964; Fuhrmann et al., 1964; Wallach and Perez Esandi, 1964).

With erythrocytes there is no doubt that the sialic acid is associated only with the plasma membrane, but the situation is less clear with more complex cells. The difficulties begin when an attempt is made to establish a quantitative relationship between the change in cell surface charge produced by sialic acid removal and the amount of sialic acid actually released, this release being apparently in considerable excess over the observed change in charge. This discrepancy can be resolved by assuming that the effective radius of curvature of sialic acid-bearing sites is much smaller than that of the cell, namely, in the order of 20–40 Å (Brinton and Lauffer, 1959; Wallach and Eylar, 1961; Eylar et al., 1962). This argument may be correct for erythrocytes, but in complex cells one must exclude a major alternative hypothesis, namely, that some of the released sialic acid comes from the cell interior. Indeed, this must be considered rather seriously, since there are a number of cell types from which sialic acid can be released without any change in electrophoretic mobility (Fuhrmann et al., 1962; Cook et al., 1963; Wallach and Perez Esandi, 1964). Moreover, there is definite evidence of sialic acid on the nuclear membranes of Hela cells (Marcus and Salb, 1965) and also on intracellular membranes of Ehrlich ascites carcinoma cells.

On the one hand, Marcus and Salb (1965) have shown that the sialic acid on nuclear membranes can be released by the action of sialidase on isolated nuclei but not on whole cells. On the other hand, similar amounts of sialic acid are released by sialidase treatment of intact and ruptured Ehrlich ascites carcinoma cells (Wallach and Eylar, 1961; Miller et al., 1963). This evidence seems to suggest that in these cells the sialic acid either is totally on the cell surface or that intracellular sialic acid is released by either penetration of the enzyme to parts of the cell interior or translocation of sialic-acid bearing sites to the outside. To clarify the situation it will be necessary both to study the kinetics of sialic-acid release from intact and ruptured cells and to measure accurately the extent of sialidase absorption in complex cells.

The status of sialic acid as a plasma membrane marker is not yet settled. Acting on the assumption that most of the sialic acid of Ehrlich ascites carcinoma cells is bound to the plasma membrane, however, we examined its distribution in subcellular fractions derived from such cells (Wallach and Eylar, 1961). These experiments showed that 87% of the sialic acid was particle-bound, 77% of it in the microsomes (Table 2). Patterson and Touster

TABLE 2

SIALIC ACID IN SUBCELLULAR FRACTIONS OF
EHRLICH ASCITES CARCINOMA
(From Wallach and Eylar, 1961)

Fractions	Sialic acid (μmole/ml cells)	%
Cells	0.382	100
Nuclei	0.012	3.2
Mitochondria	0.066	17.3
Microsomes	0.265	69.5
Soluble	0.052	13.6
Sum	0.395	103.6

(1962) found an analogous situation in liver, where 81% of the insoluble sialic acid is in the microsomes and 19% in the mitochondria. In a subsequent study (Wallach and Ullrey, 1962) it was demonstrated that the sialic acid in Ehrlich ascites carcinoma microsomes is associated entirely with "smooth" membrane vesicles. Within this category of membranes, however, the particles of lowest density show the highest concentration of sialic acid. While these results fit the hypothesis that disruption of the plasma membrane of Ehrlich ascites carcinoma cells causes its fragmentation into small vesicles, they cannot be taken as evidence that the microsomal sialic acid is associated *only* with plasma membrane fragments.

2. Membrane-associated enzymes. The usefulness of membrane-associated enzymes in tracing the absorptive regions of the plasma membranes of intestinal mucosal cells is evident from the work of Miller and Crane (1961) and Carnie and Porteous (1962). Membrane-associated enzymes involved in more common transport processes — particularly the active translocation of Na^+ and K^+ — might therefore be helpful in following other less specialized portions of plasma membranes.

We have explored the applicability of an alkali ion-activated, ouabain-sensitive ATPase from Ehrlich ascites carcinoma as a plasma-membrane marker (Wallach and Ullrey, 1964; Wallach and Kamat, 1964; Kamat and Wallach, 1965). The reasons for this choice are as follows: 1) the active transport of cations is undoubtedly a membrane-associated process; 2) it is definitely associated with the plasma membrane of erythrocytes and axones; 3) alkali ion transport is "driven" by ATP in Ehrlich ascites carcinoma cells (Aull and Hempling, 1963) and many other tissues (Whittam, 1964); 4) alkali-ion activated ATPases and alkali-ion transport mechanisms have many critical properties in common (Whittam 1964); and 5) after cell disruption, alkali-ion activated ATPase remains membrane associated.

Cell-fractionation studies show this enzyme system to be localized predominantly in the microsomal fractions from many tissues. This and the fact that it remains associated with small membrane particles derived from erythrocytes (Post *et al.*, 1960; Tosteson *et al.*, 1965) is consistent with the hypothesis that large proportions of the fragmented plasma membranes of many tissues sediment in their microsomal fractions. One cannot be secure in the use of alkali-ion activated ATPases as specific plasma-membrane markers, however, because it is not known whether ATP-driven ion transport does not also take place in some regions of the endoplasmic reticulum. Indeed, the recent studies of Chowdhury and Snell (1965) suggest that alkali-ion sensitive functions of frog skin and toad bladder are not limited to the plasma membranes of these tissues.

3. Receptors for macromolecules

A. Virus binding sites. Before animal viruses can enter susceptible cells they must attach to specific cell surface receptors (Cohen, 1963). If these receptors are located only on the plasma membrane, they would provide quantitative markers for specific regions on this structure.

Studies of the enterovirus receptors of Hela cells provide information relevant to this subject. After fractionation of Hela homogenates by differential centrifugation, most of the virus binding sites are found in the "microsomal fraction" (Holland and McLaren, 1961; Holland, 1962; Philipson and Bengtsson, 1962). This observation was first taken to indicate the fate of the disrupted membrane (Holland and McLaren, 1961; Holland, 1962). However, Holland (1962) and Holland and Hoyer (1962) proposed an alternate suggestion. They suggested that the "microsomal receptors" represent intracellular binding sites, which differ from those located on the cell surface. Their reasons were that 1) disrupted cells bind virus four times as rapidly as intact cells; 2) intact cells and also a plasma-membrane fraction prepared by the method of Neville (1960) both bind and inactivate (eclipse) virus, while microsomes can only bind virus.

The more rapid rate of virus binding by ruptured cells may, however, be due to the greater kinetic reactivity of plasma membrane receptors, once they are associated with small membrane fragments (*cf.* Holland and McLaren, 1961). Moreover, the "microsomal" fractions tested by Holland and Hoyer are crude mixtures, probably containing lysosomes and other potential inhibitors of virus inactivation. The existence of such inhibitors of virus inactivation would also account for the paradoxical observation that intact cells can eclipse virus, while cell homogenates cannot do so (Holland and Hoyer, 1962). The matter could readily be checked by testing for virus inactivation with microsomal membranes free of lysosomes and ribosomes.

There is thus some uncertainty as to the precise location of the enterovirus receptor of Hela cells, although Marcus and Salb (1965) have shown quite clearly that myxovirus receptors are present on the nuclear membrane of these cells as well as on the plasma membrane.

B. Plasma-membrane antigens. The term plasma-membrane antigens is used here to refer to substances that can be shown to reside on the plasma membrane by immunologic means such as cell agglutination (Goldberg and Green, 1959); immune cytolysis (Green *et al.*, 1959), and the use of antibodies labeled by fluorescent dyes (Möller, 1961); ferritin (Easton *et al.*, 1962); or possibly radioactive tracers. Before such antigens can be considered as specific for the plasma membrane, it must be shown conclusively that they do not occur in the cell interior.

(1) Mouse histocompatability antigens. Mouse H-2 histocompatibility antigens have been found in diverse subcellular fractions, particularly in microsomes. This has often been taken to show that these antigens occur within the cell as well as on cell surfaces, on the erroneous notion that the fractions tested were free of plasma membrane. The matter can be resolved only by accurate comparison of the amount of H_2 antigen found in whole and disrupted cells. A method adequate for this task has been developed (Wigzell, 1965), and preliminary results indicate that at least 80% of the total H-2

antigen of several cell types is located on the plasma membrane (Haughton, 1965).

(2) *Antigens involved in cell agglutination by hetero-antibodies.* We have used antibodies capable of agglutinating intact Ehrlich ascites carcinoma cells to trace the plasma membrane of these cells. (Wallach and Hager, 1962; Wallach and Kamat, 1964; Kamat and Wallach, 1965). Antibodies were prepared by immunization of rabbits and a horse, with microsomal membranes from Ehrlich ascites carcinoma. Since the agglutinating reaction is surface specific, and since at least 75% of agglutinating antibody is rapidly absorbed by intact cells in the cold, the "agglutinating antigens" must be located primarily on the cell surface, and the removal of agglutinating antibody by subcellular fractions can be used to quantify their plasma membrane content. This approach also indicates that the bulk of the disrupted plasma membrane of Ehrlich ascites carcinoma cells sediments in the microsomal fraction.

(3) *Evaluation of the "purity" of plasma membrane preparations.* A major obstacle to the purification of plasma membranes from complex cells is the difficulty of assessing their freedom from elements of "smooth" endoplasmic reticulum. Unfortunately one cannot be secure in the use of various microsomal enzymes as markers for endoplasmic reticulum until it has been proven that these enzymes do not also occur in the plasma membrane. It appears, however, that DPNH and TPNH oxidases are at least more concentrated in membranes arising from endoplasmic reticulum. We therefore consider that the presence of these enzymes in plasma membrane fractions indicates contamination with intracellular membranes. A more promising approach, involving the use of antibodies specific for intracellular membranes, is in development.

(4) *Conclusions.* It is abundantly evident that there is at present no single, reliable plasma membrane 'marker' and that multiple criteria must be used to trace the fate of this structure and of its component parts.

IV. Separation, Purification, and Subfractionation of Small Plasma Membrane Fragments

Our approach to these topics is strongly influenced by the increasing biologic evidence that neoplastic transformation is accompanied by subtle but important modification of plasma and other cellular membranes. In particular, we wish to isolate individually the membranes of the cell surface and of the endoplasmic reticulum, to compare their distinguishing functional qualities, and to define the changes wrought in these structures by the neoplastic process. Since cell rupture causes the fragmentation of much of both the plasma membrane and the endoplasmic reticulum into small vesicles, methods must be developed for the recovery of these diverse particles from amidst each other. Moreover, one must explore the possibility that not all pieces of plasma membrane or endoplasmic reticulum are alike.

We have studied these problems in the case of Ehrlich ascites carcinoma (Wallach and Kamat, 1964; Kamat and Wallach, 1965; Wallach *et al.*, 1965). According to the distribution of various "indicators," more than 70% of the plasma membranes of these cells sediment in the microsomal fraction. Calculations based on lipid analyses and estimates of the surface area of intact cells indicate, however, that not more than a third of the microsomal membrane material arises from the cell surface (Wallach *et al.*, 1965).

The microsomal membranes, whether of surface or intracellular origin, are vesicles roughly 1000 Å in diameter, bounded by charged, semipermeable "unit membranes" about 80 Å thick. All of these vesicles change in volume and density with variations of their ionic and osmotic milieu. Particles of diverse origins respond in different ways to environmental alterations, however, and this permits their separation by ultracentrifugation in suitable density gradients (Wallach and Kamat, 1964; Kamat and Wallach, 1965).

A. Theoretical considerations. To develop a rational approach to the ultracentrifugal separation of different classes of membrane vesicles, it is necessary to evaluate the factors which determine the volumes and densities of such structures.

1. Volume. Considering a vesicle as a sphere, its total volume V_T is comprised of three compartments (Fig. 1).

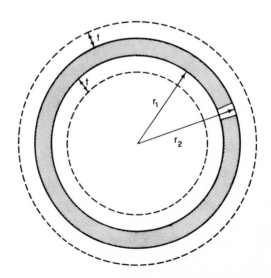

Fig. 1. Model of a membrane vesicle. See text for details.

(1) V_w is the volume of the anhydrous membrane shell, with internal radius r_1 and external radius r_2.

(2) V_h is the volume of the water of hydration associated with the membrane shell, distributed as two layers, of thickness t, one on the inside and one on the outside surface of the wall.

(3) V_f is the volume of fluid within the vesicle.

Then

$$V_T = V_w + V_h + V_f \tag{1}$$

when $t \ll r_1$, approximate expressions for V_T, V_w, V_h, and V_f are:

$$V_T = \frac{4}{3\pi}(r_2 + t)^3 \tag{2a}$$

$$V_w = \frac{4}{3\pi}(r_2^3 - r_1^3) \tag{2b}$$

$$V_h = 4\pi t (r_2^2 + r_1^2) \tag{2c}$$

$$V_f = \frac{4}{3\pi}(r_1 - t)^3. \tag{2d}$$

While the total mass of anhydrous membrane material is constant in a given particle, V_w, V_f, V_h, and therefore V_T, can vary with environmental conditions (Wallach and Kamat, 1964).

Vesicle volume depends to a large measure upon the balance between *cohesive* forces in the lipid phase and opposing electrostatic mechanisms, namely, *Gibbs–Donnan effects* and *coulombic repulsions*. Both produce expansion of V_f, and thus V_T, at low $\Gamma/2$, at pH levels away from the effective "isoelectric point," and in the absence of polyvalent counterions. In the present model, however, expansion of V_T cannot occur without some alteration of the properties of the wall. Therefore, if the wall volume V_w stays constant, the wall thickness $r_2 - r_1$ must diminish but if the wall thickness remains constant, its structural elements must become less tightly packed, the resulting voids filling with water. Alterations of the ionic environment can thus also influence V_h although this is only about 10% of V_T in the case of vesicles with radii near 500 Å. Osmotic mechanisms can act in the same or opposite direction as electrostatic effects, depending on whether the concentration of the impermeant solutes is greater within or without the vesicles.

Contraction of volume may proceed in two ways. It may proceed without alteration in shape, in which case there must be a change in wall thickness and/or wall density; or it may proceed by folding of the wall, in which instance the thickness and density of the wall may remain unaltered. In the latter situation Eq. (2a) – (2d) no longer apply directly, but can be used to calculate volumes in terms of equivalent spheres or shells.

2. *Density.* The mass of a given vesicle is made up of the masses of the three compartments, and since

$$\rho_T V_T = \rho_w V_w + \rho_h V_h + \rho_f V_f$$

$$\rho_T = \frac{\rho_w V_w + \rho_h V_h + \rho_f V_f}{V_T} \tag{3}$$

where ρ_w, ρ_h, ρ_f, and ρ_T are the densities of the anhydrous wall, water of hydration, internal fluid, and whole vesicle, respectively.

Substituting from Eq. (2a) − (2d):

$$\rho_T = \frac{\rho_w(r_2^3 - r_1^3) + \rho_h 3t(r_2^2 + r_1^2) + \rho_f(r_1 - t)^3}{(r_2 + t)^3}$$

Now, by binomial expansion:

$$(r_2 + t)^{-3} \approx r_2^3(1 - 3t/r_2) \text{ and } (r_1 - t)^3 \approx (r_1^3 - 3r_1^2 t).$$

Therefore:

$$\rho_T = \left[\rho_w[1 - (r_1/r_2)^3] + \rho_h 3t \frac{(r_2^2 + r_1^2)}{r_2^3} + \rho_f \frac{(r_1^3 - 3r_1^2 t)}{r_2^3} \right] (1 - 3t/r_2) \cdot \tag{4}$$

In very small vesicles ρ_T will approach the density of the hydrated wall, (but then second- and third-order terms in t can no longer be neglected). In very large particles ρ_T approaches the density ρ_f of the fluid within. Quite clearly, environmental variables that affect V_f and V_h can influence vesicle density.

Particle densities can be measured by means by ultracentrifugal equilibration in suitable density gradients. The actual values of ρ_T obtained for given values of ρ_w, ρ_h, and ρ_f, however, depend upon the gradient system used. This is illustrated by the following three cases:

(1) *Ficoll gradients.* In density gradients composed of nonpermeant *large* molecules such as the sucrose polymer Ficoll, osmotic effects due to the gradient itself are small and Eq. (4) applies in a straightforward manner. Ordinarily ρ_f is much smaller than ρ_w and the observed density depends markedly on V_f. Moreover, alterations of V_f resulting from electrostatic and osmotic mechanisms can produce substantial changes in ρ_T. Alterations in V_h are expected to produce less dramatic effects.

(2) *Sucrose gradients.* In density gradients composed of nonpermeant *small* solutes such as sucrose the osmotic effects of the gradient are large and lead to contraction of V_f. For this reason densities obtained in such

gradients are closer to ρ_w than in the previous case. Because V_f is already contracted, alterations of ionic environment will produce smaller changes in ρ_T. Variations in wall hydration, however, will affect ρ_T more prominently than in Ficoll gradients.

(3) *Glycerol gradients.* In density gradients composed of *permeant* solutes such as glycerol Eq. (4) simplifies, and the observed densities depend only on the densities and volumes of the wall and the hydration layers. Alterations of membrane hydration states by different experimental variables can be detected in such gradients. Gradients composed of permeant salts, e.g., NaBr also belong in this category, but in this case electrostatic effects are minimized.

The density distributions obtained when microsomal membranes are equilibrated in the three gradient types are shown in Fig. 2 (Wallach and Kamat, 1964).

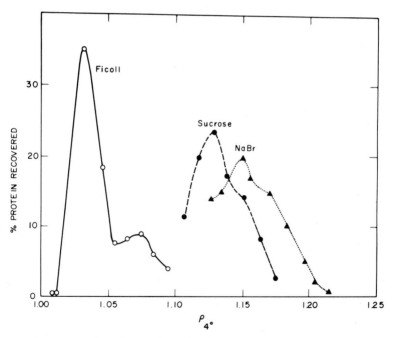

Fig. 2. Density distribution of microsomal membranes in gradients of Ficoll, sucrose and sodium bromide. Buffer—0.001 M Tris-HCl (*p*H 8.2). Material layered on top of preformed gradients. SW 39 rotor, 39,000 rpm, 14 h. Ficoll O———O; sucrose ●-----●; sodium bromide △ ....△ (Wallach and Kamat, 1964).

Our approach to the separation of various membrane classes is based upon the following reasoning:

(1) Since all the vesicles have "unit membrane" walls, it is likely that they are relatively similar in gross chemical composition and that they have a number of structural components in common.
(2) Certain plasma-membrane fragments, however, contain protein elements — enzymes, antigens — lacking in other membranes (and probably vice versa).
(3) Ionizable groups of such distinguishing proteins contribute uniquely to the ionic properties of their membrane supports.
(4) Since the ionic properties of the vesicles can affect their volumes and densities, it should be possible to effect ultracentrifugal separation of diverse membrane classes, according to their distinguishing protein constituents.

B. Separation and purification of plasma membrane vesicles. We have previously described the different effects both of variations of pH and of ionic strength on the density distributions of plasma and intracellular membranes in Ficoll gradients (Wallach and Kamat, 1964). Effects similar to those obtained by lowering of pH are produced by the addition of calcium or magnesium ions. Thus, when microsomal membranes (previously freed of ribosomes by use of a sucrose gradient) are centrifuged in Ficoll gradients which contain, in addition to 1 mM Tris HCl (pH 8.6), either calcium or magnesium, the distribution of the membrane material alters and shifts to higher densities. This is illustrated in Fig. 3, which gives the protein distributions from experiments where the membrane material was layered on top of formed gradients. The change in distribution produced by 0.1 mM calcium at $pH \sim 8$ is similar to that obtained by changing pH from 8 to near neutrality at low ionic concentration. With increasing concentrations of divalent cations the density shift becomes more pronounced as shown in Table 3.

In experiments where the material is mixed into the gradient rather than layered on top, the density changes become apparent only with $[M^{2+}] = 0.5$

TABLE 3

VARIATION OF THE MEDIAN DENSITY OF
MICROSOMAL MEMBRANES WITH $[Ca^{2+}]$*

$[Ca^{+2}]$ mM	ρ median (4°)
0.00	1.035
0.01	1.042
0.10	1.061
1.00	1.093

* Ficoll density gradients; 1mM Tris (pH 8.6)

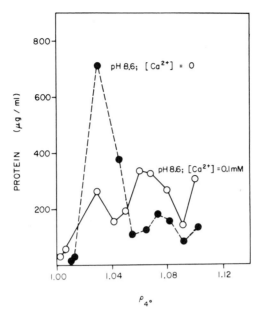

Fig. 3. Effect of 0.1 mM Ca^{2+} on density distribution of micro-somal membranes in a Ficoll gradient. Buffer—0.001 M Tris-HCl (*p*H 8.6). Material layered on top of preformed gradients. SW 39 rotor, 39,000 rpm, 14 h.

mM. This is due in large part to the different osmotic effects of Ficoll in the two experimental situations. Examination of the distribution of various markers in "mixed-in" systems, however, shows that it is primarily the membrane particles arising from the endoplasmic reticulum that undergo large density changes, either upon the addition of divalent cations or with increasing concentration of hydrogen ion. This is demonstrated in Fig. 4. In this experiment magnesium ion was used, since calcium strongly inhibits the alkali ion-activated ATPase, which is one of the enzyme markers employed in this study. At a magnesium concentration of 1mM the bulk of the membrane material is in a strongly aggregated layer with a density greater than 1.10, while the particles bearing the alkali ion-activated ATPase and the agglutinating antigen are in a zone of density 1.07. This is similar to the situation obtained at *p*H 6.5 in the absence of divalent cations. In both cases DPNH diaphorase and DPNH-cytochrome reductase are concentrated in the aggregated zone and also in a highly turbid band at density 1.02. The particles that comprise this band change to higher density only when the concentration of divalent cation is raised to 5 mM or higher.

On the basis of such observations we have developed a method for the separation of the plasma membrane vesicles from the bulk of other microsomal

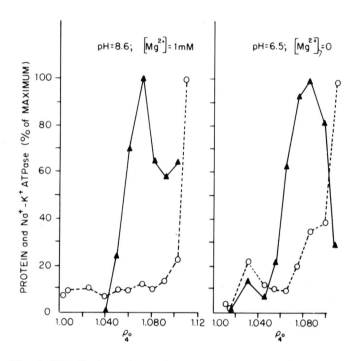

Fig. 4. Distribution of protein and alkali ion-sensitive ATPase after equilibration of Ficoll gradients. (a) *p*H 8.6; 1mM Mg^{2+}; (b) *p*H 6.5; no Mg^{2+}. Material initially distributed uniformly throughout gradients. SW 39 rotor, 39,000 rpm, 16h. Alkali ion-activated ATPase: △———△; protein ○-----○.

membranes (Kamat and Wallach, 1965). In this procedure the microsomal mixture in 0.001 M Tris-HCl (*p*H 8.6), 0.001 M Mg^{2+} is layered on a Ficoll solution of density 1.096 (4°C) of the same ionic constitution. After centrifugal equilibration the plasma membrane markers are concentrated in a layer above the barrier, while most of the other particles are in the pellet. Results obtained by this technique are illustrated in Table 4. The layer above the barrier, which consists of two closely spaced bands, contains about 20% of the applied protein, 85–91% of the agglutinating antigens, about 70% of alkali ion-activated ATPase and about 4% of the DPNH oxidase. The agglutinating antigen located in the pellet is trapped nonspecifically and appears at the top of the barrier, when the pellet material is recycled through the original separation procedure. Even after recycling, however, 20–25% of the alkali ion-activated ATPase activity persists in the pellet. Sialic acid is present

TABLE 4

SURFACE MEMBRANE SEPARATION†

Location	Protein $\%$	DPNH-diaphorase $\dfrac{mmoles}{mg \cdot min}$	Na$^+$, K$^+$-ATPase* $\dfrac{P_i\ \mu moles}{mg \cdot hr}$	Surface antigen $\Delta(\gamma\ globulin)$ mg	Sialic acid $\dfrac{\mu moles}{mg}$
At barrier	20.2	0.068	7.95	1.14	0.026
In barrier	11.5	0.213	2.80	0.12	—
Pellet	62.9	0.553	0.74	0.03	0.015

* Adenosine triphosphatase; p_i, inorganic phosphorus.
† Distribution of microsomal protein and various membrane markers after centrifugation of Ficoll-Mg barrier at 25,000 rpm for 15 hr at 4°C in SW-25 rotor; 51.5 mg of protein per tube; percentages are of total recovery.

in both fractions, but, while it makes a distinct contribution to the surface potential of vesicles in the low-density band, this is not so in the case of the high-density membranes (Wallach and Kamat, unpublished).

The two bands comprising the low-density layer in the foregoing separation can be separated in Ficoll gradients containing 0.001 M Tris-HCl (pH 8.6) but lacking magnesium ion (Kamat and Wallach, 1965). This is illustrated in Fig. 5. The agglutinating antigen and alkali ion-activated ATPase are now concentrated in the band with modal density 1.05 (4°C), which actually consists of a series of very closely spaced layers. Because of its association with plasma-membrane markers and its lower specific activity of DPNH-oxidase we consider this component to consist primarily of plasma-membrane fragments.

The other component equilibrates at density 1.024 (4°C). It has a high specific turbidity, contains sialic acid and is rich in DPNH oxidase. Its content in alkali ion-insensitive, magnesium-activated ATPase is higher than that of the plasma membrane component, but it lacks alkali ion-activated ATPase and agglutinating antigen. When this component is equilibrated in sucrose density gradients, it localizes at a density of about 1.06 (4°C). We have shown previously that vesicles which equilibrate at low densities in

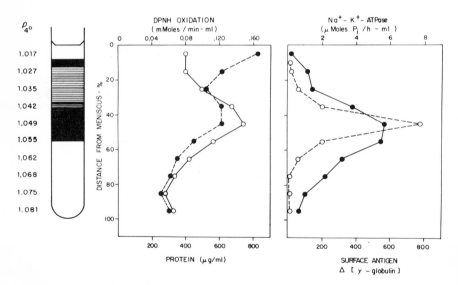

Fig. 5. Distribution of membrane "indicators" after equilibration of the low-density plasma membrane fraction in a Ficoll density gradient (SW 39 rotor, protein; ●-----●; DPNH oxidation; ●——●; alkali ion-activated ATPase; ○-----○; "agglutinating antigen." p_i—inorganic phosphorus; ρ—density. (Kamat and Wallach, 1965).

sucrose gradients have high inosine diphosphatase activities (Wallach and Ullrey, 1962). Since this enzyme appears to be concentrated in Golgi membranes, and since epididymal Golgi membranes have been shown to localize at low densities in sucrose (Kuff and Dalton, 1959), we suspect that the 1.024 component represents the Golgi apparatus of Ehrlich ascites carcinoma.

C. Subfractionation of plasma-membrane vesicles. To test for possible heterogeneity in the composition of plasma membrane vesicles we have searched for variations of density distribution with pH. One series of experiments was carried out in Ficoll, one in glycerol. In both cases the particles were initially distributed throughout the density gradients, which were then centrifuged to density equilibrium.

The results obtained in Ficoll (at ionic strength 0.01) are illustrated in Fig. 6. The maximum density (1.098) is obtained at about pH 3.3, suggesting that the apparent isoelectric point of these vesicles is near this pH. The variation of density with pH is taken to illustrate the effect of electrostatic mechanisms on V_f. Above the isoelectric point the vesicles acquire a net negative charge; below it they are positively charged. In either case, Gibbs-Donnan

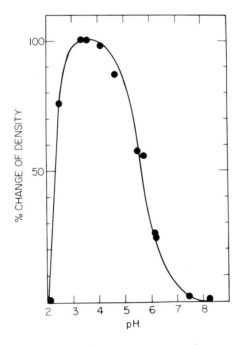

Fig. 6. Variation of density of plasma membrane vesicles with pH. Ficoll gradients. Material initially distributed uniformly throughout gradient. SW 39 rotor; 35,000 rpm; 16 h. Tris-acetate buffers. Ionic strength 0.01.

effects and direct electrostatic repulsions produce volume expansion. The apparent isoelectric point of 3.3 is identical to that obtained by light-scattering techniques (Wallach and Kamat, unpublished), and is in excellent agreement with the point of zero electrophoretic mobility of intact Ehrlich ascites carcinoma cells (Cook *et al.*, 1962). The light scattering studies also indicate that the low value for the isoelectric point is due to the contribution of sialic acid.

Despite the wide variation of density with *p*H, distributions in Ficoll gradients do not give any clear indication of heterogeneity. The situation is, however, quite different in glycerol gradients (Fig. 7), which reflect the role of various dissociable groups on the hydration of the vesicle wall. Here the maximum median density (1.177) is obtained at about *p*H 4.4; clearly the isoelectric point determined in glycerol has a different significance from that found in Ficoll. Moreover, vesicles which distribute over a narrow density range when equilibrated in Ficoll gradients, spread out over a very broad — but higher — density range in glycerol at *p*H levels away from the isoelectric point. As the *p*H is moved toward 4.4, the particles increase in density but also distribute over an increasingly narrow density range. (Near the isoelectric point this becomes extreme because of aggregation.)

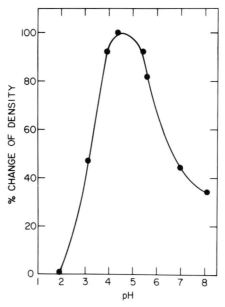

Fig. 7. Variation of density of plasma membrane vesicles with *p*H. Glycerol gradients. Material initially distributed uniformly throughout gradient. SW 39 rotor, 35,000 rpm, 16 h. Tris-acetate buffers. Ionic strength 0.01.

The data suggest that wall hydration is minimal near pH 4.4, where ρ_T approaches ρ_w, which appears to be similar for all the membrane fragments. Away from the isoelectric point, however, different particles have different degrees of hydration, which accounts for the broad range of densities in glycerol. The results show that a vesicle population of limited particle volume (V_T) and anhydrous wall density (ρ_w) can encompass membrane fragments with varied degrees of wall hydration. One must now inquire whether this heterogeneity is associated with functional diversity.

We have not yet tested this question using glycerol gradients, but data obtained by both differential and density equilibrium centrifugation in sucrose gradients indicate that the alkali-ion activated ATPase and agglutinating antigens belong to different vesicle classes (Wallach and Vlahovic, to be published).

Figure 8 illustrates one of the approaches we have employed. In this experiment C^{14}-labeled anti-microsomal membrane gamma-globulin was first absorbed to remove the bulk of antibodies common to both plasma membrane and endoplasmic reticulum. To do this the gamma globulin was reacted with a sufficient excess of the high density membrane material from the Ficoll-Mg barrier separation to bind essentially all the antibody capable of reacting with these membranes. The absorptions were carried out at 4°C for 16 hrs followed by 37°C for 30 hrs. The membrane particles and bound antibody were then sedimented by centrifugation at 50,000 rpm for 45 min. The absorption procedure removes about 80% of the labeled antibody that can be absorbed by the plasma membrane fraction, but leaves agglutinating antibody in solution. Apparently, endoplasmic reticulum and plasma membrane share many antigens, but not those involved in cell agglutination.

The residual gamma-globulin was then reacted with an excess of plasma membrane, i.e., in proportions leaving about half of the agglutinating antigen free of antibody and available for later detection. After a washing step the reacted plasma membrane material was layered on top of a sucrose density gradient buffered with 1 mM Tris-HCl (pH 8.6).

After centrifugation at 39,000 rpm for one hour, the material had distributed into a series of closely-spaced narrow layers. The tubes were then 'cut' and analyzed for protein, bound labeled antibody, residual ability to absorb agglutinating antibody, and for alkali ion-sensitive ATPase. As shown in Fig. 8, the alkali ion-sensitive ATPase is associated with the more slowly sedimenting membrane material, while the surface antigen — as measured by agglutination inhibition — is associated with the more rapidly moving particles. The distribution of C^{14}-labeled gamma-globulin shows, however, that there is no significant difference between fractions as far as antibody binding capacity is concerned. It thus appears that although all membrane fragments bind similar amounts of labeled gamma-globulin under the conditions employed, only a certain fraction reacts with agglutinating antibody.

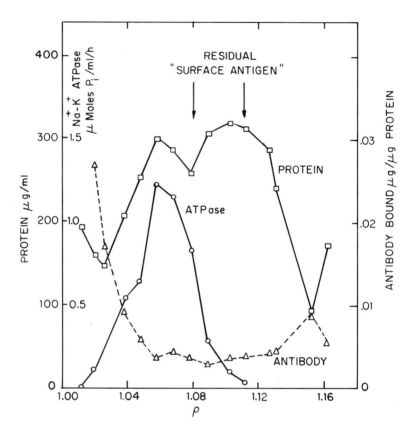

Fig. 8. Fractionation of plasma membrane material by differential centrifugation in a sucrose gradient. See text for details.

(The high levels of bound antibody at the top of the gradient are actually due to some residual free antibody.)

When the plasma membrane fraction is centrifuged to density equilibrium in sucrose density gradients, the distributions diagramed in Fig. 9 are obtained. The alkali ion-sensitive ATPase is concentrated in a series of closely spaced layers at a density of about 1.085, whereas the agglutinating antigen is located at a density of about 1.13. These results are in interesting agreement with those of Tosteson, *et al.* (1965), who found that the alkali ion-sensitive ATPase of sonicated erythrocyte ghosts is associated only with those membrane fragments that equilibrate at a density of about 1.10 in sucrose gradients.

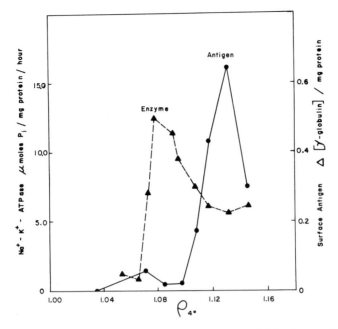

Fig. 9. Fractionation of plasma membrane material by isopycnic ultracentrifugation in a sucrose density gradient. Material initially distributed uniformly throughout gradient. Buffer—0.001 M Tris (pH 8.6). SW 39 rotor, 39,000 rpm, 16 h. (Wallach et al. 1965).

D. Conclusions. The new data suggest that disruption of Ehrlich ascites carcinoma cells leads to the fragmentation of the plasma membrane into diverse vesicle types, each bearing a different complement of the functions of the intact cell surface. This implies that the surface of these cells is organized as a mosaic of large and functionally discrete macromolecular assemblies.

REFERENCES

Ackerman, E. 1962. *Biophysical Science.* Prentice Hall, Inc. P. 236.

Ailhaud, G., D. Samuel, and P. Desnuelle. 1963. *Biochim. Biophys. Acta* 67: 150.

Al-Askari, S., D. C. Dumonde, H. S. Lawrence, and L. Thomas. 1965. *Ann. N. Y. Acad. Sci.* 120: 261.

Aldridge, W. N. 1962. *Biochem. J.* 83: 527.

Allard, C., G. de Lamirande, and A. Cantero. 1957. *Cancer Res.* 17: 862.

Anderson, H. M., and J. C. Turner. 1960. *J. Clin. Invest.* 39: 1.

Aterman, K. 1963. *The Liver*, ed. C. Rouiller. New York: Academic Press, Inc. P. 61.

Aull, F., and H. Hempling. 1963. *Am. J. Physiol.* 204: 789.

Basch, R. S., and C. A. Stetson. 1962. *Ann. N. Y. Acad. Sci.* 97: 83.

Basch, R. S., and C. A. Stetson. 1963. *Transplantation* 1: 469.

Brinton, C. C. Jr., and M. A. Lauffer. 1959. *Electrophoresis — Theory, Methods, and Applications*, ed. M. Bier. New York: Academic Press, Inc. P. 427.

Brown, A. D. 1963. *Biochim. Biophys. Acta* 75: 425.

Brown, A. D. 1965. *J. Molec. Biol.* 12: 491.

Burgos, M. H., H. W. Deane, and M. L. Karnovsky. 1955. *J. Histochem. Cytochem.* 3: 103.

Carnie, J. A., and J. W. Porteous. 1962. *Biochem. J.* 85: 620.

Casella, C. 1951. *Acta Physiol. Scand.* 21: 380.

Chowdhury, T. K., and F. M. Snell. 1965. *Biochim. Biophys. Acta* 94: 461.

Clark, B., and J. W. Porteous. 1965. *Biochem. J.* 95: 475.

Cohen, A. 1963. *In Mechanisms of Virus Infection* ed. W. Smith. New York: Academic Press, Inc. P. 153.

Cook, G. M. W., D. H. Heard, and G. V. F. Seaman. 1961. *Nature* 191: 44.

Cook, G. M. W., D. H. Heard, and G. V. F. Seaman. 1962. *Exptl. Cell Res.* 28: 27.

Cook, G. M. W., G. V. F. Seaman, and L. Weiss. 1963. *Cancer Res.* 23: 1813.

Curtis, A. S. G. 1960. *Am. Nat.* 94: 37.

Curtis, A. S. G. 1961. *Exptl. Cell. Res.* 8: S107.

Daoust, R. 1958. In *Liver Function* ed. R. W. Braver. Washington. Am. Inst. Biol. Sci. P. 3.

Davies, D. A. L. 1965. *Ann. N. Y. Acad. Sci.* 120: 230.

Deane, H. W., and E. W. Dempsey. 1945. *Anat. Rec.* 93: 401.

de Bernard, L. 1958. *Bull. Soc. Chim. Biol.* 40: 161.

Deul, D. H., and H. McIlwain. 1961. *J. Neurochem.* 8: 246.

Dodge, J. T., C. Mitchell, and D. Hanahan. 1962. *Arch. Biochem. Biophys.* 100: 119.

Draper, M. H., and A. J. Hodge. 1949. *Aust. J. Exptl. Biol. Med. Sci.* 27: 465.

Dumonde, D. C., S. Al-Askari, H. S. Lawrence, and L. Thomas. 1963. *Nature* 198: 598.

Easton, J. M., B. Goldberg, and H. Green. 1962. *J. Exptl. Med.* 115: 275.

Emmelot, P., and C. J. Bos. 1962. *Biochim. Biophys. Acta* 58: 374.

Emmelot, P., E. L. Benedetti, and P. H. Rumke. 1964. In *From Molecule to Cell, Symp. on Electron Microscopy*, 1963. Rome: 1964, Consiglio Nazionale delle Richerche, P. 253.

Emmelot, P., C. J. Bos, E. L. Benedetti, and P. H. Rumke. 1964. *Biochim. Biophys. Acta* 90: 126.

Eylar, E. H., M. A. Madoff, O. V. Brody, and J. L. Oncley. 1962. *J. Biol. Chem.* 237: 1992.

Feigin, I., and A. Wolf. 1957. *J. Histochem. Cytochem.* 5: 53.

Forrester, J. A., E. J. Ambrose, and J. A. MacPherson. 1962. *Nature* 196: 1068.

Forrester, J. A., E. J. Ambrose, and M. P. G. Stocker. 1964. *Nature* 201: 945.

Fredricsson, B. 1956. *Exptl. Cell Res.* 10: 63.

Fuhrmann, G. F., E. Granzer, E. Bey, and G. Ruhenstroth-Bauer. 1964. *Zeit. J. Naturforsch.* 19b: 614.

Fuhrmann, G. F., E. Granzer, W. Kubler, F. Rueff, and G. Ruhenstroth-Bauer. 1962. *Zeit. J. Naturforsch.* 17b: 610.

Getz, G. S., W. Bartley, F. Stirpe, B. M. Notton, and A. Renshaw. 1962. *Biochem. J.* 83: 181.

Goldberg, B., and H. Green. 1959. *J. Exptl. Med.* 109: 505.

Goldberg, B., and H. Green. 1960. *J. Biophys. Biochem. Cytol.* 7: 645.

Green, H., R. A. Fleischer, P. Barrow, and B. Goldberg. 1959. *J. Exptl. Med.* 109: 511.

Harrison, D. D., and H. L. Webster. 1964. *Biochim. Biophys. Acta* 93: 662.

Haughton, G. 1965. Personal communication.

Herberman, R., and C. A. Stetson. 1965. *J. Exptl. Med.* 121: 533.

Hers, H. G., J. Berthet, L. Berthet, and C. de Duve. 1951. *Bull. Soc. Chim. Biol.* 33: 21.

Herzenberg, L. A., and L. A. Herzenberg. 1961. *Proc. Natl. Acad. Sci.* 47: 762.

Hoffman, J. F. 1958. *J. Gen. Physiol.* 42: 9.

Hoffman, J. F. 1962. *J. Gen. Physiol.* 45: 837.

Hoffman, J. F., D. C. Tosteson, and R. Whittam. 1962. *Nature* 185: 186.

Holland, J. J. 1962. *Virol.* 16: 163.

Holland, J. J., and B. H. Hoyer. 1962. *Cold Spring Symp. Quart. Biol.* 27: 101.

Holland, J. J., and L. C. McLaren. 1961. *J. Exptl. Med.* 114: 161.

Hunter, M. J., and S. L. Commerford. 1961. *Biochim. Biophys. Acta* 47: 580.

Isselbacher, K. 1965. Personal communication.

Johnson, M. K., and V. P. Whittaker. 1963. *Biochem. J.* 88: 404.

Joly, M. 1956. *J. Colloid. Sci.* 11: 519.

Kamat, V. B., and D. F. H. Wallach. 1965. *Sci.* 148: 1343.

Kavanau, J. L. 1965. In *Structure and Function in Biological Membranes*, San Francisco: Holden-Day, Inc.

Kono, T., and S. P. Colowick. 1961. *Arch. Biochim. Biophys.* 93: 520.

Kuff, E. L., and A. J. Dalton. 1959. In *Subcellular Particles*. ed. T. Hayashi, New York: Ronald Press Co. P. 114.

Landon, E. J., and J. L. Norris. 1963. *Biochim. Biophys. Acta* 71: 266.

Manson, L. A., G. V. Foschi, and J. Palm. 1962. *Proc. Natl. Acad. Sci.* 48: 1816.

Manson, L. A., G. V. Foschi, and J. Palm. 1963. *J. Cell Comp. Physiol.* 61: 109.

Manson, L. A., G. V. Foschi, T. Dougherty, and J. Palm. 1965. *Ann. N. Y. Acad. Sci.* P. 251.

Marcus, P. I., and J. M. Salb. *Bact. Proc.* 1965. Abstr. 22: 100.

Mauro. A., and W. R. Adams. 1961. *J. Biophys. Biochem. Cytol.* 10: 177.

Mauro, A., and Q. Sten-Knudsen. 1952. *Acta Med. Scand.* 266: 715.

McCollester, D. 1962. *Biochim. Biophys. Acta* 57: 427.

McIlwain, H. 1961. *Biochem. J.* 78: 24.

Miller, A., J. F. Sullivan, and J. H. Katz. 1963. *Cancer Res.* 23: 485.

Miller, D., and R. U. Crane. 1961. *Biochim. Biophys. Acta* 52: 293.

Möller, G. 1961. *J. Exptl. Med.* 114: 415.

Morton, R. K. 1954. *Biochem. J.* 57: 595.

Neville, D. M., Jr. 1960. *J. Biophys. Biochem. Cytol.* 8: 413.

Novikoff, A. B. 1958. *Proc. Am. Assoc. Cancer Res.* 2: 331.

Novikoff, A. B. 1960. In *Cell Physiology of Neoplasia*. Texas: University of Texas Press. P. 219. Figs. 6–8.

O'Neill, C. H. 1964. In *Recent Progress in Surface Science*, Vol. 2. ed. J. F. Danielli, K. G. A. Parkhurst, and A. C. Riddiford. New York: Academic Press, Inc.

Patterson, M. K., and O. Touster. 1962. *Biochim. Biophys. Acta* 56: 626.

Philpot, J. S., and J. E. Stanier. 1956. *Biochem. J.* 63: 214.

Philipson, L., and S. Bengtsson. 1962. *Virol.* 18: 457.

Porteous, J. W., and B. Clark. 1965. *Biochem. J.* 96: 159.

Post, R. L., C. R. Merritt, C. R. Kinsolving, and C. D. Albright. 1960. *J. Biol. Chem.* 235: 1796.

Rand, R. P. 1964. *Biophys. J.* 4: 303.

Robinson, G. B. 1963. *Biochem.* 188: 162.

Rouiller, C. H., and A. M. Jezequel. 1963. In *The Liver*, Vol. 1. ed. C. H. Rouiller. New York: Academic Press, Inc. P. 195.

Schwartz, A. 1963. *Biochim. Biophys. Acta* 67: 329.

Schwartz, A., H. S. Bachelard, and H. McIlwain. 1962. *Biochem. J.* 84: 626.

Skipski, V. P., M. Barclay, F. M. Archibald, O. Terebus-Kekish, E. S. Reichman, and J. J. Good. 1965. *Life Sci.* 4: 1673.

Skou, J. C. 1957. *Biochim. Biophys. Acta* 23: 394.

Skou, J. C. 1962. *Biochim. Biophys. Acta* 58: 314.

Teorell, T. 1952. *J. Gen. Physiol.* 35: 669.

Tosteson, D. C., P. Cook, and R. Blout. 1965. *J. Gen. Physiol.* 48: 1125.

Tria, E., and O. Barnabei. 1963. *Nature* 197: 598.

Triantaphyllopoulos, S. E., and J. Tuba. 1959. *Canad. J. Biochem. Physiol.* 37: 699.

Turkington, R. W. 1962. *Biochim. Biophys. Acta* 65: 386.

Vandenheuvel, F. A. 1963. *J. Am. Oil Chem. Soc.* 40: 455.

Wallach, D. F. H., and E. H. Eylar. 1961. *Biochim. Biophys. Acta* 52: 594.

Wallach, D. F. H., and E. B. Hager. 1962. *Nature* 196: 1004.

Wallach D. F. H., and V. B. Kamat. 1964. *Proc. Natl. Acad. Sci.* 52: 721.

Wallach, D. F. H., V. B. Kamat, and F. L. Murphy. 1965. Internatl. Symp. on Invasiveness in Cancer. Paris 1965. (International Union Against Cancer.) In press.

Wallach, D. F. H., and M. V. Perez Esandi. 1964. *Biochim. Biophys. Acta* 83: 363.

Wallach, D. F. H., and D. Ullrey. 1962. *Biochim. Biophys. Acta* 64: 526.

Wallach, D. F. H., and D. Ullrey. 1964. *Biochim. Biophys. Acta* 88: 620.

Whittam, R. 1962. *Biochem. J.* 84: 110.

Whittam, R. 1964. In *The Cellular Functions of Membrane Transport.* ed. J. F. Hoffman. Englewood Cliffs, N. J.: Prentice Hall, Inc. P. 139.

Whittam, R., and M. E. Ager. 1964. *Biochem. J.* 93: 337.

Wigzell, H. 1965. *Transplantation.* 3: 423.

Wolfe, L. S., and H. McIlwain. 1961. *Biochem. J.* 78: 33.

Tumor Antigens

George Klein

Department of Tumor Biology
Karolinska Institutet Medical School
Stockholm, Sweden

At a conference dealing with cell membranes a discussion on tumor antigen must start with the question whether there is any evidence that such antigens are actually localized at the cell membrane. First, however, we must define the term *tumor antigens* as used in this paper. Since this term covers a vast area, it should be restricted. Consideration will be limited entirely to tumor antigens capable of inducing host rejection responses, and particular attention will be given to systems where such rejection occurs in the absence of any genetically determined differences between tumor and host, or, in other words, to tumor-specific transplantation reactions.

This approach will exclude tumor antigens detected by heterologous immune sera, a situation where the immunological reaction is used as a tool for analysis rather than as a method for discrimination between "self" and "nonself" components, and where the possible tumor-specific nature of any identified component will depend entirely on the composition of the normal tissue used for comparison. In such systems cellular constituents of any kind may appear to be tumor-specific if 1) the normal tissue used for comparison lacks them or contains them in insufficient concentration, and 2) the antibody-producing foreign species is capable of recognizing this difference. This kind of "antigenic profile analysis" may yield interesting information, but the same questions may be raised concerning representativeness and normal tissue homology as in the field of tumor biochemistry. Tumor-specific transplantation antigens (TSTA) are not subject to this difficulty. If consideration is limited to reactions occurring in the species of origin, and if adequate care is taken to distinguish between ordinary transplantation antigens (determined by genetic differences between donor and host) and tumor-specific antigens proper (where new cellular antigenic specificities arise in parallel with the neoplastic transformation), the reacting animal will disregard automatically the antigens of its own normal tissues, unless compartmentalization occurs, as it does with organ-specific antigens.

Tumor-specific antigens left for consideration after this restriction are essentially of two kinds. One group is detected by complement fixation, the other by their ability to induce transplantation resistance and related reactions in genetically compatible isologous hosts. Discussion will again be restricted to the second category, since complement-fixing antigens are not known to occur on the cell surface, and their possible identity or overlapping with the transplantation antigens is quite unknown. In some tumors induced by DNA viruses complement-fixing antigens are known to occur in the nucleus while in others they are localized to the cytoplasm. In contrast, there is good reason to believe that some, if not all, antigens evoking graft rejection responses are localized on the cell surface. Evidence concerning this latter point will be considered first.

Evidence Concerning Surface
Localization of Tumor Antigens

Critical consideration showed only two systems where cell membrane localization was unequivocally demonstrated. One is the H-2 iso-antigen system which induces ordinary transplantation reactions and is the strongest and best-known barrier against homotransplantation in mice. At best this can serve only as a model system for the tumor-specific antigens themselves. The reason to regard it as a model is twofold: it is the most extensively studied cellular antigen system capable of inducing rejection reactions in the homologous species, and, furthermore, there is good reason to assume that host mechanisms similar in kind, if not in degree, act against foreign H-2 antigens in tumor cells, and against the tumor-specific antigens proper.

The other system where membrane localization has been clearly shown is a tumor-specific one: this is where the new antigens are present on the surface of mouse leukemia cells, induced by various leukemogenic viruses. These antigens are capable of inducing rejection responses in genetically compatible (syngeneic) hosts; in most cases they express themselves by rendering the target cells that carry them sensitive to cytotoxicity or specific immunofluorescence upon exposure to the sera of resistant syngeneic animals. Since most of our experience in this field has been with mouse lymphomas induced by the Moloney agent, consideration will be mainly restricted to this system.

In the H-2 system membrane localization is indicated by the fact that the entire activity of iso-antisera directed against antigenic components of this system can be absorbed by intact living cell suspensions, e.g., fresh ascites tumor cells (Haughton, submitted for publication). Moreover, when living cells are exposed to anti-H-2 iso-antisera and then stained with fluorescein-conjugated rabbit-antimouse globulin, the reacting antigen is clearly localized on the cell surface and gives the appearance of a ring or, if diluted sera are used, of stained spots and sectors (Möller, 1961).

In a careful study (Haughton submitted for publication) the total H-2 antigenic activity of a known number of ultrasonically homogenized target cells was compared with the activity of the corresponding number of intact cells, by contrasting their ability to inhibit the cytotoxic activity of known anti-H-2 iso-antisera, measured by the Cr51-release test (Wigzell, 1965). The study showed that approximately 80% of the total cellular H-2 activity is expressed on the cell surface. The possibility that this figure could be an artifact, resulting from the ultrasonic destruction of H-2 antigens, was excluded by control experiments, in which antigenic extracts of known potency were exposed to the same treatment.

Comparative studies on the expression of H-2 antigens on cell surfaces have provided information on the occurrence of these antigens, and their physiological and genetic variability, in different cell types. Although it has been shown that the H-2 antigens occurred on all the mouse cells studied, the sensitivity of different cell types to the cytotoxic action of the same anti-H-2 iso-antibody varied greatly (Hellstrom, 1959). The basis for this variation may now be considered.

Variation in Surface Antigen Concentration and Cytotoxic Sensitivity in the H-2 System

First, it may be stated that a parallel difference exists in cytotoxic sensitivity *in vivo* and *in vitro*. Lymphoma and leukemia cells are almost uniformly sensitive to inhibition by anti-H-2 antibodies *in vivo* and to the cytotoxic effect of such antibodies *in vitro*, in the presence of complement. In contrast, only occasionally is it possible to find a carcinoma or sarcoma that is sensitive in either test, and the vast majority was found to be resistant in both tests [See, e.g., Hellstrom (1959) and Snell (1957).]

The mechanism of this difference has been studied by Möller and Möller (1962). Their reasoning was based on the work of Weinrach *et al.*, (1958) and Mayer (1961) on hemolysis, which showed that lytic action requires the binding of complement and at least two antibody molecules all forming a complex with the reactive site at the cell membrane. The Möllers postulated that in the presence of excess antibody and complement cytotoxic sensitivity is determined by the density of the antigenic receptors on the surface of the target cells. If the distance between two antigen-antibody complexes is too large, owing to a scarcity of antigen receptors, a critical concentration of complement would not be obtainable and the cell would be resistant. A short distance, however, would lead to a high concentration of complement within a given area and would be capable of initiating cytotoxic damage. As a first experimental approach, they selected a number of different cell types, including lymphomas, carcinomas, and sarcomas, differing in their sensitivity to the cytotoxic effect of the same anti-H-2 antibody. The density of the relevant antigenic receptors on the cell surface was compared by quantitative absorption tests, performed in parallel with measurements of the cell diameter. Absorbing ability was calculated per cell surface unit. A clear correlation, quite in line with the mechanism postulated, was found between the cytotoxic titer of an antiserum against different target cells and the absorbing ability of the same cells per unit surface area.

It follows from this concept that resistant cells should become sensitive if the proportion of antigenic sites reacting in the test could be raised sufficiently to provide an adequate density. The Möllers could accomplish this in the H-2 system, since H-2 is a compound locus that determines the specificity of a number of different antigenic components, By mixing different antisera, directed against different combinations of antigenic specificities present on the surface of the same target-cell type, it was possible to manipulate the proportion of reacting sites experimentally. The expected result was actually obtained: exposure to mixtures of two or three antisera, neither of which was cytotoxic alone, could induce significant cytotoxicity. This was not a question of simply increasing the antibody concentration, since the combined and the single sera were applied in the same final hemagglutinating titer. The results are illustrated by two representative experiments, shown in Table 1.

The same principle has been recently applied by E. Möller and Eklund (1965) to human lymph-node cells. Type ABRh + target cells were found insensitive to the cytotoxic action of anti-A, anti-B, or anti-Rh + antibodies, but sensitive to the combined action of all three.

It would thus seem that the complement-dependent killing of target cells by iso-antibody is essentially dependent on the density of the antigenic receptors on the cell surface.

Are H-2 Antigens Essential for the Integrity of the Cell Membrane?

The question may now be asked whether H-2 transplantation antigens represent essential constituents of the cell surface. This may be discussed in the light of work by this author, where tumor cell populations, homozygous

TABLE 1

CYTOTOXIC ACTION* OF SINGLE OR COMBINED ANTISERA AGAINST
SARCOMA MC1M AND CARCINOMA TA3
(After Möller and Möller (1962.)

Cell type	Antiserum	Known reactive antigenic components† (H-2)	Antiserum dilution	Cytotoxic index
MC1M	A.CA anti-A	CEKY	$\frac{1}{5}$	n.t.
ascites	A.SW anti-A	HKY	$\frac{1}{5}$	0.05
sarcoma	A.BY anti-A	ACHKY	$\frac{1}{5}$	0.10
of C3H	{ A.CA anti-A	CEHKY	$\frac{1}{5}$	0.12
origin	A.SW anti-A }		$\frac{1}{5}$	
	{ A.CA anti-A	ACEHKY	$\frac{1}{5}$	0.24
	A.BY anti-A }		$\frac{1}{5}$	
	{ A.SW anti-A	ACHKY	$\frac{1}{5}$	0.07
	A.BY anti-A }		$\frac{1}{5}$	
	{ A.CA anti-A		$\frac{1}{5}$	
	A.SW anti-A	ACEHKY	$\frac{1}{5}$	0.49
	A.BY anti-A }		$\frac{1}{5}$	
TA3	A.CA anti-A	CDEKMYB^{1}C^1	$\frac{1}{320}$	0.17
ascites	A.SW anti-A	DHKMYA^{1}C^1	$\frac{1}{40}$	0.12
carcinoma	C57L anti-A	ACDHJKMY	$\frac{1}{20}$	0.17
of strain	{ A.CA anti-A	CDEHKMYA^{1}B^{1}C^1	$\frac{1}{320}$	0.42
A origin	A.SW anti-A }		$\frac{1}{40}$	
	{ A.CA anti-A	CDEHJKMYB^{1}C^1	$\frac{1}{320}$	0.46
	C57L anti-A }		$\frac{1}{20}$	
	{ A.SW anti-A	ACDHJKMYA^{1}C^1	$\frac{1}{40}$	0.32
	C57L anti-A }		$\frac{1}{20}$	
	{ A.CA anti-A		$\frac{1}{320}$	
	A.SW anti-A	ACDEHJKMYA^{1}B^{1}C^1	$\frac{1}{40}$	0.62
	C57L anti-A }		$\frac{1}{20}$	

* Determined by the method of Gorer and O'Gorman (1956) by exposing the target cells to the antiserum *in vitro* in the presence of complement. The cytotoxic index has been calculated by subtracting the percentage of surviving cells in the antiserum-treated sample from the corresponding percentage in a sample exposed to the control serum, divided by the latter value.

† In addition to these known components, additional as yet unidentified H-2 components as well as antibodies directed against transplantation antigens *other* than H-2, may also be present, in combinations different for each antiserum.

or heterozygous for known H-2 antigens, were exposed to strong selection pressures directed against the antigens. All experimentation of this kind has been carried out with tumor cells for two reasons: these cells can be readily maintained by serial passage through animal hosts of known genotype; and, since they tend to start proliferating at a rapid rate even after transplantation to genetically incompatible hosts, they can often grow for a considerable time before being destroyed by the host reaction. Background growth of this type, prior to the onset of the selection pressure exerted by the homograft reaction, is an important requirement for these selection experiments, since rare antigenic variants could hardly be isolated by selection unless preceded by a period of more permissive growth. It seems difficult to design an analogous system with any serially passaged normal tissue. Bone-marrow transplantation through lethally irradiated hosts might be one such approach, although the irradiated state of the animals and their subsequent immunological impairment would make evaluation difficult.

Since all experiments of this kind have been carried out with neoplastic cells, it is difficult to judge whether the results obtained reflect a behavior characteristic of neoplastic cells, or could in principle apply to normal cells as well. Owing to the nature of the results obtained, however, this question is of only secondary importance in the present context.

When tumor cell populations are subject to the strong selection pressure of an incompatible host, whether untreated or preimmunized, new immunoresistant variants tend to arise, with frequencies that vary from system to system. In most cases immunoresistance is due not to antigenic *losses*, but to a reduction in the *concentration* of antigenic surface receptors: in other words, to purely quantitative changes (Möller, 1964). Such changes may make cells more resistant to the cytotoxic effect of humoral iso-antibodies, as discussed previously. In contrast, true loss of entire H-2 complexes has been conclusively demonstrated only in one situation. Tumors induced in F_1 hybrid hosts, heterozygous with regard to their H-2 composition, carry the two H-2 complexes of both parental specificities on most of their cells. When such cell populations are subjected to selection pressure directed against *one* of their two complexes, variants may emerge that have lost the now disadvantageous complex in a permanent and irreversible fashion. The missing complex does not reappear upon prolonged passage in the original F_1 hybrid host. Variant tumor sublines of this kind, specifically compatible with one parental strain, could be isolated from many different F_1 hybrid tumors, including carcinomas, sarcomas, and lymphomas.

Their loss of the entire H-2 complex of the opposite parental strain could be demonstrated by a number of independent tests such as immunizing ability, capacity to absorb known anti-H-2 antisera, and cytotoxic sensitivity in the case of the lymphomas (Klein and Klein, 1959; Klein *et al.*, 1957; Klein and Klein, 1959; Klein *et al.*, 1960; Hellstrom, 1960).

We have tried extensively to select second-step variants that have also lost their residual antigenic complex, but the results were uniformly unsuccessful. Subsequent to the loss of one complex, as described in the foregoing paragraph, the antigens of the residual complex, corresponding in specificity to the selective parental strain, were often present in increased quantities on the variant cells. This was particularly clear with the lymphoma systems, where the cytotoxic sensitivity of the target cells permitted direct tests rather than absorptions (Hellstrom, 1964a). Such variants were subjected to further selectional attempts by forcing them to grow in hosts of the opposite parental strain. Since adult mice of this latter type were now quite incompatible with the highly specific variants, newborn or antiserum-treated, "actively enhanced" animals were used, and the resulting tumors were subsequently tested in irradiated and/or untreated adults. Most variants remained specific and did not adapt to untreated adults. However some of them, in agreement with the findings of Koprowski (1955), became nonspecific, and became capable of growing progressively, not only in the opposite parental strain, but in all kinds of other genetically incompatible mouse strains as well (Möller, 1964; Klein and Möller, 1963). When tested for the residual H-2 antigens present prior to the establishment of the nonspecific sublines, it was found that these antigens have not been lost but that their concentration per cell has decreased, often considerably. This result is in agreement with what was said concerning immunoresistance and the development of nonspecific transplantation behavior in other situations.

Since, as we have noted, transplantation antigens can be regarded only as model systems, we may now proceed to the tumor-specific antigens themselves.

Tumor-specific Antigens

Table 2 presents a list of the tumor systems where specific antigenicity capable of inducing tumor cell rejection has been demonstrated by transplantation methods in genetically compatible (syngeneic) and/or autochthonous hosts.

Such antigens have been shown to occur in all chemically and virally induced tumors studied. As a rule, different individual tumors induced by the same virus cross react antigenically, while chemically-induced tumors tend to have individually distinct, nonreacting or only occasionally crossreacting transplantation antigens. The available evidence has been surveyed recently in several review articles (Old and Boyse, 1964; Sjögren, 1965; Klein, in press).

All TSTA are comparable to *weak* histocompatibility antigens. The strength of TSTA is different in different etiological groups. As an example, methylcholanthrene-induced sarcomas in mice are more "strongly" antigenic than morphologically similar sarcomas induced by dibenzathracene, and sarcomas induced by the implantation of cellophane or Millipore films are only very weakly antigenic (Prehn, 1963; Klein et al., 1963). Among the virus tumors, Moloney mouse lymphomas are strongly antigenic (Klein and Klein, 1964a), while quite similar lymphomas induced by the Gross virus are much weaker (Klein et al., 1962). Many other examples can be quoted. There is variation in the strength of TSTA even within groups of tumors induced by

TABLE 2

SYSTEMS WITH DEMONSTRATED OCCURRENCE OF TUMOR-SPECIFIC
ANTIGENS CAPABLE OF INDUCING REJECTION RESPONSES
IN ISOLOGOUS HOSTS

Chemical carcinogens	
3–methylcholanthrene	
1,2,5,6–dibenzanthracene	
9,10–dimethylbenzanthracene	
3,4,9,10–dibenzpyrene	no cross reactivity
3,4–benzpyrene	
p–dimethylaminoazobenzene	
Physical agents	
Films: Millipore filter	
Cellophane film	
Radiation: UV	
Sr^{90}	
Virus	
DNA Polyoma	
SV40	cross reaction within each group
Adenovirus 12,18	
Shope papilloma	
Mammary tumor agent	
Leukemia	
Gross	
RNA Moloney	
Rauscher	cross reaction between the groups
Friend	
Graffi	
Rous (Schmidt–Ruppin)	

the same chemical carcinogen, e.g., methylcholanthrene, or the same virus, e.g., polyoma. As a rule, tumors appearing after a short latency period in their primary host tend to turn out more strongly antigenic in subsequent transplantation tests than those that appear after a long latency period (Sjögren, 1965; Prehn, 1963).

This inverse correlation, among induced tumors, between the length of the latency period and the "strength" of specific antigenicity indicates that immunoselection occurs in the course of the neoplastic transformation and prevents the outgrowth of more antigenic cells to an increasing extent as time proceeds. The outgrowth of the more highly immunogenic cells during the early part of the latency period, after the application of chemical carcinogens like methylcholanthrene or strong oncogenic viruses like polyoma, must therefore be attributed to a depressing action of the oncogenic agent on the immune response (demonstrated for methylcholanthene, for example, by a number of workers), and/or to a more rapid growth rate of a higher autonomy of those more antigenic neoplastic variants that appear.

Various questions may now be asked, about TSTA even though only tentative answers can be given to most of them.
1. What is the evidence that these antigens are localized on the cell surface?
2. Is there any reason to assume that they are directly connected with the neoplastic phenotype of the cells?
3. What genetic information controls their specificity?
4. What role do they play during oncogenesis?

Cellular localization of TSTA. The reasons to assume that TSTAs are like H-2 antigens, localized on the cell surface are partly deductive. The host reactions capable of destroying antigenically deviating cells are mediated largely by sensitized host cells, rather than by humoral antibodies. It has been shown (Möller, 1965a) that adherence of the host lymphoid cells to the target cells is an essential first step in killing the target cells. If the foreign antigenic sites of the target cells are covered with antibody, adherence is prevented and the target cells may survive (Möller, 1963, 1965b). Since the presence of uncovered antigenic sites on the target cell surface is so essential for graft rejection, it is difficult to conceive of a transplantation antigen that would be buried inside the cell and not expressed on the surface as well. The opposite is, of course, not true: antigens expressed on the surface may be present inside the cell as well, but this is not really relevant to this discussion.

One type of tumor-specific antigen system where surface localization has been clearly demonstrated is represented by the virus-induced mouse leukemias. Our experience has been mainly with the Moloney virus-induced lymphomas in mice. Without going into the details of the evidence, which can be found in the original publications (Klein and Klein, 1964a; b; 1964; Klein, *et al.*, 1966), it may be stated that the same kind of evidence is available for surface localization as for the H-2 system. Moloney lymphoma homografts, subthreshold isografts, or homogenates induce a tumor-specific transplantation resistance in syngeneic hosts. Concomitantly, humoral antibodies are found that react specifically with Moloney lymphoma target cells in the cytotoxic and immunofluorescence tests; these antibodies can be absorbed completely and specifically by intact, living Moloney cells. Moreover, the absorbing ability of cells from a given Moloney lumphoma parallels closely their own cytotoxic sensitivity *in vitro* and *in vivo:* whenever the cytotoxic and absorption tests indicate a high surface-antigen concentration on a given cell line, they also give a higher dilution endpoint in the fluorescence test than in lines with an indicated lower antigen concentration. (In contrast, no relationship is indicated between this group of properties and virus release from a given lymphoma.) The immunofluorescence test shows, furthermore, that the reactive antigen is localized on the cell surface. The interior of the cell also contains the antigen; homogenization doubles the ability of cells to inhibit the Moloney-specific cytotoxic reaction.

Cell surface localization of tumor-specific antigens is also indicated by cytotoxic and/or immunofluorescence tests in a number of other mouse leukemia systems (cp. Old and Boyse, 1964).

Possible significance of TSTA for neoplastic behavior. We have noted that tumor cells heterozygous for H-2, which thus contain two different antigenic complexes, can readily lose one complex upon negative selection without any harm to their viability or their growth properties; while the loss of both, *or* the loss of the only one contained in a homozygous tumor cell, cannot be tolerated. This finding indicated that the presence of a certain minimum concentration of at least one H-2 antigenic complex is essential for the life of the cell. If this were not so it would be difficult to understand how tumors which have been carried in serial passage for several decades — in some cases more than half a century — and which have been exposed to the homograft reaction of laboratory mice of all kinds, nevertheless maintain certain H-2 antigens on their surface. No nonspecific tumors devoid of all H-2 antigens have ever been identified.

Experiments that are analogous to a certain extent have also been performed with some TSTA systems. In at least one case, that of polyoma-induced tumors in mice, extensive efforts have been made to establish variant cell lines devoid of the specific transplantation antigen. Sjögren (1964) carried polyoma tumor lines for 30 to 50 passages in preimmunized mice without being able to select variants with decreased antigenicity. In line with the reasoning given previously this result would indicate that tumor-specific antigenicity is related to neoplastic properties of the polyoma tumor cells. This view is reinforced by the consideration that tumor cell populations are very plastic and contain a great amount of chromosomal and other genetic or epigenetic variation. Selection of drug-resistant or immunoresistant cell variants can be readily accomplished in many systems. That this is not the case here is therefore best explained by the selective elimination of the variants.

Similar experiments, as yet unpublished, have been carried out for the Moloney system. Again there was no evidence of antigenic loss after 10 to 25 passages in pre-immunized mice and/or after repeated exposure to antiserum and complement *in vitro* prior to each inoculation. Although some decrease of immunosensitivity could be observed, indicating a somewhat decreased surface antigen concentration, there was clear evidence for antigenic persistance.

Assuming, on the basis of these admittedly scarce and, in part, still preliminary data, that TSTA systems are on the cell surface and are essential for the unlimited proliferation of the neoplastic cells, one may speculate further and infer that their existence is an expression of that change in the surface which makes the cell unresponsive to homeostatic growth-regulating forces. Whether such forces are envisaged as acting by direct cell-to-cell contact, or as mediated by circulating hormones, the cell surface must play an essential role in receiving the appropriate message and initiating adequate cellular reactions. The profound changes of the surface that lead to new antigenic specificities may involve the responsible receptor sites.

The nature of the TSTAs. One of the most important questions about the nature of the TSTAs concerns the source of the genetic information controlling them. More specifically, the question is whether this information is coded in the genome of the virus or that of the cell. Information on this point is not available for any system, and it is therefore necessary to carry out conjectural and indirect reasoning if the question is to be discussed at all.

It may be stated first that no proof has been found for any system that the rejection of the virus-induced tumor cells is dependent on the virus they release. In three cases — polyoma, Shope papilloma, and the Schmidt-Ruppin variant of the Rous virus — virus release is not a necessary condition of either immunogenicity or immunosensitivity. In the polyoma system, tumors that never release any infectious virus nevertheless can induce a good transplantation resistance in the homograft-isograft system (Sjögren, 1961). In the Shope system, papillomas of domestic rabbits, and the carcinomas derived from either domestic or cottontail rabit papillomas are nonreleasers of the virus, but they nevertheless induce transplantation resistance and are sensitive to it, even after many years of serial passage. In only one instance has loss of antigenicity been seen (Evans *et al.*, 1962). It has been suggested that this situation can arise only with DNA viruses, since they mature in the nucleus and not by budding from the cell surface. However, a similar picture was found with an RNA system: mouse sarcomas induced by the Schmidt-Ruppin variant of the Rous virus are essentially nonreleasers, but they nevertheless induce a strong graft rejection response in the homograft-isograft test (Jonsson and Sjögren, 1965).

In the polyoma and Schmidt-Ruppin systems, antiviral immunity per se was not found sufficient to obtain graft rejection if the experimental conditions were such that the virus was prevented from entering into an appropriate interaction with the host cell. Successful passive transfer of antiviral immunity against polyoma from mother to offspring, did not lead to transplantation resistance (Habel, 1962). In the Schmidt-Ruppin system, similarly, chicken-derived virus could induce antiviral immunity in adult mice but no transplantation resistance against Schmidt-Ruppin isografts. To obtain the latter it was necessary to permit virus interaction with newborn mouse cells, which leads to transplantation immunity in some mice and tumors in others (Jonsson and Sjögren, 1965).

In the systems such as the mouse leukemias, where all cell lines encountered release virus, and where continuous virus maturation occurs by budding from the cell surface, only indirect evidence could be obtained on the same point. This evidence, however, contradicts a simple antiviral hypothesis. In the Moloney system there is good correlation between the degree of immuno-sensitivity and the concentration of reactive antigen on the cell surface, as measured by the ability of the cells to absorb the antibody responsible for the specific fluorescence or the cytotoxic reaction. These qualities were not cor-related, however, with the amount of virus released by a given lymphoma, which appeared to be an independent characteristic (Klein *et al.*, 1966).

While all evidence thus speaks for cellular antigenicity, the specificity of the antigen may still be controlled by the virus genome. It could be an early virus protein, precursor substances of the virus coat, or some other product resulting from the virus-cell interaction. It is even conceivable that the presence of the virus genome or parts of it may alter the specificity of cellular iso-antigenic systems. This could happen at any level; the virus may affect the cell by altering the DNA-coded genetic information, transcription, translation, folding, assembly into appropriate patterns, etc. Since too little is known about this, however, detailed speculations do not appear to be fruitful at the present time.

Role of TSTAs during oncogenesis. Although experiments concerning immunological tumor-host relationships in transplantation systems can be considered as models of the various cell-host relationships that *may* prevail during the process of oncogenesis, they give no direct information about what actually *does* happen. They may be helpful in suggesting experiments but they do not replace the need for direct experimentation on this problem.

In discussing the possible role of immunological host responses in the course of oncogenesis, we shall attempt to consider separately humoral and cell-mediated reactions.

Some recent experiments by the authors on the role of *humoral* anti-bodies in the Moloney system may be pertinent (Klein and Klein, 1965). In adult mice of various strains, inoculation of the virus was found to induce the formation of anti-tumor antibody in high titers in approximately 30 days. Antibody was measured by cytotoxicity or immunofluorescence, with estab-lished Moloney lymphoma cells as targets. In newborn mice, on the other hand, antibody formation was deficient or delayed, and a large fraction of the animals failed to respond at all (Klein and Klein, 1965). When reinocu-lated as adults, the previously nonresponsive animals still did not react, thus appearing to be truly tolerant. These animals not only failed to make anti-tumor antibody, but also failed to react in transplantation tests against antigenic tumor cells and did not develop virus-neutralizing antibodies.

Similar findings were reached previously by Rubin with avian lympho-matosis virus. He found that infection through the egg was associated with persistent viremia, absence of antiviral antibody, and a sixfold increase of visceral lymphomatosis (Rubin, 1962). Immunological tolerance seems to prevail in two other vertically transmitted virus systems as well: AKR mice, transmitting the Gross virus from parent to offspring are unable to react against the cellular antigen specific for this leukemia (Axelrad, 1965), and mouse strains transmitting the mammary tumor agent through the milk cannot be made resistant against the mammary cancers that arise in them, while agent-free sublines of the same strains can be readily immunized (Attia *et al.*, 1965).

We have made an attempt to study whether humoral antibodies may play any inhibitory or enhancing role for leukemia development in the mouse Moloney system. Comparing various mice inoculated when newborn, with the virus (Klein and Klein, 1965) it was found that animals developing significant antibody levels tended to develop leukemia later than tolerant animals. Both categories developed leukemia, however, and the difference was restricted to the length of the latency period. This result indicates that humoral antibodies are fighting an ultimately losing battle against the development of the virus-induced leukemia. This conclusion was strengthened by other experiments: when 0.05–0.1 ml of mouse anti-Moloney serum was injected twice weekly for two months into mice inoculated with the virus at two weeks of age there was a clear-cut delay in the appearance of leukemia, and a certain reduction in the final incidence. These experiments show that humoral antibodies do not seem to play an enhancing, positive role in this system, and further, that they may have a certain inhibitory effect.

Immunological *surveillance* mechanisms have been postulated to play an important role in eliminating potentially neoplastic antigenic tumor cells, arising by spontaneous cellular changes or as a result of chemical or viral oncogenesis in the adult organism. This mechanism has also been suggested as the evolutionary basis of the homograft reaction (Burnet, 1964). If so, one may expect, on the basis of the information available on transplantation systems, that cell-mediated host reactions may play a more important role for surveillance than humoral antibodies. This prediction is supported by the finding that thymectomy of newborn animals may increase the incidence of both chemically and virally induced tumors (Defendi and Roosa, 1964; Ting and Law, 1965; Miller, 1964; without necessarily affecting the production of humoral antibodies directed against the oncogenic virus (Ting and Law, 1965). It remains to be seen, however, whether immunological surveillance mechanisms are the only ones that the organism has at its disposal to eliminate potentially neoplastic cells.

The efficiency of immunological surveillance is hampered by several factors, as mentioned before. They can act only if the neoplastic transformation has changed the cell surface in such a way as to make it clearly antigenic, i.e., foreign to the antibody-forming system. This change is more pronounced in some cases than in others, as shown by the wide variation in the "strength" of antigenicity among tumors, which has been mentioned. As an example, with methlycholanthrene-induced mouse sarcomas it is much easier to build up resistance in syngeneic hosts, and a stronger resistance is attained than with sarcomas induced by the implantation of films. Lymphomas induced by the Moloney agent are much more "strongly" antigenic than morphologically indistinguishable lymphomas induced by the Gross virus. Even when a tumor is clearly antigenic, immunological surveillance can be efficient only if the specific antigen(s) reach the antibody-forming centers in time. A number of restrictions can be envisaged that limit the efficiency of this afferent arm. The same is true for the efferent arm: the immune response must act on the target in time and hit it in the right way, not in the left-handed way it sometimes uses when it achieves enhancement instead of rejection. In enhancement, the humoral antibodies probably reach the target first and, by coating the foreign antigenic sites exert two effects: they diminish antigen release (afferent inhibition), and they protect the sites from host-cell mediated graft destruction by preventing recognition and/or attachment (efferent inhibition), as previously discussed.

This reasoning leads to the conclusion that immunological surveillance, although it undoubtedly exists and probably plays a more important role in some systems than in others, can hardly be the only mechanism established by evolution for the protection against potentially neoplastic cells. Other and more locally efficient mechanisms must be sought. One may envisage tissue homeostatic forces, capable of eliminating cells with a changed surface structure and correspondingly impaired ability to respond to the growth regulating mechanisms of the organism. In fact, immunological responses may be a special case of such a more general mechanism. The work of Hellström on syngeneic preference and allogeneic inhibition (Hellström, 1964a; b;) may reflect the possible existence of some such mechanisms. The findings of Erna Möller (1965a), suggest that there may be a connection between "allogeneic inhibition" and immunological response; in fact, the cell-mediated immune responses may represent a specialized function, inherent in the immunologically competent cells working within the larger framework of a more general mechanism of tissue homeostasis.

REFERENCES

Attia, M. A., K. B. DeOme, and D. Weiss. 1965. *Cancer Res.*, 25: 451.

Axelrad, A. A. 1965. *Progr. Exp. Tumor Res.* 6: 31.

Burnet, F. M. 1964. *Brit. Med. Bull.* 20: 154.

Defendi, V., and R. A. Roosa. 1964. In *The Thymus. The Wistar Institute Monograph* no. 2: 121.

Evans, C. A., R. F. Weiser, and Y. Ito, 1962. *Cold Spring Harbor Symp. Quant. Biol.* 27: 287.

Gorer, P. A., and P. O'Gorman. 1956. *Transplantation Bull.* 3: 142.

Habel, K. 1962. *J. Exptl. Med.* 115: 181.

Haughton, G. *Transplantation.* Submitted for publication.

Hellström, K. E. 1959. *Transplantation Bull.* 6: 411.

Hellström, K. E. 1960. *J. Natl. Cancer Inst.* 25: 237.

Hellström, K. E. 1963. *Nature* 199: 614.

Hellström, K. E. 1964a. *Nature* 201: 193.

Hellström, K. E. 1964b. *Science* 143: 477.

Jonsson, N., and H. O. Sjögren. 1965. *J. Exptl. Med.* 122: 403.

Jonsson, N., and H. O. Sjögren. 1965. *Exptl. Cell Res.* 40: 159.

Klein, E. In *Immunopathology, 4th Internatl. Symp. Monte Carlo,* ed. P. Grabar. Basel/Stuttgart: Schwabe & Co. Publishers. In press.

Klein, E., and G. Klein. 1959. In *Biological Problems of Grafting,* P. B. Medawar, Chairman, Les Congrès et Colloques de l'Iniversité de Liège, vol. 12. pp. 453, Université de Liège, Belgium, Pp. 380–399.

Klein, E., and G. Klein. 1964a. *J. Natl. Cancer Inst.* 32: 547.

Klein, E., and G. Klein. 1964b. *Nature* 204: 339.

Klein, E., and G. Klein. 1965. *Cancer Res.* 25: 851.

Klein, E., and G. Klein. 1966. *Nature.* 209: 163.
Nature. Submitted for publication.

Klein, E., and G. Klein, and K. E. Hellström. 1960. *J. Natl. Cancer Inst.* 25: 271.

Klein, E., G. Klein, and L. Revesz. 1957. *J. Natl. Cancer Inst.* 19: 95.

Klein, E., and E. Möller. 1963. *J. Natl. Cancer Inst.* 31: 347.

Klein, G., and E. Klein, 1959. In *Genetics and Cancer. 13th Ann. Symp. on Fundamental Cancer Res.,* ed. R. W. Cumley, M. Abbot, and J. McCay, Austin, Univ. of Texas. Pp. 359, 241–270.

Klein, G., and E. Klein. 1964. *Science* 145: 1316.

Klein, G., E. Klein, and G. Haughton. 1966. *J. Natl. Cancer Inst.* 36: 60f.

Klein, G., H. O. Sjögren, and E. Klein. 1962. *Cancer Res.* 22: 955.

Klein, G., H. O. Sjögren, and E. Klein. 1963. *Cancer Res.* 23: 84.

Koprowski, H. 1955. *Nature* 175: 1087.

Mayer, M. M. 1961. *Cancer Res.* 21: 1262.

Miller, J. F. P. A. 1964. *Science* 144: 1544.

Möller, E. 1964. *J. Natl. Cancer Inst.* 33: 979.

Möller, E. 1965a. *Science* 147: 873.

Möller, E. 1965b. *J. Exptl. Med.* 122: 11.

Möller, E., and A. E. Eklund. 1965. *Nature* 206: 731.

Möller, E., and G. Möller. 1962. *J. Exptl. Med.* 115: 527.

Möller, G. 1961. *J. Exptl. Med.* 114: 415.

Möller, G. 1963. *J. Natl. Cancer Inst.* 30: 1205.

Old, L. J., and E. A. Boyse. 1964. *Ann. Rev. Med.* 15: 167.

Prehn, R. T. 1963. *Canad. Cancer Conf.* 5: 387.

Rubin, H. 1962. *Cold Spring Harbor Symp. Quant. Biol.* 27: 441.

Snell, G. D. 1957. *Cancer Res.* 17: 2.

Sjögren, H. O. 1961. *Virol.* 15: 214.

Sjögren, H. O. 1964. *J. Natl. Cancer Inst.* 32: 661.

Sjögren, H. O. 1965. *Progr. Exptl. Tumor Res.* 6: 289.

Ting, R. C., and L. W. Law. 1965. *J. Natl. Cancer Inst.* 34: 521.

Weinrach, R. S., and D. Q. Talmage. 1958. *J. Infect. Dis.* 102: 74.

Wigzell, H. 1965. *Transplantation* 3: 423.

The Behavior of Normal and Malignant Cells in Tissue Culture [1]

H. Rubin

Department of Molecular Biology and Virus Laboratory
University of California
Berkeley, California

The existence of multicellular organisms depends on the adhesion of cells subsequent to their division. When cells undergo differentiation, the degree of adhesion both to like cells and to unlike cells becomes altered. The adhesional change determines the degree of movement and the position of the cells, which in their turn profoundly affect further cellular development.

Changes in adhesion obviously involve changes in the structure of the cell surface, and therefore all embryological studies are concerned with the surface of cells to some extent. There are only a few experimental situations, however, in which the effects of the surface structure of cells can be studied in a manner largely isolated from other effects. One such situation is the selective aggregation and sorting out of cells as it has been studied by Moscona (1960). Another is the phenomenon of contact inhibition among fibroblastic cells in tissue culture as studied by Abercrombie (Abercrombie and Ambrose, 1962).

Both sets of investigations have contributed to our knowledge of the specificity of cell surfaces in metazoan cells, and it would be useful to examine briefly some of the observations and conclusions from these studies. When disaggregated cells of two different tissue types are placed together in a rotating flask, the cells aggregate at random into clusters. Within the clusters

[1] This investigation was supported by research grants CA 04774 and CA 05619 from the National Cancer Institute, Public Health Service.

the cells sort themselves out into homologous groups. The cells apparently adhere more strongly to cells of their own type than to cells of another type. Therefore, cells observe a brand of specificity in aggregating only with others of the same cell type. The specificity is not highly discriminating, however, since the cells are just as likely to adhere to like cells of another species, or even vertebrate class, as they are to those of their own species and class. In other words, a fibroblast forms aggregates with fibroblasts, be they from mice or chickens. Kidney and retinal cells also recognize their own type regardless of source. The cells may then be said to display tissue specificity in their adhesion, but to display no species specificity.

Contact inhibition results in the failure of normal fibroblasts to overlap other fibroblasts when these cells are cultured on a solid substrate. The failure of one cell to move over another is apparently due to the adhesion formed between two cells immediately upon contact between their plasma membranes. Epithelial cells seem to be subject to similar restraints, but a rigorous statement cannot be made about the role of the cell surface in contact inhibition between such cells because the quantitative techniques used to study contact inhibition between fibroblasts are not applicable to epithelial cells.

Sarcoma cells, partially or completely, escape from contact inhibition, and consequently can be seen moving over each other and over normal cells. Fibroblasts from mice and chickens impose contact inhibition upon one another. It would appear, therefore, that contact inhibition and the sorting out of cells both display tissue, but not species, specificity.

While both techniques have enriched our knowledge about surface interactions between cells, they have not yet given us the versatile tools for measuring, in a quantitative way, the functional integrity of isolated cell-membrane components. I should like to describe, therefore, a technique that appears to offer promise as a biological assay for functionally intact isolated components of the cell membrane. The technique turns to advantage the inability of very small numbers of normal cells in tissue culture to multiply without lag in a sustained manner. This deficiency can be corrected by the use of "conditioned" medium obtained from large numbers of cells (Rubin, 1966). The component that facilitates the growth of small numbers of cells can be concentrated by sedimentation at $50,000 \times g$ and is therefore a very large molecule, compound molecule, or aggregate of molecules. The growth enhancing effect is tissue, but not species, specific. Cells which undergo the malignant transformation as a result of infection by Rous sarcoma virus (RSV) release a substance that counteracts the effect of the conditioning factor.

In an analysis of these observations, which I shall present in the discussion, I suggest that the biologically effective component of conditioned medium is a structural subunit of the cell membrane that diffuses into the medium. In the presence of high concentrations of cells, this component achieves an equilibrium between medium and cell surface. In the presence of small numbers of cells, the equilibrium is shifted toward the loss of this component from the cell surface, which results first in vacuolization and leakage, and finally, in death of the cell. The loss can only be compensated by providing medium rich in this component, obtained from large numbers of cells. In this view we shall have to think of the cell membrane not as a static structure, but one in constant dynamic equilibrium with its environment. We shall be in honorable company in doing so, since this was precisely the view of such notable figures in biology as R. Chambers (Chambers and Chambers, 1961) and Holtfreter (1943).

The Growth of Chick Embryo Cells
As a Function of Cell Concentration

Figure 1A shows the growth rates of cells started at different cell concentrations. In general we have found that chick embryo cells in our medium grow optimally only when their initial number in a 50 mm dish is higher than 5×10^4. Below this concentration they grow at a reduced rate, or experience a lag of a few days before growth begins.

The Effect of Condition Medium
On the Growth of Small Numbers of Cells

In Figure 1B it can be seen that small numbers of cells grow at almost the maximum rate when a conditioned medium is present. The conditioned medium is obtained by adding the regular medium for 24 hours to a confluent culture of chick embryo cells. The medium is used after centrifuging out any floating cells. It is partially depleted of nutrients and, therefore, can support the growth of cells only to a limited extent unless fresh nutrients are added.

Assay of Conditioned Medium and
Optimal Conditions for Collection

An assay was developed for the growth enhancing activity of conditioned medium. It consisted of diluting the conditioned medium in varying proportions with fresh medium and determining the increase in cell population at 5 or 6 days. The assay was used to determine the optimal time and conditions

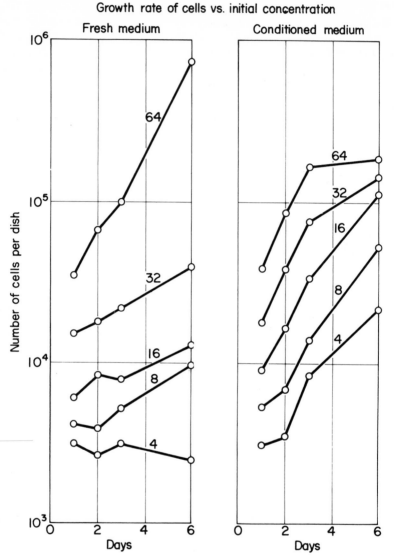

Fig. 1. *Left:* Growth rate of chick embryo cells (fibroblasts) as
a function of starting concentration of cells. Cells were plated on
groups of 50 mm plastic petri dishes, and the number present on
each succeeding day was determined by trypsinizing and counting
cells in a Coulter Counter. The number on each curve multiplied
by 10^3 gives the number of cells initially plated, not all of
which are attached to the dish. The medium was 199 plus 10 per
cent tryptose phosphate broth, 4 per cent calf serum and one per
cent chicken serum. *Right:* The same except the medium had
been conditioned for 24 hours by incubation in the presence of
large numbers of cells.

for collecting the conditioned medium. The results are shown in Fig. 2. It can be seen that conditioned medium with optimal activity is produced only when the cells used to supply the conditioning factor reach a concentration of about 10^7 per 100 mm dish. This concentration of cells is about 50 times that which is required to initiate sustained exponential growth in dishes of this surface area. It is apparent that the substance responsible for enhancing the growth of small numbers of cells must, to a large extent, be utilized in the immediate vicinity of the cell.

Properties of the Growth Enhancing Factor in Conditioned Medium

The growth enhancing factor can be sedimented from conditioned medium by centrifuging at $50,000 \times g$ for 12 to 16 hrs. Although the material responsible for the biological activity is removed from the supernatant fluid, it cannot be recovered from the pellet. It appears in the highly viscous fluid that lies immediately over the pellet.

The properties of the growth enhancing factor are summarized in Table 1.

TABLE 1

PROPERTIES OF THE GROWTH ENHANCING FACTOR IN
CONDITIONED MEDIUM

1. Sedimented into viscous layer overlying pellet at $50,000 \times g$ for 16 hrs.
2. Retained by dialysis tubing.
3. Passes over Sephadex G-25 column.
4. Inactivated at 56°C for 30 min.
5. Becomes inhibitory to growth upon sonic oscillation.
6. Passes HA Millipore filters (0.45 μ), (0.22 μ).
7. Gradually inactivated by repeated freezing and thawing.
8. Inactivated at pH 8.5 but not at pH 5.5-8.0.

Specificity of the Growth Enhancing Activity of Conditioned Medium

Conditioned medium was prepared from mouse embryo fibroblasts and from chicken embryo fibroblasts, and the growth enhancing activity of each was tested on both types of cells. It can be seen in Fig. 3 that mouse and chicken cells responded to conditioned medium from fibroblasts regardless of species source. Mouse cells did not grow as well as chicken cells in our medium, and therefore did not respond as well as chicken cells to conditioned medium from either source. The response of chicken cells to mouse cell conditioned medium was not as marked as their response to chicken cell con-

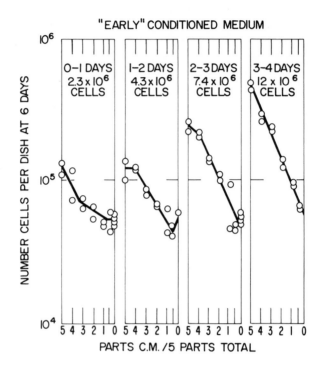

Fig. 2. The efficacy of variously conditioned media in enhancing the growth of small numbers of cells. Medium was conditioned by incubation with primary cultures of chick embryo cultures for 24 hours at various times after seeding the cultures. The number of cells in the conditioning culture is shown at the top of each panel. The conditioned medium was diluted with increments of fresh medium to a total of 5 ml per dish, and 10^4 chick embryo cells were added. The extent of growth at 6 days was determined. C.M. = Conditioned medium.

ditioned medium, but comparison of all the results indicates that this was merely due to a lower concentration of the growth enhancing factor obtained from the mouse cells. This is not surprising, since the cultures from which the mouse cell conditioned medium was obtained had fewer cells than the cultures from which the chicken cell conditioned medium was obtained.

Conditioned medium was prepared from cultures of chick kidney epithelium. These cultures were prepared from the fairly large clumps of tubule cells that remained after limited tryspin treatment of kidneys from newly hatched chicks. The use of clumps was necessary, because characteristic epithelial outgrowth does not occur from isolated single cells. The conditioned

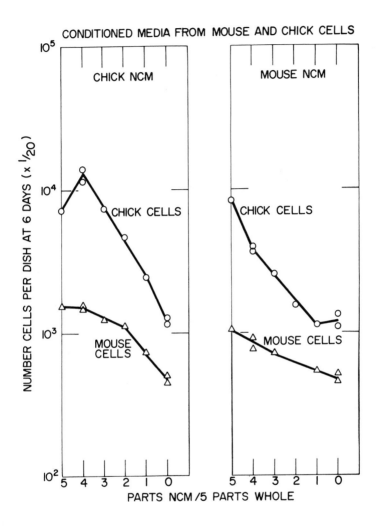

Fig. 3. Absence of species specificity of conditioned medium. Large numbers of fibroblasts from chick and mouse embryos were used to condition medium. Each conditioned medium was used to culture small numbers of fibroblasts from chick and mouse embryos. The mouse cells grew more slowly and to a more limited extent in this medium than did the chicken cells. N.C.M. = Normal conditioned medium.

medium prepared from the kidney cultures after they had become confluent failed to enhance the growth of fibroblasts (Fig. 4). Unfortunately, studies have not yet been done on the effects of conditioned media on epithelial cell outgrowth because of the requirement that epithelial cultures be initiated

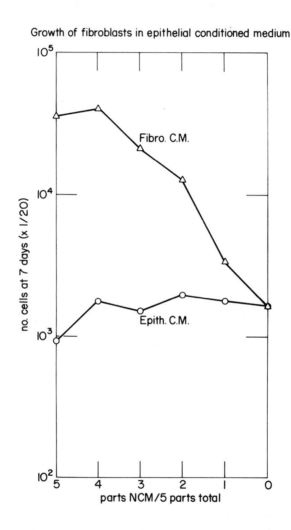

Fig. 4. Tissue specificity of conditioned media. Conditioned media were prepared from cultures of clustered chick embryo kidney epithelial cells, and from chick embryo fibroblasts. Both types of conditioned media were used to support the growth of small numbers of fibroblastic cells for seven days.

with clumps. In such a case it is difficult to create the conditions — low cell concentrations at the *local* level — which create the need for conditioned medium. As far as the studies have gone, however, they indicate that the growth enhancing factor is tissue, but not species, specific.

The Malignant Transformation

Chick embryo cells can be infected in tissue culture with a concentration of Rous sarcoma virus which will cause the morphological transformation of a high proportion of the cells within three to four days. As a result of this transformation, the cells become indistinguishable in appearance and behavior from cultivated Rous sarcoma cells obtained initially from chicken tumors. The alteration is therefore referred to as the malignant transformation.

The Rous sarcoma cells grow vigorously if surrounded by normal cells, but when they constitute a large fraction of the cells in culture their growth is poor. The poor growth of the Rous sarcoma cells can be corrected, when the total number of cells is small, by keeping them in the presence of a conditioned medium obtained from normal cells.

These findings suggested that Rous sarcoma cells were either producing inadequate amounts of the conditioning factor, or inactivating what was produced. It was found that infected cells produced the conditioning factor at a normal or slightly elevated rate until they underwent the morphological transformation. At this time they began to produce a medium which markedly inhibited rather than enhanced cell growth (Figs. 5 and 6). The inhibitory activity could neither be removed from the medium by ultracentrifugation, nor could it be concentrated in this way. Therefore, on first appearance, the growth inhibitory material in Rous conditioned medium seems to be smaller than the conditioning factor.

Since the inhibitory factor appears at the same time as the morphological transformation becomes evident, it is a question whether its appearance is the cause or the consequence of the transformation. When Rous conditioned medium is added to normal cells they assume a more rounded appearance than usual, and become vacuolated. Since they resemble Rous sarcoma cells in these characteristics, it is certainly possible that the material released by Rous sarcoma cell is responsible for their altered appearance and perhaps even for their altered behavior.

When the Rous conditioned medium is diluted, it frequently turns from an inhibitor to an enhancer of cell growth. This indicates that the transformed cells are still capable of producing a conditioning factor, but that its presence is masked by the inhibitor. Experiments are underway to find out if the inhibitor acts directly on the conditioning factor.

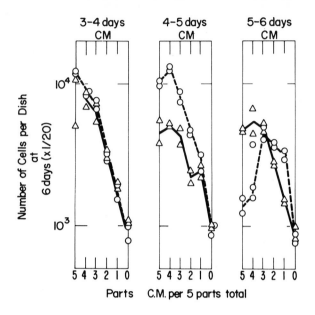

Fig. 5. Appearance of toxic factor at the time of cell transformation by RSV. A group of cultures of chick embryo fibroblasts was heavily infected with RSV and another group left uninfected. The infected culture became heavily transformed between the fifth and sixth day. Conditioned medium was prepared daily beginning three days after infection and used to support the growth of small numbers of chick embryo fibroblasts.

Conditioned medium from

△———△ normal cells

○ - - - ○ RSV-infected cells.

Discussion

I should like now to consider the evidence that components of the cell surface can diffuse into the medium and that the resulting loss can lead to cell damage. From the work of Lovelock (1954), it is known that lipids and lipoproteins from the surface of red blood cells diffuse rapidly into the medium, and are also replaced into the membrane from the medium. The equilibrium concentration of these components in the medium increases with the prior time of storage of the cells, and decreases with the number of washings. If the washing is very extensive, lipids and lipoproteins are released into the medium only in proportion to the fraction of cells that lyse. The rate of

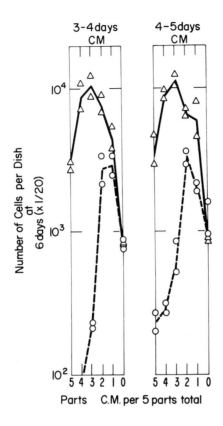

Fig. 6. Same as Fig. 5 except cultures transformed about third day after infection.

removal of lipids and lipoproteins from the red blood cells can be speeded up, and lysis increased, if a neutral absorbent such as alumina is added. To quote Lovelock, "It is almost as if a proportion of the cells were sacrificed to maintain a necessary minimum concentration of cell components in the suspending medium." The rate of loss of the cell components can be greatly retarded by adding plasma to the cells. Although the cells can survive the removal of a considerable fraction of lipid from the surface, the extensive removal of lipoprotein leads to cell lysis.

Lovelock infers that the membrane is composed of lipoprotein units, rather than of a bimolecular lipid leaflet "with a sprinkling of antigenic and antisphering protein." Gent and coworkers (1964) expressed a similar notion regarding the constitution of the myelin sheath surrounding nerve cells.

The membranes of pleuropneumonia-like organisms, which have a typical unit membrane structure when seen by electronmicroscopy, are also composed of discrete lipoprotein units (Razin et al., 1965) as are the membranes of certain bacteria which grow in high salt concentrations (Brown, 1965).

In addition to these analogies there is more direct, but less precise, evidence that the membranes of fibroblasts are composed of lipoprotein units, and that these can diffuse from the surface. Rosenberg (1960) has found that the attachment of cells to glass in the absence of serum is accompanied by the extrusion of material from the cells to form a microexudate. The microexudate is a monomolecular film containing protein and lipid. It may cover up to 100 times more area than covered by the visible cell, with a monomolecular film containing protein and lipid. Thus, when a low concentration of cells is spread on a dish, we may expect a rapid loss of lipoprotein from the cell surface in analogy to the loss of lipoprotein from red blood cells in the presence of alumina. Furthermore, we may expect this lipoprotein to be denatured at the fluid-solid interface, and thereby lost for service to the cell.

Let us now consider the proposition that the conditioning factor described here is a lipoprotein and constituent of the cell membrane. The evidence is obviously incomplete, and the proposition inevitably speculative, but it must at least be granted heuristic value. Like lipoproteins in general, the conditioning factor is a very large molecule, or aggregate of molecules, since it can be sedimented at 50,000 $\times$ g, passes over sephadex G25, and is retained by dialysis tubing. It is extremely sensitive to inactivation by physical treatments. Sonic oscillation, small increases in pH, and short exposures to 56°C temperature destroy its biological activity, Such extreme sensitivity to various physical treatments is characteristic of lipoproteins, and probably arises from the weak bonding between lipid and protein (Gurd, 1960).

The tissue specificity of the conditioning factor and the absence of species specificity are consistent with its being a component of the cell surface. Both the specific sorting out of cells and contact inhibition of cell movement are determined by the surface character of cells, and exhibit the same type of specificity as does the growth enhancing activity of conditioning factor. If it can be firmly established that the conditioning factor is indeed an intact macromolecular component of the cell membrane, the assay technique described here could provide the quantitation necessary for precise studies of the specificity of cell surfaces. The sensitivity to inactivation of the conditioning factor indicates that its effect will not register unless it is in its pristinely native state. Therefore it should be possible to characterize physically the functional state of the subunits of the cell membrane.

The assay for conditioning factor has disclosed a sharp difference between normal and sarcoma cells, which only becomes evident when the latter manifest their malignant properties. The most characteristic manifestations of malignancy such as the loss of contact inhibition, the capacity to invade tissues and to metastasize to distant sites, are likely to be due to changes in the surface of malignant cells. Another property of malignant cells is their increased permeability to macromolecules (Busch, 1962), and this is certainly due to changes in the cell surface.

In searching for the molecular basis of the altered behavior of malignant cells, it might be useful to consider substances known to alter the properties of cell membranes. For instance, it has been shown that very low concentrations of surface active agents such as ionic and nonionic detergents cause changes in membrane permeability (Seufert, 1965). Surface active agents of lipoidal nature are also produced by cells during infection with certain viruses, and are responsible for some of the pathological changes which accompany virus infection. For example, infection of chick embryos with Sendai virus leads to the production of lysophosphatides which cause the hemolysis of red blood cells (Rebel et al., 1962). Treatment of a variety of cells with high concentrations of Newcastle disease virus leads within a few hours to fusion between membranes of individual cells and consequent giant cell formation (Kohn, 1965). This action of the virus can be abolished with phospholipases from various animal sources, suggesting that the substance which disturbs the membranes is a phospholipid. Hemolysis and fusion apparently result from the action of similar substances.

I have observed that the transformation of cells by Rous sarcoma virus is most pronounced when the infected cells are overlaid with an agar rich in sulfated polysaccharides. This effect on infected cells can be mimicked by adding dextran sulfate to a fluid medium. The sulfated polysaccharides are, of course, anionic polyelectrolytes with strong surface activity. I have found that dextran sulfate in very low doses inactivates the conditioning factor, and in higher doses, disrupts cells. It is probable, therefore, that surface active agents accentuate the malignant transformation by disrupting the cell membrane. This raises the question whether the cell itself produces surface active agents that play the same central role in causing the malignant transformation as they cause in hemolysis and fusion of cells. The view that it does is supported by reports of the appearance of new phospholipids in cancer cells (Kosaki et al., 1958), and of striking quantitative changes in the polar lipid constituents of cancer cells (Rapport and Graf, 1961). Therefore, we are now investigating the possibility that phospholipids or other surface active agents play a role in effecting the malignant transformation. The assay for conditioning factor promises to be a sensitive tool in guiding us in the search for the molecular basis of the malignant transformation.

REFERENCES

Abercrombie, M., and E. J. Ambrose. 1962. *Cancer Res.* 15: 332.

Brown, A. D. 1965. *J. Molec. Biol.* 12: 491.

Busch, H. 1962. *An Introduction to the Biochemistry of the Cancer Cell.* New York: Academic Press, Inc. Pp. 354–363.

Chambers, R., and E. L. Chambers. 1961. *Explorations into The Nature of the Living Cell.* Cambridge, Mass. Harvard University Press.

Gent, W. L. G., N. A. Grigson, D. G. Gammack, and J. H. Raper. 1964. *Nature* 204: 553.

Gurd, F. N. 1960. In *Lipide Chemistry*. By D. J. Hanahan. New York: John Wiley and Sons, Inc.

Holtfreter, J. 1943. *J. Exptl. Zool.* 93: 251.

Kohn, A. 1965. *Virol.* 26: 228.

Kosaki, T., T. Ikada, Y. Kotani, S. Nakagawa, and T. Saka. 1958. *Science* 127: 1176.

Lovelock, J. E. 1954. *Nature* 173: 659.

Moscona, A. A. 1960. *J. Comp. Cell Physiol.* Suppl. 1: 65.

Rapport, M., and L. Graf. 1961. *Cancer Res.* 21: 1225.

Razin, S., H. J. Morowitz, and T. M. Terry. 1965. *Proc. Natl. Acad. Sci. U. S.* 54: 219.

Rebel, G., R. Fontanges, and L. Colobert 1962. *Ann. Inst. Pasteur* 102: 137.

Rosenberg, M. D. 1960. *Biophys. J.* 1: 137.

Rubin, H. 1966. *Exptl. Cell Res.* 41: 131.

Rubin, H. 1966. *Exptl. Cell Res.* 41: 149.

Seufert, W. D. 1965. *Nature* 207: 174.

The Cell Surface
and Specific Cell Aggregation[1]

Tom Humphreys

Department of Biology
Massachusetts Institute of Technology
Cambridge, Massachusetts

The cell surface is important in many functions and properties of animal cells, especially those involving interactions of a cell with surrounding cells and with body fluids. Such cell interactions must participate in the developmental organization of cells into organs and tissues. The earliest investigators of cell organization implicated cell surfaces in these interactions (Galtsoff, 1925a; Holtfreter, 1939; Weiss, 1941) and present day ones still do, although the nature of the cell surface components participating in these cell surface reactions has remained obscure (Moscona, 1959; Steinberg, 1963b; and many others).

Many other aspects of cell function and behavior are also nearly always theoretically related to cell surface reactions. The cellular control reaction, contact inhibition (Abercrombie and Heaysman, 1954), is generally thought of as a cell surface reaction. Malignant transformation of cells by viruses appears related to a cell surface change (Habel, 1962; Rubin, 1962). Tissue transplantation antigenicity, selective transport macromolecules (Roth and Porter, 1964) and ions (Post, et al., 1960), transmission of embryonic induction (Grobstein, 1961), and many other cell functions have been related to properties of the cell surface.

Despite the apparent importance of the cell surface in these cellular functions, there is little evidence relating them to a biochemically or cyto-

[1] This work was supported in part by NSF grant GB-2021.

logically defined entity of the cell surface; none of the foregoing examples can be so related. Only in the case of receptor sites for the attachment of certain viruses to cells (Stone, 1947; Klenk and Uhlenbruck, 1958) does a body of knowledge exist that relates cell function (if viral invasion can be called such!) to a biochemical entity of the cell surface. There are, of course, most elegant studies on cell surface antigens (Morgan, 1949; Morgan, 1960; Watkins, 1966), but unfortunately no function can be demonstrated for the surface groups, although it is easy to speculate how such specific groups might participate in certain cell-surface functions.

Why is there virtually no direct information about the functional components of the cell surface? The answer is not simple, but from the cytological point of view few morphological clues to functional structures of the cell surface are available, since for the most part the material coating animal cells is small, indistinct, and unstructured when examined by present techniques (Revel, 1966). Biochemical examination of these problems is difficult because the animal cell-surface coat is small and not highly differentiated from the rest of the cell, and setting up an *in vitro* assay system for cell surface functions such that the functional components could be purified is not a trivial task. How does one isolate cell surfaces so that selective transport of molecules or contact inhibition can be evaluated? The work to be described here is an attempt to devise such an *in vitro* system for cell aggregation and specific cell sorting. Although it is not an ideal solution and probably cannot be considered strictly an *in vitro* system in the biochemical sense, some results have been obtained, and the system appears promising.

The general problem is to determine the physiological or molecular basis for the arrangement of cells in the metazoan organism. That is, to isolate, assay, and characterize the macromolecular and biochemical reactions that order cells into tissues, organs, and organisms. In general the sorting out of two different kinds of cells aggregating from a mixed suspension of dissociated cells has been taken as an experimental expression of these reactions. The sorting of cell types was first observed by Wilson in 1907 during his classical experiments showing the regeneration of sponges from dissociated cells. He found that when cells from two species of sponges, which were different colors, were mixed, the respective colored cells of each species aggregated with their own kind. Later, Galtsoff in 1925 (1925b) showed that cell sorting occurred among the different cell types of one species during the reformation of a sponge from dissociated cells. It was not until 1939, however, when Holtfreter published his famous experiments showing specific affinities of amphibian germ layer cells that the role these sorting reactions might play in normal development was emphasized. Almost immediately Weiss and Tyler (Weiss, 1941; 1947; Tyler, 1947) related selective cell association to possible cell surface specificities and extensively developed the possibilities such reactions might have in guiding normal morphogenesis. Ever since, investigators have been stimulated to study cell sorting as an expression of the mechanisms of normal morphogenesis and have tried to relate this morphogenetic behavior to cell surface properties (Spiegel, 1954; Gregg and Trystad, 1958; Humphreys, 1963, and many others).

Cell Aggregation in Vitro

In what form can a reaction such as cell aggregation and cell sorting be transferred to an *in vitro* system? The simplest possibility is to have a system for assaying and manipulating chemically the reactions which make whole cells adhere. Since it was not clear how to proceed toward this objective directly, a secondary guiding principle was chosen. Find the least complicated experimental system in which cell sorting occurred and begin an investigation of its parameters with the intent of eventually developing an *in vitro* system.

Species-specific aggregation of interspecific mixtures of dissociated sponge cells (Wilson, 1907) appeared to be the most promising for several reasons. First there were only two kinds of cells, and during sorting between certain species these two kinds separated completely from one another. Second, sorting could be easily and unequivocally ascertained by examining the color of the living cells when species of different colors were used. Third, the tissue and cells could be maintained in nonsterile, simple, defined salt solutions. These characteristics, which proved to be important in these studies, were not true for any other system. The major disadvantage of this system was that its simplicity rendered it suspect as a model for morphogenesis.

There were many experimental problems, but these were shared with virtually all other possible selections. Two critical ones had to be overcome to make sponge aggregation experimentally useful; a chemically reversible dissociation procedure and a direct assay for aggregation were required. A single species of sponge, *Microciona prolifera*, was chosen to attack these experimental problems, since earliest investigators (Wilson, 1907; Galt-soff, 1925a) found this species most amenable to experimentation. All experiments described refer only to this species unless explicitly stated otherwise.

The first of the difficulties had not been previously recognized in any investigation and the success of this work revolved around its solution. If the macromolecules that cause cells to adhere were to be isolated and the biochemical reactions involved in cell adhesion to be studied *in vitro*, the dissociation procedure must not destroy these macromolecules, but must instead reverse the intermolecular reactions normally participating in cell adhesion. Previously sponges had been dissociated mechanically by squeezing the tissue through fine silk. This method obviously was not suitable. Dissociation of other tissue was usually done with proteolytic enzymes, which also did not meet the necessary requirements. If the literature on cell adhesion is reviewed with the idea of a reversible, chemical dissociation in mind, the necessity of calcium ions for cell adhesion is very striking in virtually every organism examined (Steinberg, 1958). This characteristic, however, had not been widely used for routine dissociation procedures. If removal of calcium ions dissociated sponge cells, it would prove to be a method which met the requirements listed.

When sponge tissue was soaked in calcium-and magnesium-free sea water (CMF-SW), the cells separated from one another (Fig. 1). Removal of divalent cations thus did dissociate sponge cells. I have termed cells dissociated by this method as *chemically dissociated cells* (cd cells) to distinguish them from *mechanically dissociated cells* (md cells), which have been squeezed through cloth (Humphreys, 1962; 1963).

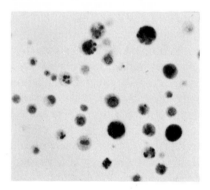

Fig. 1. Chemically dissociated sponge cells. All cells are separate. Note the wide range in cell size representing the various types of sponge cells. Line indicates 10μ.

The need for a direct assay for aggregation had been recognized by other investigators (Gerisch, 1959; Moscona, 1961), and their solution was relatively easy to apply to sponges. In all previous studies on sponges, aggregation had been assayed by allowing cells to migrate together on a glass surface. This assay had an unacceptable ambiguity since any treatment which affected cell migration would affect the extent of cell adhesion. This was easily overcome by letting the cells aggregate suspended in a continuously swirled suspension in shaker flasks (Moscona, 1961). Under these conditions the cells aggregated whenever they were mutually adhesive, since they were brought randomly together by the agitated medium.

When chemically dissociated sponge cells were returned to complete artificial sea water at the normal summer-temperature environment of the sponges, 20–25°C, they began to aggregate very rapidly in shaker flasks. Within 15 min ragged clusters of loosely adhering cells had formed. By one hour the aggregates had reached almost maximum size and were irregular, 0.1 to 0.2mm masses of closely adhering cells. Between 6 and 12 hr the aggregates became smooth spheres and remained in this condition for days (Fig. 2).

If, however, the cells were put under exactly the same conditions, except in sea water free of calcium and magnesium ions, they could not aggregate. If calcium ions were added to a concentration between 0.01 to 0.1 M the cells aggregated as if they were in complete sea water. Magnesium in similar concentrations allowed aggregation to proceed almost normally except the final size of aggregates was somewhat smaller. Strontium or barium did not support aggregation when added in these concentrations, nor did they inhibit aggregation in the presence of calcium ions. These results, along with the results from dissociation, show that the divalent cations, calcium and magnesium, specifically function in the adhesion of sponge cells.

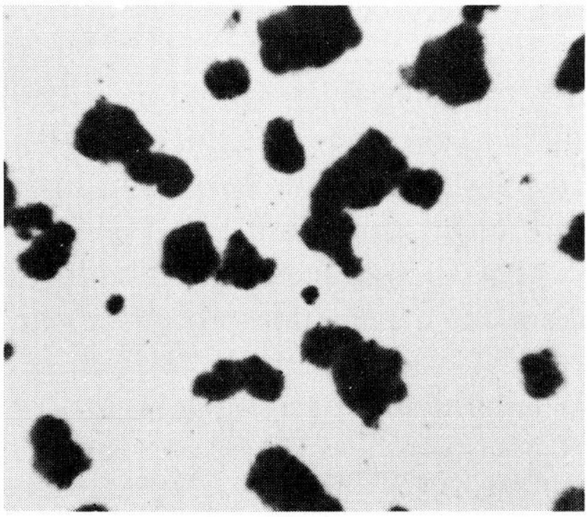

During a series of experiments to examine the parameters of aggregation in the shaker flasks, it

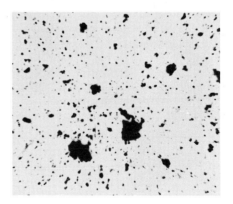

Fig. 2. Aggregates of chemically dissociated cells formed in shaker flasks at 22°C. 24-hour culture (×26).

was noted that the chemically dissociated cells in sea water did not readhere extensively at temperatures below 5°C (Fig. 3). Galtsoff (1925a) described similar behavior with mechanically dissociated sponge cells aggregating on glass. He found that low temperatures slowed cell migration and concluded that the cells did not aggregate because they failed to move about and come in contact under such conditions. In the shaker flasks the cells are, at least theoretically, brought together by the shaking and the lack of aggregation must be a failure of adhesion. According to the original hypothesis, however, the removal of divalent cations should not destroy macromolecules and should be reversible when divalent cations are returned.

Were these assumptions incorrect? Mechanically dissociated cells might provide a test. Certainly cells dissociated by squeezing through fine cloth should have a complete complement of macromolecules and should be able to adhere at 5°C if shaking actually brought the cells together. The md cells did adhere at 5°C. In a few hours they formed irregular compact aggregates similar to those formed in one hour at 22°C. These aggregates of md cells did

Fig. 3. Chemically dissociated cells in shaker flasks at 5°C. A portion of these cells have adhered into small clumps but most have remained single. 24-hour culture (×26).

not proceed beyond this stage at 5°C but proceeded normally when the temperature was raised to 22°C. Although the low temperature did not inhibit cell adhesion, it appears to have inhibited the cell movement necessary for the rounding up of aggregates (Galtsoff, 1925a). These results indicated strongly that the md cells had some macromolecules which the cd cells had lost during their dissociation in CMF-SW.

This missing factor was soon found. If some of the CMF-SW supernatant from the dissociation procedure was added to the cd cells which had been returned to complete sea water, these cells could also aggregate at 5°C exactly as could the md cells (Fig. 4).

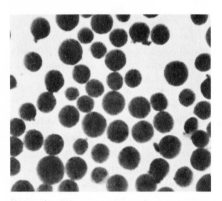

Fig. 4. Chemically dissociated cells in shaker flasks at 5°C to which supernatant solutions from dissociation have been added. A factor in the supernatant has allowed these cells to aggregate extensively at 5°C. 24-hour culture (×26).

How should these results be interpreted? Soaking sponge tissue in CMF-SW apparently broke certain intermolecular bonds dependent on divalent cations; and the cell surface molecules, which held the cells together, dissolved from the cells. If the divalent cations were returned to the cells by transferring them to sea water, these molecules were left behind and the cells were devoid of the necessary molecules to adhere to one another. If the cells were maintained at 22°C, they would resynthesize the molecules and aggregate; but at 5°C the synthetic machinery was inhibited and the cells could not aggregate. If both the divalent cations and the dissolved cell surface molecules were added back to the cd cells at 5°C, however, the molecules spontaneously returned to their position between the cells and bound them together, making the cd cells aggregate at 5°C. This would indicate that sponge cells are held together by cell surface materials that attach to each cell and hold them together by bonds involving divalent cations. This interpretation fits the results very well but leaves many questions which must be examined before it can be accepted. For this reason the material isolated from the cells will be called "aggregation factor" or just "factor" until its nature is more firmly established.

If we return to the problem of transferring the phenomena of aggregation to an *in vitro* system we see certain of the reactions necessary for cell adhesion have been dissociated from the cell and can be manipulated experimentally. Although the reactions separated from the cells could be extended, e.g., a cell-membrane preparation (Warren *et al.*, 1966; Wallach, 1966) could be substituted for the whole cells, this was not attempted. Instead the system, as it has been described, was used to test the hypothesis presented and to further elucidate mechanisms of aggregation.

One refinement of the system described was necessary. The assay for the aggregation factor, adhesion of cd cells at 5°C, had to be quantitated. Serial one-half dilution as used for immune sera to determine a titer proved suitable. Aliquots from a serial dilution were added to a series of flasks containing a fixed number of cells, and the greatest dilution where aggregation occurred was noted. For most preparations a distinct transition from aggregation to no aggregation occurred at some dilution providing a distinct end point. The amount of factor activity at the end point was defined as one unit.

The interpretation presented for the aggregation factor depended upon two assumptions which cannot be accepted casually. 1) It was assumed that the factor which caused cells to adhere at 5°C was the same material that normally held them together in the intact sponge and was not just a stray substance that agglutinated cells (Schmitt, 1941; Steinberg, 1963a; Katchalsky et al., 1959). 2) It was assumed the factor was a cell-surface component that physically participated in holding cells together.

Several observations supported the first assumption. Aggregates produced by the factor were morphologically identical to aggregates formed by the processes of the cell itself in about one hour at 22°C, when they were examined either in the living state or in histological sections. The factor aggregates would remain suspended in this intermediate state as long as the temperature was low, but the adhesions of these arrested aggregates were functional, since any time the factor aggregates were raised to 22°C, they would proceed to round up through the same sequence that normal aggregates follow after one hour. Finally, the adhesion caused by the factor specifically required calcium and magnesium ions. Thus, morphologically, functionally, and chemically the adhesion caused by the factor appeared normal to the extent these characteristics could be tested.

If the factor physically binds the cells together as postulated, it should not come off the cells except when calcium and magnesium are removed, and should be taken up by the cells as they aggregate. This was the case: tissue could be mechanically disrupted in sea water, and md cells could be homogenized in sea water without the release of detectable factor. (Homogenizing cd cells in CMF-SW also did not release factor.) Only when divalent cations were removed such that the cells dissociated, did the factor come off the cells. The cells also took up factor from the supernatant solution in which they aggregated at 5°C. If aliquots of a cell suspension were serially aggregated by a single preparation of factor, about one unit of activity was removed per 10^7 cells caused to aggregate. This activity was not lost if the same cells were caused to aggregate again and again in the same factor preparation by mechanically breaking up the aggregates periodically. This indicates that the factor binds to the cells when it causes them to adhere.

Although these observations support the conclusion that the aggregation factor normally functions to physically hold cells together, they do not prove it. The evidence that I shall present in the remainder of the paper will not be a proof either. Let us proceed with an analysis of the system along other lines, however, with the hope that we may return to this point when enough information about the factor is available to devise a critical set of experiments.

Cell Sorting and the Aggregation Factor

At this point it was very clear how to proceed to the problem of cell sorting and cell surface specificity: determine the specificity of the factors isolated from two different kinds of cells. The most important implication of specificity, assuming the factor is a cell-surface material, would be that cell-surface reactions guide sorting out during species-specific aggregation of sponges. This has not been previously demonstrated for any system, and only when the factor is shown to be a cell surface material that normally holds cells together will this proof be complete for sponges. Since the nature of the factor is not yet fully established, the specificity of the factor only correlates with specificity of normal aggregation and provides a very striking similarity between aggregation caused by the factor and normal aggregation. Specificity would also rule out any suggestion that the factor was a substance like DNA (Steinberg, 1963a) or basic proteins (Schmitt, 1941; Katchalsky et al., 1959), which generally cause cells to agglutinate nonphysiologically.

A second species of sponge, *Haliclona occulata* (*Ho*), was found, which aggregated specifically when mixed with *Microciona prolifera* (*Mp*), and which yielded an aggregation factor upon dissociation. *Ho* was found to behave in the shaker flasks essentially as *Mp* except cd cells of *Ho* aggregated to form small aggregates at 5°C or even minus 2°C. When cells from these two species were mixed in a single shaker flask at 22°C, the cells of each species aggregated only with cells of its own species, forming two sets of aggregates: *Mp* forming orange ones; *Ho* forming lavender ones.

First, the specificity of the factors was tested by adding the factor of one species to the cells of the other species at 5°C. In both cases the heterologous factor even in large excess had no effect; the cells only aggregated into small aggregates as they would have if they had been in plain sea water. The same amount of factor added to homologous cells would cause the cells to form giant aggregates (Fig. 5a-d).

Second, the ability of the factors to cause cells to sort out and aggregate separately from mixed suspensions was examined. In both cases if the factor of one species was added to a cell suspension containing cells of both species, the homologous cells formed large aggregates, leaving behind the heterologous cells as if they were in plain sea water at 5°C. If the factors from both species

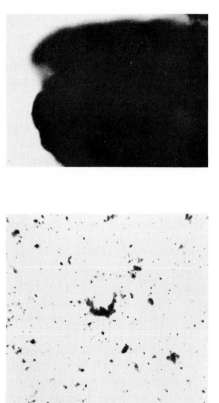

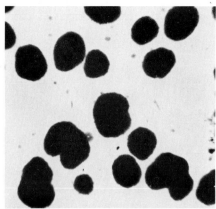

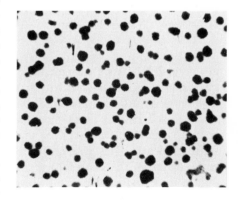

Fig. 5. Species specificity of the aggregation factor. a. Aggregation of chemically dissociated Mp cells in high concentrations of Mp factor at 5°C. The cells aggregate into one large cylindrical aggregate. Only an end of the aggregate is shown in the photograph. b. Aggregation of chemically dissociated Ho cells with high concentrations of Ho factor. c. Aggregation of Mp cells in Ho factor at 5°C. d. Aggregation of Ho cells in Mp factor at 5°C. The cells do not respond to heterologous factor at all but aggregate exactly as they would in plain sea water at 5°C. 24-hour culture (×26).

203

were added to a mixed suspension, the cells of both species began to aggregate immediately with cells of their own species and separate aggregates of each species were formed simultaneously (Fig. 6). The factors simulated normal cell sorting by these two species of sponges and proved to be completely specific. The results of these combinations demonstrate that there is no cross reaction between the cells of one species and the factor of the other species; otherwise, some cross specific aggregation would have occurred in some of the various mixtures. If the factor is a cell-surface material, then the complete specificity of cell surface reactions has been shown to be the basis for species-specific sorting of cells between these two species of sponges.

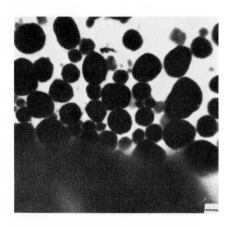

Fig. 6. Species specific cell sorting caused by the aggregation factors. Mp and Ho cells were mixed and Mp and Ho factors added. The cells aggregated only with others of their own species and sorted out under the influence of their individual factors. A large Mp aggregate appears out of focus across the bottom of the picture with many Ho aggregates above. 24-hour culture (×26).

The Aggregation Factor

What is the chemical and physical nature of the aggregation factor? Do its characteristics conform to the expectations of a cell-surface material? What do its characteristics suggest about the way it functions? Examination of these questions using *Mp* factor has yielded some interesting and suggestive, but far from conclusive, ideas.

The first characteristic noted about the factor was its extremely labile nature. Freshly prepared factor lost all of its activity within one to three days at 0°C or frozen at minus 20°C. Since calcium ions participated closely in the function of the factor, CaCl₂ was added to a preparation of freshly isolated factor in an attempt to stabilize activity. Factor which had more than about 0.001 M CaCl₂ added proved to be indefinitely stable at 0°C. This suggested that calcium ions were necessary for the functional integrity of the aggregation factor molecule. This was confirmed by removing calcium ions with the chelating agent EDTA. Addition of 0.001 M EDTA to a fresh preparation of factor immediately and irreversibly destroyed activity. If the EDTA was saturated with calcium ions before its addition to the factor or 0.002 M CaCl₂ was added to factor before the EDTA, the EDTA had no effect on activity. Calcium ions are necessary for the maintenance of the functional integrity of the factor. It is not clear how this requirement for calcium ions is related to their requirement for aggregation, but it is not unusual for enzymes to be stabilized against denaturation by substrates and cofactors.

The factor proved to be nondialyzable and heat labile. In 0.002 M $CaCl_2$ all activity was lost in less than 5 min at 56°C and in 1 hr at 45°C. No detectable activity was lost in 1 hr at 37°C.

Centrifugation of the factor preparations showed that all activity was completely sedimented at 100,000 g for 90 min. This sedimentation behavior was more accurately characterized using the quantitative assay to test the *activity* of fractions from sucrose density gradients (Humphreys, 1965a). All activity layered onto the gradient was found to sediment in a single sharp peak (Fig. 7). This result shows that the aggregation factor is a uniformly sized particle. Assuming a density of about 1.2 to 1.3, the sedimentation constant of the factor may be calculated (Martin and Ames, 1961) to be approximately 100 S. If it were spherical, the particle would have a molecular weight of about 10,000,000 and a diameter of some 300Å.

Chemical analysis of the factor shows that it contains protein and polysaccharide but no detectable nucleic acid (Humphreys, 1965a). The prep-

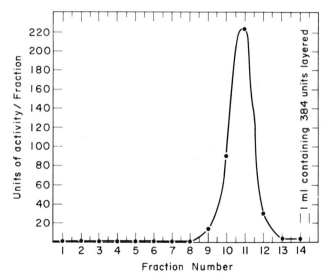

Fig. 7. Zone sedimentation of sponge aggregation factor. The active material sediments as a single sharp peak at about 100S. One milliliter of a concentrated extract was layered on to a linear sucrose gradient and centrifuged for two hours at 25,000 rpm in a Spinco SW25 rotor at 5°C. (Humphreys, 1965a). Fractions were assayed for aggregation factor by testing their ability to make cells adhere in a continually swirled suspension at 5°C.

aration could be somewhat purified by a differential centrifugation which collected 50 to 80% of the activity. It consisted of collecting a pellet of active material after a 90-min centrifugation at 100,000 g of a supernatant solution that was previously centrifuged for 30 min at 50,000 g. This pellet was purified about three times and contained 0.22 μgm protein and 0.20 μgm polysaccharide per unit activity. Accurate analysis of the active fractions from the sucrose gradient was not possible because polysaccharide in the sucrose produced a high polysaccharide background down the gradient, and the protein content at the level of the activity was very low. The latter was somewhat less than 0.03 μgm per unit activity. No peak of protein or polysaccharide was associated with the peak of activity, and a large proportion of both substances was at the top of the gradient.

It is not clear what relation these figures bear to the actual makeup of the active material, since no way is known to ascertain the purity of the preparations examined. It is clear that only a small amount of protein is associated with the activity, but this could conceivably represent the active material. Polysaccharides are usually found in most cell-surface materials that have been characterized, and these results would agree with such a conclusion. Certainly, however, this is now little more than a guess. One point is clear: the original extract can be purified considerably.

Extraction of aggregation factor preparations by gently mixing with lipid solvents partially destroys activity. Chloroform destroys about 90%, ether and benzene about 75%. All these solvents cause a precipitate at the interphase. Interpretation of these results is difficult, but they could mean the factor has a lipid component.

Another approach to the composition of the factor is to test the ability of chemically dissociated cells to aggregate and resynthesize the missing factor in the presence of specific inhibitors of protein synthesis (Humphreys, 1965b). When puromycin (200 μgm/ml) or ethionine (0.01 M) was added to chemically dissociated sponge cells of either Mp or Ho, protein synthesis was immediately lowered to less than 10% of controls. This had no direct effect on aggregation. In puromycin the cells died after about 6 hr, but in ethionine the cells remained healthy and aggregated for at least two days. This clearly demonstrated that concurrent protein synthesis was not necessary for aggregation and suggested the factor did not contain protein. It was possible, however, that the protein necessary for aggregation was stored in the cell and was only secreted during aggregation. If this was the case, the store could theoretically be exhausted by repeatedly redissociating the cells in CMF-SW and making them aggregate again and again in ethionine. This could not be done; after redissociation and reaggregation five times in ethionine the cells could still reaggregate normally in ethionine. Although the cells may just have had a large store of protein, this result suggests a high molecular weight protein made by the ribosomal mechanism of protein synthesis is not a constituent of the factor. This result does not detract from the possibility that the factor contains polypeptides in a glycoprotein with short peptides synthesized enzymatically.

What does this information suggest about the aggregation factor and the nature of the cell surface? Certainly as yet no strongly consistent interpretation can be presented, but some ideas have emerged that might be worth developing, since they suggest experiments with this system and others.

The sedimentation of the factor as a single sharp peak is the most striking observation and suggests a definite cytological constituent. It could be either some known structure to which the active material has attached or a previously unrecognized cell structure responsible for holding cells together. Of the known cytological particles only ribosomes approximate this size closely and the absence of nucleic acid eliminates them. If the activity has attached to some unrelated cell particulate, it most likely is an unknown one. It seems probable that the active material is itself particulate and represents a new cell organelle.

If these structures are accepted as organelles of the cell surface that hold cells together, several other observations in the literature, which could not previously be interpreted can now be interpreted.

(1) Direct observation of the cell surface by shadowing techniques for the electron microscope has revealed 100 to 300 Å "granules" on the surfaces of several cell types (Hillier and Hoffman, 1953; Coman and Anderson, 1955; Newell and Berwick, 1958; Berwick, 1959; Catalano et al., 1960; Haggis, 1960; Davis et al., 1961).

(2) The lipid membranes of adjacent cells are nearly always separated by about 100 to 200 Å in sectioned material examined by the electron microscope (Robertson, 1960), although the material is not seen because it is badly fixed (Coman and Anderson, 1955) or unstained (Revel, 1966).

(3) Membranes of nonadhesive red blood cells are separated by 100 to 200 Å when agglutinated with antibodies (Easty and Mercer, 1962) and remain this far apart when the red cells are centrifuged into a pellet (Robertson, 1960).

The estimated size of the factor particle, 300 Å, approximates the dimensions given in these three other observations. All four observations could be combined and interpreted by the conclusion that the basic unit of the cell surface was a 100 to 300 Å organelle that made up the cell surface coat, or to use a term recently coined by Bennett (1963), glycocalix.

Obviously the new cytological particle being proposed does not cover all cases of the cell surface coat. It seems most likely that the 100 to 300 Å particle is the structure on cells whose surface is not specialized. In the many instances where specializations are observed, different structures must exist (Fawcett, 1965).

To summarize, the sponge aggregation factor appearing to have the properties of a cell-surface material that binds cells together is a uniformly sized particle of about 100 S and 100 to 300 A in diameter. A general hypothesis suggested by this observation — that the cell surface coat, or glycocalix, which appears on many cells consists of particles this size — unifies several observations in the literature. With the sponge aggregation factor these organelles were isolated and assayed by their function of making cells aggregate, and were shown to be capable of directing species specific aggregation of cells. Such cell-surface organelles, however, may be important for many other cell-surface properties. They may carry the antigenic determination of red cells and may make the red cells nonadhesive. They may be sources of transplantation antigens of tissue cells. Changes at the time of malignant transformation of cells by viruses may involve these organelles. The sodium- and potassium-dependent ATPase of cell membranes might be associated with such particles. Further possibilities need not be enumerated, but it is hoped that these ideas can be experimentally examined, not only in sponges, but in other cell types by asking such questions as, "What do sponge cell surfaces look like with and without factor?" "Do factor preparations have ATPase activity?" "Are the cell surface viral antigens associated with particles of this size?"

ACKNOWLEDGMENT

It is a pleasure to acknowledge the assistance of Miss Margaret Uehara and Mr. Kenneth Ault.

REFERENCES

Abercrombie, M., and J. E. M. Heaysman. 1954. *Exptl. Cell Res.* 6: 293.

Bennett, H. S. 1963. *J. Histochem. Cytochem.* 11: 14.

Berwick, L., 1959. *Cancer Res.* 19: 853.

Catalano, P., P. Nowell, L. Berwick, and G. Klein. 1960. *Exptl. Cell Res.*, 20: 633.

Coman, D. R., and T. F. Anderson. 1955. *Cancer Res.* 15: 541.

Davis, J. E., H. N. Green, and P. W. Tymms. 1961. *Nature* 191: 923.

Easty, G. C., and E. H. Mercer. 1962. *Exptl. Cell Res.* 28: 515.

Fawcett, D. W. 1965. *J. Histochem. Cytochem.* 13: 75.

Galstoff, P. S. 1925a. *J. Exptl. Zool.* 42: 183.

Galtsoff, P. S. 1925b. *J. Exptl. Zool.* 42: 223.

Gerisch, G. 1959. *Naturwissenschaften* 46: 654.

Gregg, J. H., and C. W. Trystad. 1958. *Exptl. Cell Res.* 15: 358.

Grobstein, C. 1961. *Exptl. Cell Res.* Suppl. 8: 234.

Habel, K. 1962. *Cold Spring Harbor Symp.* 22: 433.

Haggis, G. H. 1960. *Proc. Roy. Phys. Soc. Edinburgh* 28: 115.

Hillier, I., and J. F. Hoffman. 1953. *J. Cell. Comp. Physiol.* 42: 203.

Holtfreter, J. 1939. *Arch. f. Exp. Zellf.* 23: 169.

Humphreys, T. 1962. Ph.D. dissertation. The Univ. of Chicago, Ill.

Humphreys, T. 1963. *Develop. Biol.* 8: 27.

Humphreys, T. 1965a. *Exptl. Cell Res.* 40: 539.

Humphreys, T. 1965b. *J. Exptl. Zool.* 160: 235.

Katchalsky, A., D. Danon, A. Nevo, and A. de Vries 1959. *Biochim. Biophys. Acta* 33: 120.

Klenk, E., and G. Uhlenbruck. 1958. *J. Physiol. Chem.* 311: 227.

Martin, R. G., and B. W. Ames. 1961. *J. Biol. Chem.* 236: 1372.

Morgan, W. T. J. 1949. *Exptl. Cell Res.* Suppl. 1: 228.

Morgan, W. T. J. 1960. *Proc. Roy. Soc. London* B 151: 308.

Moscona, A. 1959. *Symp. Soc. Study of Growth and Develop.* 18: 45.

Moscona, A. 1961. *Exptl. Cell Res.* 22: 455.

Newell, P. C., and L. Berwick. 1958. *Cancer Res.* 18: 1067.

Post, R. L., C. R. Merritt, C. R. Kinsolving, and C. D. Albright. 1960. *J. Biol. Chem.* 235: 1796.

Revel, J. P. 1966. This symposium.

Robertson, J. D. 1960. *Prog. Biophys. Biophys. Chem.* 10: 343.

Roth, T. F., and K. R. Porter. 1964. *J. Cell Biol.* 20: 313.

Rubin, H. 1962. *Cold Spring Harbor Symp.* 22: 441.

Schmitt, F. O. 1941. *Symp. Soc. Study of Growth and Develop.* 3: 1.

Spiegel, M. 1954. *Biol. Bull.* 107: 149.

Steinberg, M. S. 1958. *Amer. Natl.* 92: 65.

Steinberg, M. S. 1963a. *Exptl. Cell Res.* 30: 257.

Steinberg, M. S. 1963b. *Science* 141: 401.

Stone, J. D. 1947. *Aust. J. Exptl. Biol.* 25: 137.

Tyler, A. 1947. *Symp. Soc. Study of Growth and Develop.* 6: 7.

Wallach, D. F. H. 1966. This symposium.

Warren, L., M. C. Glick, and M. K. Nass. 1966. This symposium.

Watkins, W. 1966. This symposium.

Weiss, P. 1941. *Growth, Third Growth Symp.* Suppl. 5: 163.

Weiss, P. 1947. *Yale J. Biol. Med.* 19: 235.

Wilson, H. V. 1907. *J. Exptl. Zool.* 5: 245.

The Surface Components of Cells[1]

Jean-Paul Revel and **Susumu Ito**

The Department of Anatomy,
Harvard Medical School
Boston, Massachusetts

One of the most important contributions of electron microscopy to biology has been the discovery of the major role membranes play in the organization of cells. Because of its great resolving power the electron microscope has also proved extremely useful in studies of the molecular organization of membranes. Examination of ultrathin sections of cellular membranes viewed at high magnification in the electron microscope reveals that each consists of a trilaminar structure in which two electron dense layers, each about 20 Å wide, are separated by a lighter zone approximately 35 Å thick. This common configuration has been designated the "unit membrane." Studies on the formation of nerve myelin (Robertson, 1959) revealed that the myelin sheath is continuous with the plasma membrane of the Schwann cells. One could assume, therefore, that information on the structure of the myelin sheath obtained in the polarized light microscope studies of Schmidt (1936) and the data derived from X-ray diffraction (Schmitt *et al.*, 1941; Finean, 1956; 1962) also would apply to the cell membrane. On the basis of this information Robertson (1964) proposed that the outer dense layers in the electron microscope image of the cell membrane represented layers either of protein, or other nonlipid material, while the intervening lighter zone corresponded to a bimolecular leaflet of phospholipid and cholesterol. According to this interpretation the unit membrane of electron microscopists is the morphological

[1] This work was supported by grants GM 11380 and GM 10182 from the U. S. Public Health Service. One of us (J. P. Revel) is the recipient of a Research Career Development Award.

counterpart of the cell membrane model proposed by Davson and Danielli (Harvey and Danielli, 1938) some 30 years ago.

Recent work has provided evidence for the existence of still other types of molecular organization in cell membranes, and has also emphasized the possible physiological importance of surface components situated outside of the usually recognized limits of the classical unit membrane. In this presentation current concepts of membrane structure will be reviewed, and some of the surface specializations that may play an important role in determining specific membrane properties will be described. A consideration of the importance of these so-called surface coats to the function of membranes leads us to suggest that the concept of the cell membrane be extended to encompass such surface specializations.

The Organization of Lipids in
Cell Membranes and Model Systems

The interpretation of the electron optical image of cellular membranes as a protein-lipid sandwich has been tested by the examination of artificial membrane preparations (myelin figures), which can be produced by exposing purified phospholipids to an aqueous environment. X-ray diffraction studies of hydrated phospholipid preparations show patterns that are compatible with the presence of bimolecular leaflets of lipids, separated by an aqueous phase of variable width (Baer et al., 1941). After fixation in permanganate, a procedure especially suited for the demonstration of unit membranes, or in osmium tetroxide, myelin figures were found to have patterns similar to actual cellular membranes, i.e., two dark lines bounding an interzone of lower electron density (Stoeckenius, 1959; Revel et al., 1958). In myelin figures prepared from phospholipids alone, the dark lines obviously cannot represent proteins. The ready reaction of osmium with unsaturated compounds originally led to the assumption that the electron density observed, reflected the deposition of reduced osmium at double bonds in the fatty acid residues of the phospholipids. If this were so, a bimolecular leaflet of phospholipid should then be imaged in the electron microscope as a single dark line (bounded by two clear spaces). To account for the inverse pattern observed (a clear space bounded by two dark lines), Stoeckenius postulated that each leaflet was actually quadrimolecular. A model of such a structure should be accommodated within the observed membrane dimensions, although a bimolecular leaflet would provide a much better fit.

Finean (1959), however, was able to demonstrate that saturated cephalin (but not lecithin) reacts with osmium tetroxide. Since the image obtained with such saturated phospholipids was similar to that observed with unsaturated compounds, it was postulated that certain end groups as well as ethylenic linkages could interact with osmium tetroxide. Stoeckenius (1962a, b), in turn, working with heavy metal soaps of unsaturated fatty acids, also reached the conclusion that the density observed in the electron microscope was associated with the polar ends of the molecule rather than with the fatty acid backbone. It is logical, therefore, to consider a bimolecular lipid leaflet as the basic unit of organization of myelin figures.

The concept of a bimolecular leaflet as the sole structural basis for the organization of cellular membranes has recently been questioned and the new evidence seems to indicate that other molecular arrangements can occur. Dourmashkin et al., (1962) found that treatment with saponin revealed a regular array of pores in erythrocyte and other membranes. These authors suggested that the pores represented areas from which lipid components had been extracted by the action of saponin, leaving behind only a protein framework. Further investigations by Bangham and Horne (1962) and Glauert, Dingle, and Lucy (1962) clearly established that similar patterns could be obtained by addition of saponin to purified or even synthetic phospholipids as a result of the formation of micellar structures containing saponin. A careful study of such micelles and of myelin figures by negative staining techniques led these authors to conclude that the demonstration of a unit membrane structure in electron micrographs of sectioned material does not necessarily denote the presence of a bimolecular leaflet of phospholipids, as a membrane formed of closely packed micelles could give the same image. Lucy (1964) has speculated that at least part of the cell membrane could consist of micelles arranged to form "pores" some 4 Å in radius, dimensions very close to the values obtained by Paganelli and Solomon (1957) for the pore size in erythrocytes, or by Lindemann and Solomon (1961) for the intestinal mucosa.

The studies of Luzzati and Husson (1962) on the phase diagram of phospholipid-water systems, and the correlated work of Stoeckenius (1962a) on the morphology of lipids in various phases, also emphasize that the bimolecular leaflet is only one of many arrangements possible in a lipid-water system. Of particular interest is the finding of a hexagonal phase containing long and narrow water channels. The authors point out that any such structures, if present in cell membranes, might revert to the lamellar phase as a result of the near-freezing temperatures commonly used in fixation for electron microscopy.

Patterns reminiscent of those postulated in model systems have also been reported in observations of cellular membranes. Sjöstrand (1963), in an analysis of various cellular membranes, concluded that smooth-surfaced elements of the endoplasmic reticulum and the mitochondria had a globular pattern, instead of the lamellar one reported for the plasma membrane. A particulate organization in mitochondrial membranes has also been described by Fernandez-Moran (1962).

Robertson (1963) has published electron micrographs of an electrical synapse in which a hexagonal array of subunits can clearly be seen. The plasmalemma in the nonsynaptic areas does not show this array. A similar pattern is also seen in the lamellae of the rod outer segment of the retina (Robertson, 1964). Finally, Benedetti and Emmelot (1965) have recently reported the existence of a hexagonal pattern on the surface of isolated liver plasma membranes examined by negative staining techniques. The micellar arrangement was absent in membranes kept at 2°C, but was present at 37°C, perhaps because of phase transitions such as those described by Luzzati and Husson. It must be emphasized that the samples examined by Emmelot and Benedetti were not "fixed" in the usual sense of the word, and therefore cannot be compared directly with illustrations of membranes in fixed tissues.

One is left with some doubts about the basic macromolecular architecture of cell membranes, if indeed there is a single architectural pattern common to all. Much of our difficulty arises from uncertainties introduced by the preparative techniques required to view a thin section of a cell in the electron microscope. How far can we go in interpreting in molecular terms details seen in such a section? How much is the molecular architecture of the living membrane modified by interaction with the fixative, or by the removal of water during the embedding procedure? Even the thinnest sections (100–200 Å) used in electron microscopy are thicker than the subunits seen in cell membranes by such techniques as negative staining. The relative thickness of a section could easily lead to superimposition of various small substructures, so that only the external and internal boundaries of membranes can be seen giving the typical trilaminar pattern. On the other hand, much evidence other than electron microscopic observation such as direct analyses (see Gortner and Grendell in Davson, 1962), X-ray diffraction (see Finean, 1962), polarization optics (Schmidt, 1936), and capacitance measurement (Pauly et al., 1960; Davson, 1962), support the idea of a trilaminar leaflet as a continuous lipid phase. This is therefore accepted as the basis of organization of most cell membranes. None of these methods, however, would eliminate the possibility that a small percentage of the cell surface could be constructed differently (Lucy, 1964).

The Non-lipid Components of the Cell Membrane

Up to this point we have emphasized the arrangement of the phospholipid backbone of cellular membranes and have neglected the material other than lipids that may play a role in the structural organization of these membranes. Recent evidence, however, indicates that extraction of much of the lipids from mitochondrial fractions (Ball and Barnett, 1957) and even from intact mitochondria (Fleischer et al., 1962) does not greatly alter their appearance of the membranes although it does impair function. Mitochondrial function can, however, be restored by replacement of the lipid. Evidence for the presence of nonlipid materials was obtained early by Danielli and Harvey (see Harvey and Danielli, 1938) who deduced the presence of protein by comparing the surface tension of membranes with that of oil droplets in water or in protein solutions. Chambers (see Davson, 1962) studied the role of the extraneous coats on egg cells by observing the coalescence of the cells with oil droplets before and after removal of the surface coat. Further evidence for the presence of materials associated with the cell membrane also comes from light-polarization studies of myelin, which indicate the presence of a radially oriented component presumed to be lipid; and a tangentially oriented one, thought to represent protein. Direct chemical analysis of both isolated plasma membranes (O'Neill, 1964) and erythrocyte ghosts (Ponder, 1961) shows significant amounts of protein and carbohydrate material. There is specific evidence for the presence of sialic acid on the surface of various cell types (Cook, et al., 1961) as well as immunologically active polysaccharides (Morgan, 1960). The presence of carbohydrates has also been postulated as the possible basis for cellular adhesion (see, for example, Moscona, 1961), and there is good histochemical and biochemical evidence for the presence of enzymatic activities, i.e. protein, notably ATPase (see Novikoff et al., 1962) and alkaline phosphatase (Mölbert et al., 1960).

It is worth noting that while model systems of membranes always appear to be symmetrical, the plasma membrane of various cell types is commonly asymmetrical. This observation originally prompted Robertson to postulate an electron-dense protein layer facing the intracellular environment, and a polysaccharide or mucoprotein coat of relatively low density facing the extracellular space. It must be remembered, however, that since a trilaminar membrane can be observed even in the absence of proteins, the asymmetry of plasma membranes could also result from a different lipid composition of the inner and outer leaflets of the cell membrane (Finean, 1962).

Experiments performed in collaboration with Drs. Wallach and Maurice (unpublished), while shedding no particular light on the molecular architecture of the membrane, serve nevertheless to emphasize the important role proteins play in the macromolecular organization of membranes. Micelles of egg-yolk phosphatidyl ethanolamine prepared by the slow injection of ether solution of phospholipids into buffer solution, show a high degree of internal organization (Fig. 1). Presumably a shell of lipid forms around each droplet as it comes into contact with the aqueous medium. As the ether slowly diffuses out of the center of the droplets, the lipid films that form must take on a precise geometrical pattern to allow appropriate orientation of all of the molecules trapped inside the droplets. In the presence of protamine, however, this order is disrupted by the interaction of the basic groups on the protein with the negatively charged phospholipids and a completely different pattern of

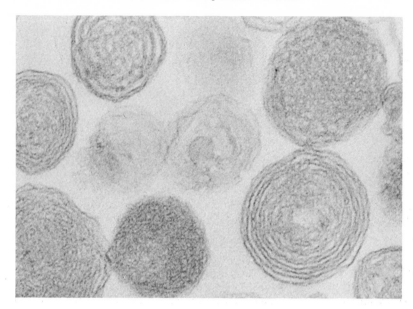

Fig. 1. Globular myelin figures of complex internal structure produced by slow injection of solutions of phosphatidyl ethanolamine into an aqueous buffer. The characteristic appearance of such a preparation can be altered by changing the conditions under which they are allowed to form. About 60,000 ×.

organization results (Fig. 2). The illustrations clearly show that under appropriate conditions, the presence of nonlipid material can strongly influence the organization of some artificial membrane systems.

Another example of the striking influence of nonlipid material on the behavior of model systems is found in the patterns formed when proteolipids (fluff) isolated from liver microsomes is allowed to hydrate. Characteristic of such preparations is the formation of extremely well organized membrane systems extending in three dimensions (Fig. 3). While no attempt has been made to construct a model of such a pseudocrystal, they seem to bear a fortuitous resemblance to the cristae mitochondriales described by Pappas and Brandt (1959) in the amoeba, *Chaos chaos*. It is believed that the protein moiety of the proteolipids imposes restrictions on the type of organization that can be achieved, and thus leads to the formation of distinctive structures. Obviously the study of the behavior of these systems may have some value in illustrating how various organelles, each with a different and specific morphology, can all be formed by membranes that may possess a similar basic molecular architecture.

The interaction of various proteins with phospholipid monolayers has been intensely studied and has yielded valuable information about the possible

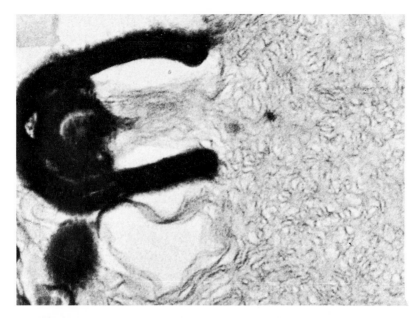

Fig. 2. A preparation similar to that illustrated in the previous figure, but for the presence of protamine in the aqueous phase. Instead of the globular structures shown in Fig. 1 one now finds large expanses of membranous sheets (at the right) as well as some more discrete, extremely dense structures, which probably represent areas where the artificial membranes are very tightly packed. About 60,000 ×.

types of interaction between lipids and proteins. Eley and Hedge (1956), for example, using films of lecithin or cephalin and bovine plasma albumin and insulin, showed that at least two layers of protein were adsorbed at the lipid-water interface. The first layer appears to be completely denatured, the second essentially native. With cephalin, both the phosphate group and the amino group may interact with the protein peptide linkage, while in the case of lecithin there seems to be ionic bonding only. Haydon and Taylor (1963) have discussed problems involved in protein-lipid interactions. Stoeckenius (1959; 1962b) has published electron micrographs of myelin figures prepared in the presence of globin. One remarkable micrograph (Stoeckenius, 1959) shows a defect in the protein coat, and provides graphic evidence of the effect of adsorbed protein on the appearance of myelin figures, i.e., a thickening and an increased electron density of the outer members of the trilaminar leaflets.

How much of the information obtained on model systems can directly be applied in evaluating actual membrane structures is a very difficult question. The electron micrographs provided by Stoeckenius show structures very

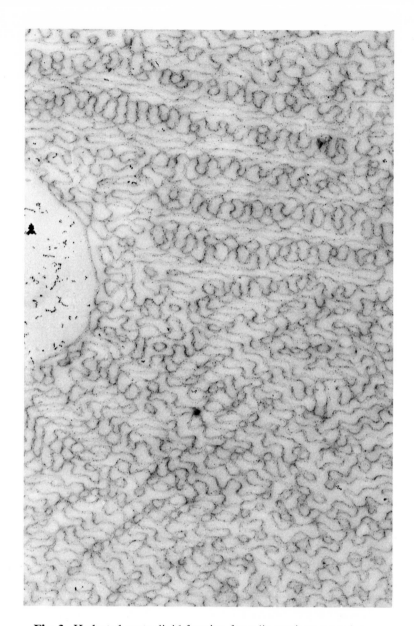

Fig. 3. Hydrated proteolipid fraction from liver microsomes have a tendency to form large "pseudo crystalline" membranous structures. The regular array has been cut at various angles producing different appearances in various areas of the micrograph. Pure phospholipids have never been observed to form such structures, and it is believed that the non-lipid component of this artificial preparation plays a major role in determining the morphological organization of the preparation. About 25,000 ×.

similar to what is observed in the cell membrane. Reconstituted bimolecular leaflets show electrical properties similar to those measured in cell membranes (Mueller, *et al.*, 1962; Thompson, 1964), and there is data indicating that such systems can be "activated" and become "excitable." On the other hand, model systems are usually prepared from relatively simple compounds, and do not contain the proteolipids, lipopolysaccharides, glycolipids, etc., known to be present in cell membranes. Undoubtedly, real membranes in which such "specific" compounds or complexes are present will differ to some extent from the idealized membrane structure, as deduced mainly from model systems. It seems likely, however, that in cell membranes the layering of the various membrane constituents is not necessarily as sharp as in model systems. Various enzymes, possibly present as lipoproteins, are probably incorporated in the fabric of the particular membranes (see, for example, proposed models of mitochondrial membranes). Wherever membranes have a micellar organization it is also possible to conceive of globular protein as part of the membrane itself.

Cell Membrane Components Found
Outside of the Unit Membrane Structure

Until a few years ago, although electron microscopists were aware of the presence of various substances at the surface of the animal cell, they usually could not detect any material outside of the unit-membrane complex. Recent improvements in the preparative techniques used in most laboratories have greatly facilitated the visualization of some extraneous substances or surface coats, and no doubt many others remain to be described. At the same time, the introduction of histochemical methods applicable at the electron microscope level has permitted studies of the distribution of several enzymes, and has also allowed us to localize some classes of polysaccharides in or on the plasmalemma.

One extremely common type of surface coating consists of exceedingly fine filaments extending radially from the plasmalemma. Such filaments were originally described by Yamada (1955) as "antennullae microvillares" on the free surface of the gall-bladder epithelium. At present, this type of surface specialization is commonly referred to as "fuzz" since it imparts a hirsute appearance to the cell membrane. The thickness of the fuzzy coat and the amount of the surface membrane covered by it varies greatly. While some free living organisms such as the amoebae may be completely invested by such a layer, only the free surface of certain epithelial cells of higher organisms seem to have this layer. In certain cell types such as ova, erythroblasts, and Kupffer cells, a material similar to fuzz occupies small patches, or lines small invaginations of the cell surface. In other cells, while there is no visible surface coating, the presence of one can be inferred from the results of histochemical tests.

The Surface Coat of the Amoeba

While little is known of the role or the composition of the surface coating of many cell types, the coating found on the surface of the amoeba has been extensively studied and much information has been obtained about its nature and function.

The plasma membrane of the amoeba has long been believed to be particularly thick and to have associated with it "an invisible, elastic, viscous, water insoluble, mucous or mucous-like coat" (Lewis, 1958). The surface of the amoeba is periodic acid-Schiff positive (Brandt, 1958), a fairly good indication of the presence of polysaccharides. It can be stained metachromatically with Toluidine blue, and also reacts with the phthalocyanin dye, Alcian blue — two reactions generally indicative of the presence of acid polysaccharides. Examination with the electron microscope reveals that the cell membrane, contrary to early belief, is not especially thick and has a clearly defined symmetrical unit-membrane structure. Outside of the cell membrane, however, there is a thick layer of amorphous material of very low electron density, from which numerous fine filaments extend (Fig. 4). It is likely that the presence of this coat misled early investigators concerning the thickness of the plasma membrane.

Studies on the uptake of proteins by the amoeba have shown that the first step in the process is a binding to the cell surface of the material to be absorbed. This step is usually reversible, and is unaffected either by the presence of metabolic inhibitors or by cold. Extensive investigations by Chapman-Andresen (1962) have shown that only compounds carrying a positive charge can be absorbed. Using the electron-dense positively-charged colloidal micelles of thorium dioxide (Thorotrast) as a tracer *in vivo*, Brandt and Pappas (1960) were able to demonstrate that the fuzzy coat of the amoeba was the site of this binding. Both ferritin (iso-electric point 4.4) and methyl-esterized ferritin are bound to the surface coat of the amoeba. Washing of the cells at a pH over 5, after adsorption had taken place at a lower pH, removes ferritin but not the methylated derivative, which still carries a net positive charge (Nachmias and Marshall, 1961). The surface coat apparently behaves very much like a biological cation exchange resin, in concentrating material at the surface of the organism prior to ingestion. The fixed charges of the coat are believed to be sulfate residues attached to polysaccharide found on the surface. This is indicated by the light microscopical histochemical reactions we have mentioned already and also by the analyses of isolated cell membrane fractions from amoeba (Nachmias and Marshall, 1961). O'Neill

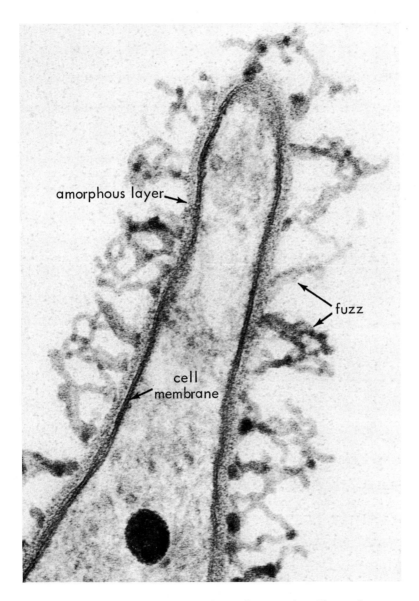

Fig. 4. A thin pseudopodium from the amoeba *Chaos chaos* shows the structural components of the cell surface. The tri-laminar cell membrane underlays an amorphous layer 200–300 Å thick. Fairly coarse filaments of the "fuzz" layer seem to end in knobby structures which rest on the amorphous layer. About 120,000 ×.

(1964) was able to show the presence of galactose, mannose, and glucose as well as amino acids in isolated cell membranes. He found no sialic acid, but did not investigate the presence of sulfate residues.

Further evidence for the presence of acidic polysaccharides in the fuzz layer of the amoeba surface has recently been obtained by employing a histochemical reaction developed for use in the electron microscope (Revel, 1964). Earlier studies on the ultrastructure of cartilage matrix indicated that colloidal thorium at pH 2 could be used to detect acidic glucoseaminoglycans in thin sections of material prepared for the electron microscope. Where this electron stain is applied to thin sections of amoebae, large masses of colloidal particles are seen associated with the fine filaments of the surface coat (Fig. 5). The plasma membrane itself is clearly resolved but there is no reaction over it,

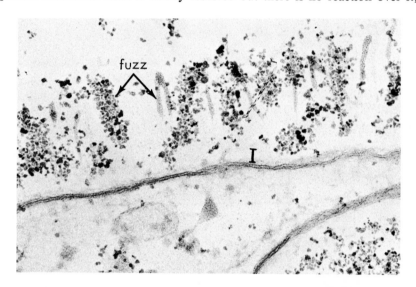

Fig. 5. Positively charged colloidal thorium particles applied to a thin section at low pH, are bound by the filaments of the fuzz which are exposed at the surface of the section. Some of the fuzz filaments are not stained because they are completely surrounded by the embedding plastic and can therefore not bind the colloidal particles. Note that the thorium particles seem to delineate structures wider than the fuzz filaments. It may be that the filaments represent only the core of a structure, part of which is not visualized here. No amorphous coat, such as that shown in the previous figure is demonstrated here, but its location (⊢—⊣) is indicated by the absence of fuzz filaments (and of thorium particles) next to the cell membrane. Of the three recognizable components of the surface complex only the fuzz filaments appear to stain, i.e., contains groups of a pK lower than 3. About 90,000 ×.

suggesting the absence of acid mucopolysaccharides in the unit membrane itself. The amorphous coat which lies between the fuzz and the plasma membrane of the organisms does not seem to stain either. In fact, Brandt and Pappas (1960) as well as Nachmias and Marshall (1961) have shown that *in vivo* this amorphous layer is impermeable to ferritin. One may wonder, therefore, whether the amorphous layer, distinguishable from the fuzz both by its behavior *in vivo* and by its staining reaction, may not be formed of material of a different nature than the rest of the surface. O'Neill (1964) has indicated that the solubilized surface complex of the amoeba contains only one major and two very minor antigens, a finding which would suggest that the coat is composed of a homogeneous material. Possibly the filaments and the amorphous material of the surface coat represent two components of the same molecular complex, part of which would be rich in strongly acidic groups and the other not. The nature of the attachment of the fuzz to the plasma membrane is not known. There is some evidence that mechanical factors, e.g., saturation with thorium, which would perhaps stiffen the fuzz and physiological mechanisms can separate the membrane from the fuzz.

Binding of material to the surface of the amoeba induces the onset of pinocytosis or phagocytosis by an unknown mechanism that may involve the release of calcium ions from binding sites on the surface (Christiansen and Marshall, 1965). In either process, both plasma membrane and associated external layers become internalized. Christiansen and Marshall have estimated that during a single 24-hour growth cycle the cells consume ten times the amount of plasmalemma present at the surface at any one time, and presumably an equivalent amount of fuzz. Once the cell surface has become internalized, it seems that the extraneous layers become detached from the plasmalemma proper (Hayward, 1963; Nachmias and Marshall, 1961), and in electron micrographs of preparations stained with thorium one can visualize vacuoles containing food organisms and tightly packed balls of stained material, which probably represent the cast-off surface coat (Fig. 6).

No direct evidence has as yet been produced concerning the site of synthesis of the new cell surface that must be formed to offset the depletion of the surface which occurs during feeding. Circumstantial evidence indicates that new membrane may be added by fusion of intracellular vacuoles with the plasmalemma.

Previous studies on protein synthesis in the cartilage cell (Revel and Hay, 1963) have provided evidence for the hypothesis that the Golgi vacuoles fuse with the cell surface during the secretion of cartilage matrix materials. It is possible that the membrane limiting the Golgi vacuoles thus becomes part of the cell membrane. It has also been shown that isotopically labeled sulfate, glucose, galactose, and acetate are all selectively incorporated in the Golgi zone shortly after exposure of the cells to the precursors (Godman and Lane, 1964; Petersen and Leblond, 1964; Revel, unpublished). Actually the vacuoles

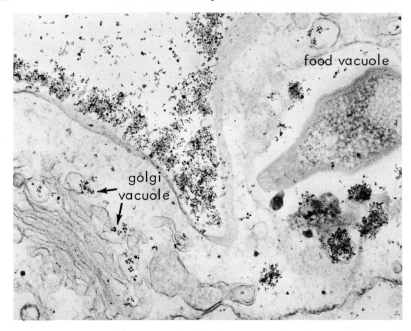

Fig. 6. A bacterium is found in a food vacuole in the cytoplasm of an amoeba. The interiorized cell surface which forms the wall of the phagocytic vacuole has lost its fuzzy coat, and stainable material is now found only in patches or balls of material. It is not clear how the surface membrane lost by ingestion is regenerated (see text). It is possible, however, that the acid polysaccharide stained in the Golgi vacuoles may represent cell surface precursor material. About 40,000 ×.

of the Golgi area seem to be the only intracellular compartment containing acid polysaccharides of high enough molecular weight to be preserved by the routine processing of electron microscope specimens (Revel, 1964). In the amoeba, as in the cartilage cell, one can detect acid polysaccharides in the vacuoles of the Golgi apparatus (Fig. 6). If one assumes that this represents newly synthesized polysaccharides, then it becomes tempting to postulate that a secretory process similar to that suggested for the cartilage cell is involved in the replacement of depleted cell surface. Instead of being released in the extracellular environment, as it is with cartilage, however, the polysaccharide would remain attached to the cell membrane to form fuzz.

The Surface Coat of the Intestinal Epithelium

As we have indicated earlier, the plasma membranes of various cell types of vertebrates are also adorned with a fuzzy coat. Of particular interest

among these is the surface of the intestinal epithelium, where the fuzzy surface coat is especially abundant in man, bats, and cats (Fig. 7) (Ito, 1965). The
plasma membrane limiting the intestinal microvilli is relatively thick, and
very asymmetrical (Fig. 8, inset). The outer leaflet of the trilaminar membrane has a very low electron density and bears a branching mat of fine filaments arranged more or less perpendicular to the surface. In the light microscope the outer edge of the striated border, i.e., the region corresponding to
the tips of the microvilli as seen in the electron microscope, stains heavily
with the Schiff reagent after periodate oxidation. It is also metachromatic
after staining with Toluidine blue and with Alcian blue. The striated border
itself is less intensely stained than its outer layer, probably because the filaments of the coat are longer at the tips of the microvilli than on their side.
In the intestine, as in the amoeba, the use of the colloidal thorium stain
(Revel, 1965) on thin sections allows a clear identification of the filaments
of the fuzz as the site of the polysaccharide detected in the light optical
preparations. No polysaccharide is detected at the lateral surface of the cells
where a fuzzy coat is absent. Attempts at removing the fuzz with papain,
trypsin, lysozyme, pronase, neuraminidase, and hyaluronidase have all
failed. N-acetylcysteine, a powerful mucolytic agent, also was without effect
on the surface coat of the microvilli. Conversely, defuzzing seems to occur
readily in cells that have been exfoliated from the epithelium during the normal cell renewal cycle of the intestinal lining. It is likely that the fuzz represents an integral part of the surface membrane complex, rather than an adsorbed layer of mucus. Further evidence along these lines has been provided
by the use of autoradiography at the electron microscope level (Ito and Revel,
1964). After exposure of intestinal mucosa *in vitro* to tritiated glucose, galactose, and acetate, and also after treatment with $S^{35}O_4$, there is at first an in-
tense labeling of the epithelial cells (Fig. 7). Chase experiments show that
much label eventually accumulates in the fuzz in the course of a few hours,
while the cell cytoplasm loses its radioactivity (Fig. 8). The label also eventually disappears from the cell surface, implying a constant renewal of the surface coat.

The role played by the fuzzy coat of the intestinal absorptive cells is
obscure. There are few indications of a role similar to that of the extraneous
layers in the amoeba. While thorotrast binds readily to the fuzzy coat of the
living amoeba, little if any can be found associated with the intestinal fuzz
when it is exposed to these colloidal particles *in vivo*. It has not yet been
possible to test the hypothesis that various digestive enzymes are associated
with the surface coat, although they are known to be localized in or on the
microvilli (see Ugolev, 1965). Alkaline phosphatase, however, one enzyme
whose activity can be studied in the electron microscope, appears to be
localized close to the outer leaflet of the cell membrane rather than in the
peripheral parts of the fuzzy filamentous structures. One might argue that in
the intestine the fuzz plays a role quite opposite to that of the surface coats in

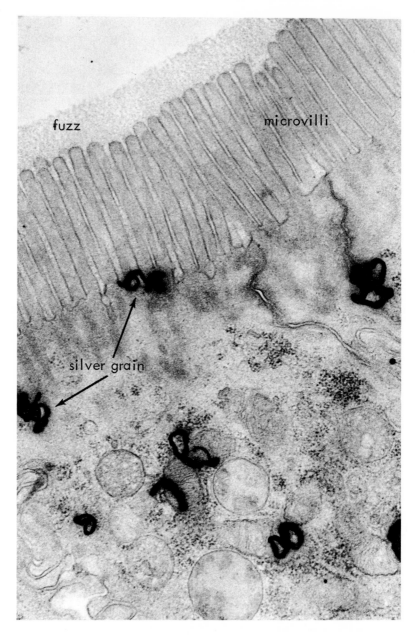

Fig. 7. An electron micrograph of an autoradiogram of a cat intestinal cell 15 minutes after administration of H²-glucose. Silver grains, indicating the presence of insoluble radioactive material, are found only in the cytoplasm of the cells. No radioactivity is associated with the microvilli or their fuzzy coat after such a short incubation. About 30,000 ×.

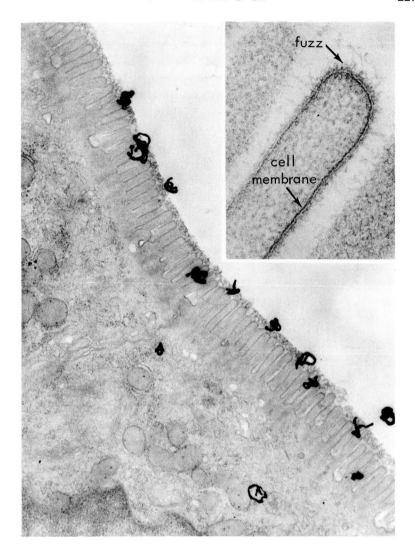

Fig. 8. After 15 minutes in H³-glucose followed by 105 minutes of incubation in the presence of an excess of cold glucose, most of the radioactivity is now associated with the fuzzy coat of the microvillar border. There are only two silver grains over the cyto-plasm of the cell. The inset illustrates the appearance, at a high magnification, of the tip of a microvillus in the rat, a species in which the fuzzy coat is poorly developed. The short fuzz filaments are in close contact with the asymmetrical plasma membrane. Slightly longer fuzz filaments are found at the very tip of the microvillus. About 15,000 ×, inset about 100,000 ×.

amoebae. Because of the relatively high pH prevalent in much of the intestinal tract, it is likely that most amphoteric substances will bear a net
negative charge. Thus undigested protein might be prevented from approach-
ing the cell surface because it is large enough to interact with the meshwork
of fuzz filaments. The interstices between the filaments are wide enough,
however, so that small molecules such as amino acids, might be allowed to
pass freely, irrespective of their charge. The fuzz might thus play some role
in the preliminary screening of the stuffs presented to the surface of the
intestinal cells.

Partial Surface Coats

In both the amoeba and in the intestinal epithelium there appears to be a
continuous fuzzy coating at the free surface of the cells. Other cell types,
however, seem to have a discontinuous surface component; a most striking
example of such a structure is provided by the so-called coated vesicles found
associated with the surface of various cell types. The coated vesicles are
characterized by the presence of short filaments or a mat of amorphous
material on the extracellular face of the cell membrane, while bristle-like
projections extend inward from the cytoplasmic face. Both Roth and Porter
(1964) and Anderson (1964) as well as Stay (1965) have shown that yolk proteins are selectively absorbed by such vesicles in the insect egg. In the mos-
quito, the rapid accumulation of yolk proteins after a blood meal results in a
15-fold increase in the number of these "bristle vesicles" (Roth and Porter,
1964). It is believed that the coated vesicles found in many other tissue cells
probably function in a similar fashion. An interesting illustration of this role
is found in the uptake of iron, in the form of ferritin, by erythroblasts (Bessis
and Breton-Gorius, 1956; Fawcett, 1964). While the plasma membrane of
the immature nucleated red cells is mostly smooth, small patches covered
with short filaments can be recognized on the external surface of the plasma
membrane (Fig. 9, inset). These patches appear to invaginate as ferritin is
adsorbed onto these fine projections. The similarity of these observations to
those in amoebae raises the question of the presence of acid polysaccharides
in such areas of the erythroblast cell membrane. The results of attempts at
staining thin sections of bone marrow with colloidal thorium were negative
in the erythroblasts, though other cells in the bone marrow biopsies were positive, indicating that the stains used were effective (Fig. 9). While it is danger-
ous to put much faith in negative results, one could consider this finding as
consistent with a specific uptake of some materials at the expense of others.
An acidic polysaccharide might have allowed the binding of too wide a spectrum of substances to be compatible with specificity of uptake.

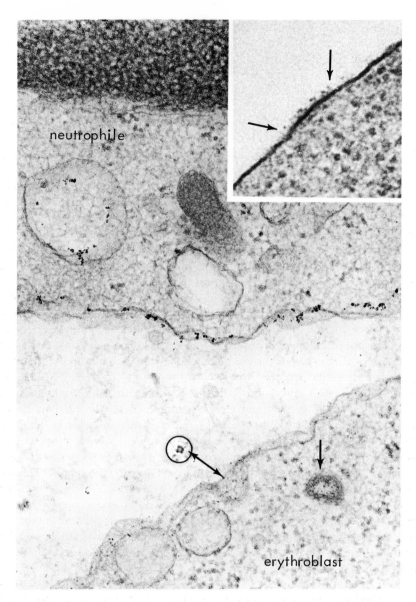

Fig. 9. Patches of fuzz-like material found at the surface of erythroblasts (inset, at arrows), seem to invaginate and enter the cytoplasm of the cell (arrow at bottom right), during the uptake of ferritin by the cells. The ferritin is seen as very small electron dense particles, one of which is greatly magnified (double headed arrow) to show the typical tetrad structure. The material coating the fuzzy vesicles cannot be stained with colloidal thorium at pH 2. The surface of a neutrophile, as well as an intracellular vacuole, however, do stain with thorium, even though no coat material can be visualized directly. About 75,000 ×. Inset about 150,000 ×. Ferritin particle, 400,000 ×.

Invisible Surface Coats

Another interesting example of surface coating is that observed in leucocytes of the neutrophilic series (neutrophils or neutrophilic metamyelocytes). In these cells no surface coating has been found that can directly be visualized in the electron microscope, yet after treatment of thin sections with colloidal thorium at pH 2, particles of stain were found just outside of the cellular membranes (Fig. 10). While these results are still preliminary in nature, they bring to mind the observations of Chapman-Andresen (1957) on the induction of pinocytosis in leukocytes by plasma protein fractions. Northover (1961) indicated that phagocytosis by leukocytes was adversely affected by proteins carrying a net negative charge; and with globulins, enhanced by a net positive charge. These findings suggest a resemblance between phagocytosis in leucocytes and the absorptive process, as we understand it, in the amoeba. In fact, as in the case of the amoeba, charged groups are present on the surface of sheep leukocytes (Wilkins et al. 1962a, b). The exact nature of these groups is unknown. Their pK, as determined by electrophoresis of leukocytes in 0.145M NaCl, is about 3, and it is inferred that the group may represent a carboxyl, either in protein or some other material present at the cell surface. Further evidence for the presence of strongly bound polar material at the surface of the leukocyte can be found in the experiments of Mudd and Mudd (1930) who showed clearly that polymorphonuclear cells, in contrast to red blood cells, are not capable of becoming wet with oil. One might imagine that the surface component of leukocytes demonstrable by colloidal thorium staining is at least partly responsible for the specific properties of the neutrophilic leukocyte. It may play a role in such processes as the adhesion of these cells to capillary walls during inflammation and in the chemotactic and phagocytic response. Although our experience with this interesting system is still limited to only a few observations, it must be emphasized that only cell membranes of neutrophilic polymorphonuclear cells have thus far been stained with colloidal thorium. While the granules of the basophiles do stain, the plasma membranes of the other white blood cells show no reaction.

Some mature erythrocytes, however, in contrast to erythroblasts described earlier, seem to stain occasionally (Fig. 10). The reason for the erratic staining properties is not understood, but in all positive cases the distribution of micelles of colloidal thorium was extremely distinctive. Here, in contradistinction to what was observed in any of the other cell types examined, the stain was not deposited next to the cell membrane, but directly on it. This may be related to the observation of Mudd and Mudd (1930) that the erythrocyte could be readily wetted by oils, showing the plasma membrane to have nonpolar groups close to the surface. We presume that the staining of the erythrocyte membrane reflects the presence of sialic acid within the membrane and not as a surface coat external to the membrane. In fact, in their investi-

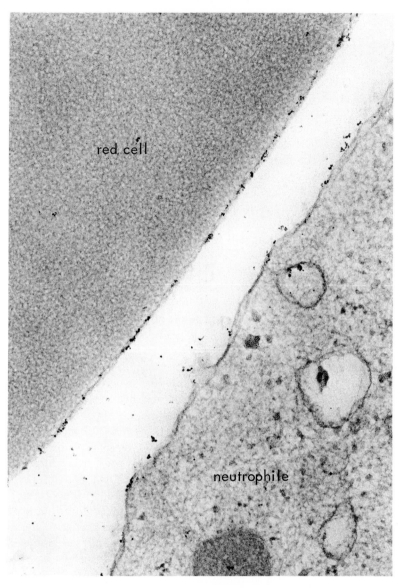

Fig. 10. This figure allows a comparison of the distribution of acidic groups of low pK on the cell membrane of a red blood cell and of a neutrophile. Colloidal thorium particles are found at some distance to the neutrophile, rather than on the membrane itself. This suggests that the invisible coat material of the neutrophile may extend some 200–300 Å away from the cell surface. In the case of the red cell, however, the particles of colloidal thorium obscure the cell membrane itself, as if the charged groups were part of the membrane structure proper. About 60,000 ×.

231

gation of the charged groups of the red-cell membrane, Cook, Heard, and Seaman (1961) were led to postulate that not all of the sialic acid was found in the electrophoretic shear plane. If our preliminary observations prove correct, it may be that some of the sialic acid residues seemingly embedded in the membrane itself, may be neutralized by positively charged groups, and thus be rendered electrokinetically ineffective. Sialic acid has been demonstrated at the surface of Ehrlich cells by the binding of positively charged colloidal metal particles (Gasic and Berwick, 1963). The methods used, however, could not have indicated an intramembranous localization. Information available on the localization of blood group substances shows them associated with the cell surface (Lee and Feldman, 1964).

In the course of this presentation we have attempted to review some of the recent advances in our understanding of the morphology of cell surfaces. More and more evidence suggests that polysaccharide, or mucoprotein coats — be they cryptic as in the red blood cell and neutrophil or clearly visible as in the other cell types discussed — are not peculiar to bacteria and cells of higher plants. The chitinous polysaccharide exoskeleton of insects and the extraneous coats of ova of many vertebrates and invertebrates, far from being particular cases, may be but the expressions of a trait common to many cell types. Obvious limitations have led us to consider only specializations of the free surface of cells. It will suffice to remind the reader that surface coats are also found at the base of epithelial cells in the form of a basement membrane lamina, that muscle cells are invested by a similar material, while the cells of the connective tissues are completely surrounded by an extracellular matrix again rich in polysaccharides. Indeed the prevalence of polysaccharide containing substances in close apposition to many cells has led Bennett (1963) to use the term "glycocalyx," a carbohydrate husk or shell, to describe this material. It is hoped further work will allow us to get a better idea of the relationship between what one might call the plasma membrane proper and its surface specializations. The surface components play important and specific roles in the cell economy. It may well be that in the future our present concept of the cell membrane will have to be expanded to accommodate various surface components in a "greater-membrane" concept. It seems appropriate to conclude by recalling the words of Robert Chambers (1940):

"Many of the physical properties which have been determined as of the cell surface belong more to the extraneous coatings than to the actual protoplasmic surface of the cell."

REFERENCES

Anderson, E. 1964. *J. Cell Biol*. 20: 131.

Baer, R. S., K. J. Palmer, and F. O. Schmitt. 1941. *J. Cell. Comp. Phys*. 17: 365.

Ball, E. G., and R. J. Barrnett. 1957. *J. Biophys. Biochem. Cytol*. 3: 1023.

Bangham, A. D., and R. W. Horne. 1962. *Nature* 196: 952.

Benedetti, E. L., and P. Emmelot. 1965. *J. Cell Biol.* 26: 299.

Bennett, H. S. 1963. *J. Histochem. Cytochem.* 11: 2.

Bessis, M. C., and J. Breton-Gorius. 1956. *Compt. Rend. Soc. Biol.* 150: 1903.

Brandt, P. W. 1958. *Exptl. Cell Res.* 15: 300.

Brandt, P. W., and G. D. Pappas. 1960. *J. Biophys. Biochem. Cytol.* 8: 675.

Chambers, R. 1940. *Symp. Quant. Biol.* 8: 144.

Chapman-Andresen, C. 1957. *Exptl. Cell Res.* 12: 397.

Chapman-Andresen, C. 1962. *Compt. Rend. Trav. Lab. Carlsberg* 33: 73.

Christiansen, R. G., and J. M. Marshall. 1965. *J. Cell Biol.* 25: 443.

Cook, G. M. W., D. H. Heard, and G. V. F. Seaman. 1961. *Nature* 191: 44.

Davson, H. 1962. *Circulation* 26: 1022.

Dourmashkin. R. R., R. M. Dougherty, and R. J. C. Harris. 1962. *Nature* 194: 1116.

Eley, D. D., and D. G. Hedge. 1956. *J. Coll. Sci.* 11: 445.

Fawcett, D. W. 1964. *J. Histochem. Cytochem.* 13: 75.

Fernandez-Moran, H. 1962. *Circulation* 26: 1039.

Finean, J. B. 1956. In *Biochemical Problems of Lipids.* London: Butterworths, P. 127.

Finean, J. B. 1959. *J. Biophys. Biochem. Cytol.* 6: 123.

Finean, J. B. 1962. *Circulation* 26: 1151.

Fleischer, S., G. Brierley, H. Klourven, and D. B. Slautterback. 1962. *J. Biol. Chem.* 237: 3264.

Gasic, G., and L. Berwick. 1963. *J. Cell Biol.* 19: 223.

Glauert, A. M., J. T. Dingle, and J. A. Lucy 1962. *Nature* 196: 953.

Godman, G. C., and N. Lane. 1964. *J. Cell Biol.* 21: 353.

Harvey, E. N., and J. F. Danielli. 1938. *Biol. Rev.* 13: 319.

Haydon, D. A., and J. Taylor. 1963. *J. Theoret. Biol.* 4: 281.

Hayward, A. F. 1963. *Compt. Rend. Trav. Lab. Carlsberg* 33: 535.

Ito, S. 1965. *J. Cell Biol.* 27: 475.

Ito, S., and J. P. Revel. 1964. *J. Cell Biol.* 23: 44A.

Lee, R. E., and J. D. Feldman. 1964. *J. Cell Biol.* 23: 396.

Lewis, W. H. 1958. *Anat. Rec.* 130: 426.

Lindemann, B., and A. K. Solomon. 1961. *J. Gen. Phys.* 45: 801.

Lucy, J. A. 1964. *J. Theoret. Biol.* 7: 360.

Luzzati, V., and F. Husson. 1962. *J. Cell Biol.* 12: 207.

Mölbert, E. R. G., F. Duspiva, and O. H. von Deimling. 1960. *J. Biophys. Biochem. Cytol.* 7: 387.

Morgan, W. T. J. 1960. *Proc. Roy. Soc. Biol.* 151: 308.

Moscona, A. A. 1961. *Nature* 190: 408.

Mudd, S., and E. B. H. Mudd. 1930. *J. Gen. Phys.* 14: 734.

Mueller, P., D. O. Rudin, H. Titien, and W. C. Wescott. 1962. *Circulation* 26: 1167.

Nachmias, V. T., and J. M. Marshall. 1961. In *Biological Structure and Function*, Vol. II. ed. Goodwin and Lindberg. New York: Academic Press, Inc. P. 605.

Northover, B. J. 1961. *Nature* 189: 574.

Novikoff, A. B., E. Essner, S. Goldfischer, and M. Heus. 1962. In *The Interpretation of Ultrastructure*, ed. R. J. C. Harris. New York: Academic Press, Inc. P. 149.

O'Neill, C. H. 1964. *Exptl. Cell Res.* 35: 477.

Paganelli, C., A. K. Solomon. 1957. *J. Gen. Phys.* 41: 259.

Pappas, G. D., and P. W. Brandt. 1959. *J. Biophys. Biochem. Cytol.* 6: 85.

Pauly, H., L. Packer, and H. P. Schwann. 1960. *J. Biophys. Biochem. Cytol.* 7: 589.

Peterson, M., and C. P. Leblond. 1964. *J. Cell Biol.* 21: 143.

Ponder, E. 1961. In *The Cell*, Vol. II. ed. Brachet and Mirsky. New York: Academic Press, Inc. P. 1.

Revel, J. P. 1964. *J. Microscopie* 3: 535.

Revel, J. P., and E. D. Hay. 1963. *Zeitshc. f. Zellforsch.* 61: 110.

Revel, J. P., S. Ito, and D. W. Fawcett. 1958. *J. Biophys. Biochem. Cytol.* 4: 495.

Robertson, J. D. 1959. *Biochem. Soc. Symp.*, *Cambridge* 16: 3.

Robertson, J. D. 1963. *J. Cell Biol.* 19: 201.

Robertson, J. D. 1964. In *Cellular Membranes in Development* ed. M. Locke New York: Academic Press, Inc. P. 1.

Roth, T. F., and K. R. Porter. 1964. *J. Cell. Biol.* 20: 313.

Schmidt, W. J. 1936. *Z. Zellforsch. Mikr. Anat.* 23: 657.

Schmitt, F. O., R. S. Baer, and K. J. Palmer. 1941. *J. Cell Comp. Physiol.* 18: 31.

Sjostrand, F. S. 1963. *J. Ultrastructure Res.* 9: 340.

Stay, B. 1965. *J. Cell Biol.* 26: 49.

Stoeckenius, W. 1959. *J. Biophys. Biochem. Cytol.* 5: 491.

Stoeckenius, W. 1962a. *J. Cell Biol.* 12: 221.

Stoeckenius, W. 1962b. In *The Interpretation of Ultrastructure* ed. R. J. C. Harris. New York: Academic Press, Inc. P. 349.

Thompson, T. E. 1964. In *Cellular Membranes in Development* ed. M. Locke. New York: Academic Press, Inc. P. 83.

Ugolev. A. M. 1965. *Physiol. Rev.* 45: 555.

Wilkins, D. J., R. H. Ottewill, and A. D. Bangham. 1962a. *J. Theoret. Biol.* 2: 165.

Wilkins, D. J., R. H. Ottewill, and A. D. Bangham. 1962b. *J. Theoret. Biol.* 2: 176.

Yamada, E. 1955. *J. Biophys. Biochem. Cytol.* 1: 445.

The Molecular Basis of Complementarity

Structural Basis of Antibody Specificity

David Pressman

Roswell Park Memorial Institute
Buffalo, N.Y.

The specificity of cell surfaces arises from the ability of the cell surface to combine with some substances or surfaces and not with others. For structures to combine with each other, they must exert sufficient mutual force of attraction or binding to hold themselves together, or else be held together by an outside force. The forces of attraction are short-range forces and require that the interacting groups approach each other very closely, i.e., are essentially in contact with each other.

Many biological combinations appear to have a close complementariness of fit, either a receptor molecule about its substrate or of two interacting regions on larger structures. Then, enough of the weak short-range attractive forces such as van der Waal's attraction, charge interaction, hydrogen bonding, dipole interaction, hydrophobic interaction, and entropy increases involved in stripping water from charged and polar areas, can provide the energy to hold the molecules together (Pauling *et al.*, 1943; Pressman, 1958; Karush, 1962; and Singer, 1965). Actually hydrophobic interaction and entropy increases can be considered outside forces, since they result from the properties of water molecules after they are removed from the region of interest. Specificity depends on two conditions: 1) that the substance has a configuration fitting the combining region and 2) that it has a proper arrangement of hydrophobic groups, charged groups, etc., to interact with hydrophobic groups and oppositely charged groups, etc., of the receptor site. Substances with configurations that do not fit the combining site sterically, or that lack a sufficient amount of the proper complementary arrangement of interacting groups, do not bind.

Antibodies are good models of biological binding regions, as they bind with great selectivity. This is shown by their ability to combine with certain substances and not with others, and to differentiate between very closely related substances. Moreover, as shown by the pioneer studies of Obermayer and Pick (1906) and of Landsteiner (1945; Landsteiner and Lampl (1917)), antibodies can be formed almost at will against simple substances of known chemical configuration. This is done by coupling a known compound with an antigenic substance, protein or otherwise, and injecting it into an animal. The resulting antibodies have the ability to combine with the hapten against which they were formed and with closely related substances. The effect of changes in structure on the strength of bonds can be determined, and the extent of the complementariness and the regions important for binding of antibody with hapten can be mapped out.

By the study of such systems it has been found that the antibody fits closely around a portion of the surface of the hapten, so that there is a close complementary steric fit. If the hapten has a charged group, a complementary oppositely charged group can be found in the combining region of the antibody molecule in the position where it can react with the charge on the haptenic group. The importance of many structures for specific combination with antibody molecules has been determined.

The antibody is not directed against the whole of the hapten group, that is, it does not engulf it, but seems, instead, to be directed against a particular portion of the haptenic surface (Fig. 1). This may be due to the fact that during antibody formation only a small part of the haptenic group may be exposed, since the hapten may be lying along the surface of the carrier antigen, either on its face or its side, rather than extended from the surface of the carrier antigen. It may, however, be because the antibody combining region is rather limited in size and can interact with only a partial segment of the hapten.

The antibody that is formed is quite heterogeneous with respect to combining site, and antibodies formed against even a single hapten species [such as dinitrophenylribonuclease with the dinitrophenyl group on the lysine number 41, (Eisen et al., 1964)] contain a mixture of antibody molecules with different specificities, as shown by different combining constants with a 2, 4-dinitrophenyl hapten.

The fit of the antibody around the hapten cannot be perfect, because the extent of complementariness is limited by the ability of the polypeptide chains of the antibody to orient closely around the antigenic structures. This ability, in turn, is dependent on the flexibility of the backbone and side groups of the polypeptide chain in the antibody molecule. Since the atoms of the antibody combining region are the same size as the atoms composing the antigen, and since they occupy space and are bound to other atoms, the

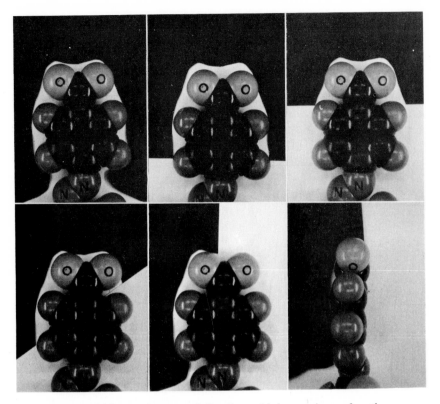

Fig. 1. Different degrees of fit of combining regions of anti-*p*-azobenzoate antibodies.

antibodies are limited in their capacity to form a close complementary fit around antigenic structures (Fig. 2).

These two factors, fit and energy of reaction for the combining regions, are basic considerations in the study of interactions of any biological binding site.

Structural Features of Importance

Much information concerning the complementary nature of antigen and antibody combining sites, and the closeness of fit and forces involved, has been derived from the studies of antibodies against simple substances of known chemical and steric configurations. The structural features of importance can be evaluated by a study of the interaction of these antibodies with other substances of known configuration related to the original one.

Closeness of fit. As an example, antibodies formed against the *o*-, *m*-, and *p*-azobenzoate groups appear to fit closely around the van der Waals outline of the groups, which are shown in Fig. 3 (Pressman *et al.*, 1954). Benzoate ion itself combines quite well with these antibodies. If a chlorine is substituted for a hydrogen in the para position, Fig. 4, the hapten combines even more strongly with the anti-*p*-azobenzoate antibody than does the unsubstituted benzoate. Apparently, the chlorine is accommodated in the position occupied by the azo group of the immunizing hapten and provides increased interaction energy relative to the hydrogen. Similarly, ortho-

chlorobenzoate combines more strongly with antiorthoazobenzoate antibody, and the metachlorobenzoate combines more strongly with the antimeta-azobenzoate antibody than does benzoate. When the substituent is in a position other than the position of attachment, the result is generally a reduced combination because of steric interaction, as pictured in Fig. 4. Investigations of this nature show the very close fit of the antibody around the benzoate group.

Just how closely the antibody fits around a particular hapten was determined for the benzoate grouping by measuring the extent of combination of the various chloro-substituted phenol-azobenzoates with the antibodies directed against the *o*-, *m*-, and *p*-azo-

Fig. 2. Representation of the combining region of an anti-*p*-azobenzoate antibody showing atoms of which the antibody is composed.

benzoates. The van der Waals outlines of the haptens, against which the antibodies were formed, are shown superimposed on the test hapten in Fig. 5.

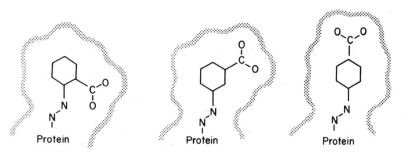

Fig. 3. Van der Waals outlines of ortho, meta and para azobenzoate ions against which antibodies are directed.

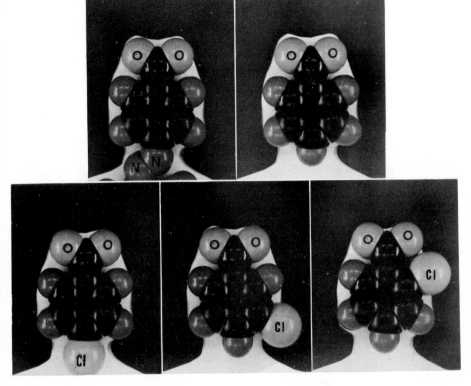

Fig. 4. Effect of substitution on fit of azobenzoate and benzoate into combining region of anti-para-benzoate antibody. A chloro group is accommodated in the para position but not in the ortho and meta positions due to steric hindrance.

Free energies of combination with antibody relative to that of benzoate ion itself ΔF_{rel}[1] are also given. A summary of the results is shown in Fig. 6, where the numbers around the van der Waals outline of the injected hapten indicate the effect of a chlorine present in the corresponding position on the free energy of combination of hapten with antibody. Similar effects of substitution have been observed with several systems.

[1] ΔF_{rel} is the relative free energy change for the binding of a hapten to antibody, and is the value of ΔF° relative to the value for the unsubstituted hapten.

$$\Delta F_{rel} = \Delta F^\circ_{hapten} - \Delta F^\circ \text{ substituted hapten.}$$

K_{rel} is the relative binding constant for the binding of a hapten and is the value of K_{rel} to the value for the unsubstituted hapten.

$$K_{rel} = \frac{K_{hapten}}{K_{unsubstituted\ hapten}}.$$

Then $\Delta F_{rel} = -RT\ln K_{rel}$.

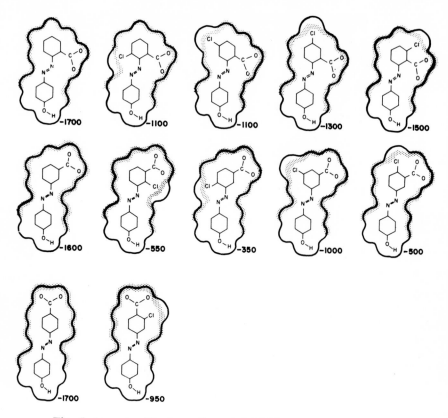

Fig. 5. Van der Waals outline of inhibiting azochlorobenzoate hapten superimposed on outline of the injected hapten group. Numerical values are for ΔF_{rel} compared to value for benzoate.

Antibodies against some haptens appear to show a closer fit than do antibodies against other haptens. For example, antibodies against the 4-azophenyltrimethylammonium group (Pressman *et al.*, 1946) and the $p(p'$-azophenylazo)-phenylarsonate ion seem to fit less closely around the haptens than do antibodies against the *p*-azobenzenearsonate (Pauling *et al.*, 1944), the *p*-azobenzoate (Pressman and Siegel, 1953; Pressman *et al.*, 1944), or the $p(p'$-azophenylazo)-benzoate antibodies (Nisonoff and Pressman, 1957). This is shown in Table 1, where it can be seen that meta- and ortho-methyl substituents do not interfere with the combination with the former set of antibodies but only with the latter group. Indeed, alpha-naphthyl derivatives show increased combination with the former, whereas decreased combination is observed with the latter; this indicates that antibodies of the first group can accommodate large substituents on one side, while the others cannot. The increase, where observed, is probably due to either the increased van der

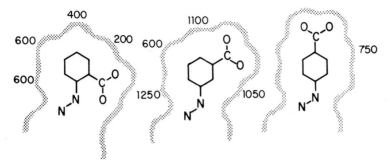

Fig. 6. Effect of chlorosubstituent in indicated position on the free energy of combination of (p'-hydroxyphenylazo)-benzoates with antibody. Numerical values are for ΔF_{rel}.

Waals attraction of the naphthalene for the antibody or, perhaps, the water displacement.

Importance of the benzene ring when present. The benzene ring is important in the combination with anti-p-azobenzoate antibody, for example. Replacement of a benzene ring by a methyl group to give acetate reduces the binding energy to a very low level. Displacing the benzene ring by about 1.5 Å, and tilting it by inserting a methylene group to give phenylacetate, displaces it from its complementary position with respect to the carboxylate, and combination does not take place. Similarly, replacing the benzene ring by cyclohexane, which is somewhat thicker and does not have the polarizability of the benzene ring, causes a large decrease in combination energy. The proper orientation of the benzene ring is very important in many hapten systems (Table 2).

When the benzene ring is replaced by the thiophene ring (Pressman, unpublished) — which has a size and shape very similar to the benzene ring, as is evidenced by the mixed crystals formed by thiophene and benzene — the combination is equally as good as when the benzene ring is next to the carboxylate group. It is interesting that the antibody can differentiate between the compound where the sulfur is in the 2 and where it is in the 3 position. Pyridine is also well accommodated, but the degree of combination depends on the position of the nitrogen in the ring (Pressman and Siegel, 1957). Furan and pyrrole rings, which are also planar, are accommodated although not as well as the thiophene ring (Table 3).

Using antibody to the D-phenyl-(p-azobenzoylamino) acetate group, Karush (1956) made a comparison of the binding of benzoylamino acetate and D-phenyl-(benzoylamino) acetate. The contribution by the phenyl group to the free energy of combination was − 4.2 kcal.

TABLE 1

CLOSENESS OF FIT IN VARIOUS PARA-AZOHAPTEN SYSTEMS

Hapten*

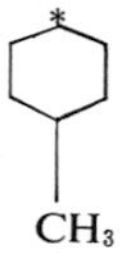

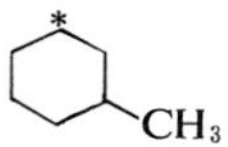

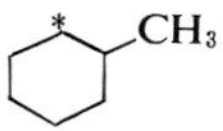

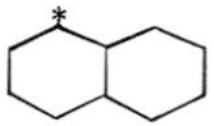

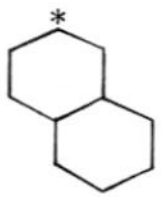

Relative Binding Constants

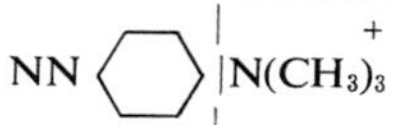

Hapten Specific Antibody	1	2	3	4	5	6
NN⬡ |N(CH$_3$)$_3^+$	1.0	1.45	0.86	1.05	2.0	
NN⬡ |AsO$_3$H$^-$	1.0	2.7	1.10	1.00	2.9	3.90
NN⬡⬡ |AsO$_3$H$^-$	1.0	1.9	0.78	0.21	0.52	6.00
NN⬡⬡ |COO$^-$	1.0	1.8	0.21	0.03	0.03	1.98
NN⬡⬡ |COO$^-$	1.0	3.0	0.66	0.08	0.18	10.0

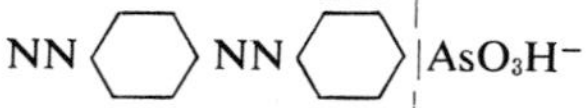

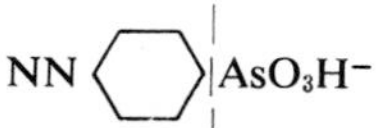

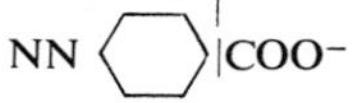

*The asterisk (*) represents $N(CH_3)_3^+$, AsO_3H^-, or COO^- depending on the antibody system used.

VAN DER WAALS ATTRACTION DUE TO BENZENE RING

SYSTEM		HAPTEN	
		⬡— H_3C-	⬡CH_2^-
		K_{rel}	
$-NN-⬡-AsO_3H^-$	1.00	0	0
$⬡-AsO_3H^-$ (−NN−)	1.00	0	
$⬡-AsO_3H^-$ (−NN)	1.00	0	
$-NN-⬡-NN-⬡-AsO_3H^-$	1.00	0	0.05
$-NN-⬡-C{O^- \atop O}$	1.00	0	0
$-NN-⬡-NN-⬡-C{O^- \atop O}$	1.00	0	0
$-NN-⬡-\overset{O}{C}CH_2CH_2C{O^- \atop O}$	1.00	0.12	
$-NN-⬡-\overset{O}{C}NHCH_2C{O^- \atop O}$	1.00	.01	
$-NN-⬡-NHCOCH_2CH_2C{O^- \atop O}$	1.00	.05	0.18
$-NN-⬡-N(CH_3)_3^+$	1.00	.10	(.5)

Charge. When the antibody is formed against a charged group, the presence of the charge on the hapten is important for combination. Thus, antibody against the *p*-azobenzoate group shows essentially no combination with the nitrobenzene group, in which the charged carboxylate of benzoate is replaced by the uncharged nitro group, even though both groups have the same size and shape. Specificity for the nature of the charged group in this system is shown by the fact that if the carboxylate is replaced with the charged groups sulfonate or arsonate, there is essentially no combination. This is apparently because these charged groups are too large to be accommodated by the antibody directed against the carboxylate grouping.

Antibody against the benzenearsonate group combines well with the benzenearsonate and the benzenephosphonate group, with which it cross reacts extensively and is very closely related structurally. It does not react with the benzenesulfonate, benzoate, methylphenylarsinic acid, or the stibonic acid, which also bear a negative charge, but apparently are not accommodated (Pressman *et al.*, 1945).

When the antibody is directed against a hapten with two charged groups close together, as in antibody against the 4-azo-orthophthalate group (Pressman and Pauling, 1949) or the 5-azoisophthalate group (Pressman, unpublished), two charges are required on the hapten for strong combination to take place. A single charge, as in benzoate or even in the more sterically similar *o*-nitrobenzoate (or *m*-nitrobenzoate), is insufficient. In the ortho- and meta-phthalate systems, the energy contribution of the charge interaction is so large, that the rest of the structure of the hapten is of lesser importance. Thus, substituents on the ring are more easily accommodated.

Strong direct evidence for a charge on antibody in juxtaposition to a charge on the hapten is shown by the interaction of positively charged phenyltrimethylammonium group with its specific antibody (Pressman and Siegel, 1953). By comparing 4-azophenyltrimethylammonium group (coupled to H-acid) and the 4-azophenyltertiarybutylbenzene (similarly coupled) (which has the same size and shape as the phenyltrimethylammonium ion but lacks the charge), a factor of 8 was found in relative combining constants for the reaction of these two substances with the antibody (Fig. 7). This represents a free energy of interaction due to the positive charge of about 1,150 cal, assuming that the other interactions for the two groups are the

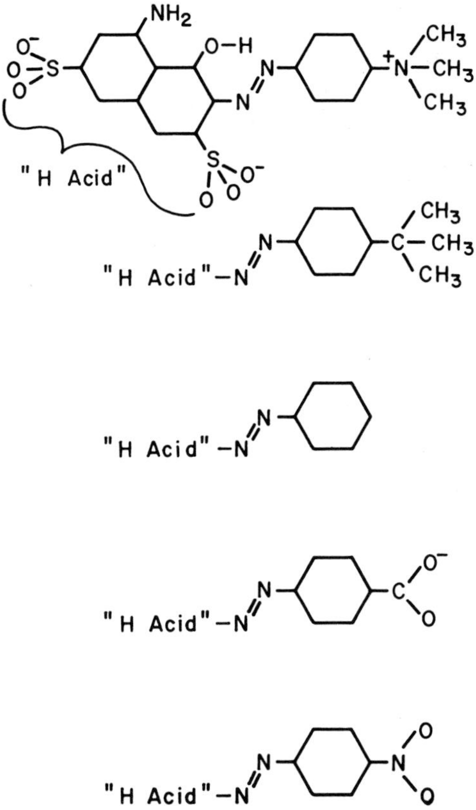

Fig. 7. Haptens used for charged interaction measurements, the trimethylammonium group *vs.* the isosteric tert butyl group and the hydrogen (benzene). The carboxylate *vs.* the isosteric nitro group.

same. Calculation of the distance between the positive charge of the hapten and the corresponding negative charge on the antibody that would give an electrical energy of interaction of this magnitude, shows a negative charge on antibody within about 8 Å from the positive charge on the hapten. This indicates a carboxylate on the antibody in juxaposition to the trimethylammonium group. These groups are therefore within 3 Å of the distance of closest possible approach (Fig. 8). Calculation was made on the basis of

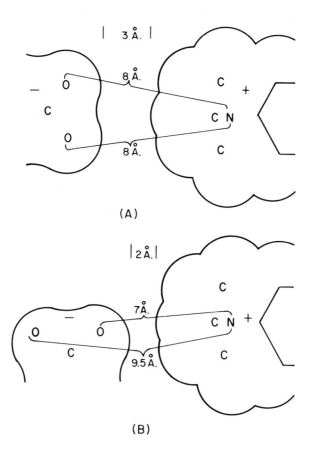

Fig. 8. Apparent distance of approach of trimethylammonium group of hapten to carboxylate of antibody.

Schwartzenbach's (1936) evaluation of the effect of distance between charges in water on the free energy of interaction (Schwartzenbach, 1936). If the tertiarybutylbenzene group is replaced by the benzene group, Fig. 7, the tertiarybutyl group, in occupying the space which accommodates the trimethyl ammonium group of the homologous hapten, contributes 3 kcal to the free energy of combination.

Chemical reaction proved that a carboxylate in the combining site of the antibody molecule is directed against the positive ion (Grossberg and Pressman, 1960).

The strength of combination of related haptens with this antibody is a function of the ion radius. The antibody combines with both the phenyltrimethylarsonium ion and the phenyltriethylammonioum ion, and the constant decreases as the ion radius increases (Table 4).

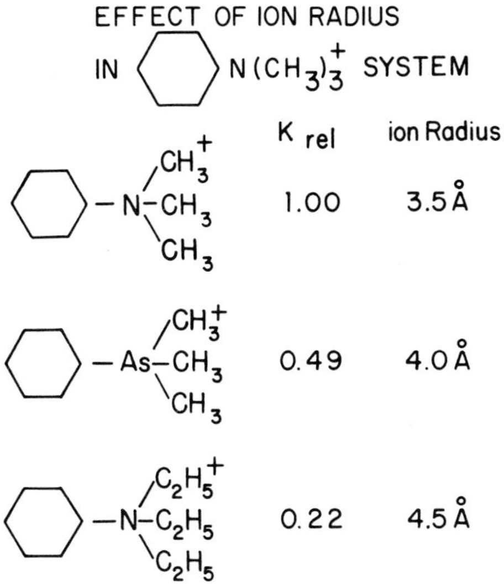

EFFECT OF ION RADIUS

IN ⟨⟩ N$(CH_3)_3^+$ SYSTEM

	K rel	ion Radius
⟨⟩—N$\overset{/CH_3^+}{\underset{\backslash CH_3}{-CH_3}}$	1.00	3.5 Å
⟨⟩—As$\overset{/CH_3^+}{\underset{\backslash CH_3}{-CH_3}}$	0.49	4.0 Å
⟨⟩—N$\overset{/C_2H_5^+}{\underset{\backslash C_2H_5}{-C_2H_5}}$	0.22	4.5 Å

When antibody is formed against a negative hapten group, p-(p'-azophenylazo)-benzoate ion (Nisonoff and Pressman, 1957a), similar evidence of an opposite charge on the antibody is seen. When the combination with H-acid p-azobenzoate and H-acid p-azonitrobenzene were compared, a difference of over 5,000 cal/mole free energy of combination was observed. If we assume that both the nitro group and the carboxylate group have similar shapes and sizes, this difference in energy would arise from a separation of charge of 4.5 Å, which is about equivalent to the distance of closest approach for a charge on the carboxylate and the charge on an ammonium group.

Uncharged groups. When antibody is directed against 3 azo- or 4 azo-nitrobenzene group, the nitro group accounts for an appreciable amount of free energy of interaction (Nisonoff *et al.*, 1959). The nitro group contributes 4 kcal of free energy of combination, as shown by a comparison of nitro-benzene derivative with the benzene derivative. For combination with antibody to the 3,5-dinitroazobenzene group or antibody to the 2,4-dinitro-azobenzene (Farah *et al.*, 1960), both nitro groups are important just as both carboxylate groups are important for combination of phthalate with anti-4-azophthalate antibody. Removing one nitro group results in a reduction of over 2 kcal in free energy of interaction.

The hydrocarbon residue is also important when the antibody is directed against it. Thus, antibody against *p*-azobenzoylleucine does not combine well with benzoylglycine (Kreiter and Pressman, 1964). The converse is also true; antibody against *p*-azobenzoylglycine does not react with benzoyl-leucine. In the latter case the effect is steric lack of accommodation, while in the former the α hydrogen of glycine does not contribute to the interaction with antibody as does the α isobutyl group of leucine.

Configuration and conformation. Antibody formed against one optical isomer usually does not fit the antipode. Thus, as Karush (1956) has shown, antibody to the D-phenyl-(benzoylamino) acetate reacts with the D-hapten but only very poorly with the L-hapten. Since the antibody fits the hapten in the complementary manner that a glove fits a hand, the change from the D to the L configuration interferes much more with combination than a change in the size of the group, just as a right hand will fit into a right hand glove, even of a different size, much better than into a left glove of correct size.

Another factor that can affect fit is the flexibility of the hapten. If the hapten group is an extended chain, the antibody may be formed against a particular preferred orientation of the chain. This appears to be the situation with the azosuccinanilate group (Pressman *et al.*, 1948), as first pointed out by Landsteiner and van der Scheer (1934). This group seems to exist in a coiled configuration in aqueous solution, since antibodies formed against it combine well with succinanilate ion and also with the (cis) maleanilate ion, but combine only poorly with the (trans) fumaranilate ion. Such cyclization of succinanilate could be stabilized by hydrogen bond formation between the carboxylate and the NH group, or perhaps through resonance in the carboxyl group (Fig. 9). Benzoylpropionate seems to exist in the coiled configuration also. It combines well with antibody against the succinanilate ion, and anti-body prepared against the *p*-azobenzoylpropionate group combines better with the (cis) maleanilate ion than with the (trans) fumaranilate ion.

Another example of configurational factors is shown by antibody to the 4-azophthalate ion (Pressman and Pauling, 1949). Although the carboxylate group of benzoate ion is coplanar with the benzene ring, this cannot be the

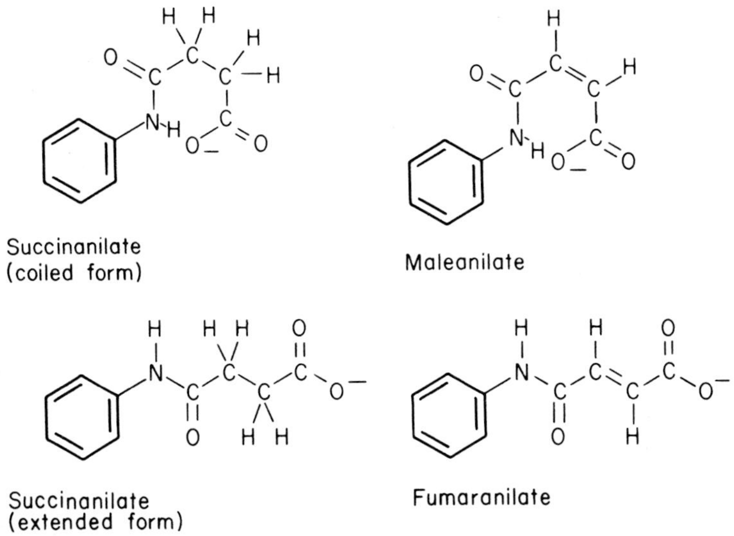

Succinanilate
(coiled form)

Maleanilate

Succinanilate
(extended form)

Fumaranilate

Fig. 9. Extended and coiled forms of succinanilate compared with fumaranilate and maleanilate.

situation for the carboxyl groups of phthalate ion. The carboxylates are tilted relative to each other. This is reflected in the ability of the antibody to combine with the o-sulfobenzoate group, although benzene sulfonate does not combine with anti-p-azobenzoate antibodies. The accommodation of a sulfo in place of a carboxylate by antiphthalate antibody may well be because the antibody is formed against a much thicker charged region due to the tilting of the groups in the phthalate system; whereas, the antibody may be formed against the flat carboxylate group in the benzoate and cannot accommodate the sulfonate group.

Hydration. Another factor that affects fit is the hydration of the molecule. Water of hydration can act sterically as a substituent on the molecule. The nitrogen of the pyridine ring is hydrated in aqueous solution. This water of hydration is a factor in the reaction with antibody. Antibodies against the o-, m-, and p-azobenzoate ions and p-(p′-azobenzeneazo) benzoate ion react with the pyridine carboxylate ions, picolinate, nicotinate, and isonicotinate, as though there were a large substitituent (water) on the ring in the position occupied by the nitrogen atom (Pressman and Siegel, 1957; Nisonoff and Pressman, 1957). The various quinoline carboxylate ions also combine with these antibodies as though a large substituent on the ring was corresponding to the position of the nitrogen group. These results are consistent with hydration of the ring nitrogen atom. In the combination of antibody formed against the 4-azophthalate ion with pyridine dicarboxylate and with pyrazine dicarboxylate, the relative combining constants are 0.20 and 0.05, indicating a large steric factor due to hydration of one- and two-ring nitrogen atoms (Pressman and Pauling, 1949).

Pyridine retains its water of hydration (Nisonoff and Pressman, 1957) when antibodies are formed against the 3-azopyridine group. This is indicated by a region being present in the antibody site that can accommodate a benzene ring with large substituents attached in place of the pyridine ring with water attached. This "hole" is very large and will accommodate large groups, e.g., iodo.

Hydration is not limited to the nitrogen atom, but is probably an important factor with all the various groupings that are either charged or form hydrogen bonds. The energy required to strip water from hydrated small ions is of the order of 50 kcal/mole or more, and this value is much greater than the free energies of combination or heats of combination of antibody and antigen as determined. It may well be that structures written for many physiologically active substances that neglect the water of hydration are grossly incorrect with respect to their effective steric configurations.

Chemical Nature of the Combining Region of Antibody

The combining region of antibodies directed against different haptens are necessarily different since they have different specificities. Besides differences in complementary configuration, antibody directed against a positive charged group such as a p-azophenyltrimethylammonium group, is different from antibody formed against the negatively charged p-azobenzoate group. In this instance, the difference in charge contributes to the specificity since charge interaction is an important part of antibody-antigen combination. The antibody directed against the positively charged group has a negative charge in the combining region; the antibody against a negative group has a positive charge in the combining region. The presence of these charges has been shown experimentally by the demonstration that the combining region with a negative charge attracts inorganic cations nonspecifically (Grossberg et al., 1962a), while the region with a positive charge attracts anions (Pressman et al., 1961). Antibodies to an uncharged group do not attract either type of ion preferentially (Pressman, unpublished).

The negative charge in the combining region of antibody to the positive charge must necessarily be due to a carboxylate group (Grossberg and Pressman, 1960). When such antibodies are treated with diazoacetamide, which is known to esterify carboxylate ions, the ability of the antibody to bind hapten is lost. The greater the degree of reaction, the greater the number of carboxyl groups esterified, the greater is the loss of activity. Binding activity can be recovered by exposure of the esterified antibody to alkali which hydrolyses the ester, liberating the charged carboxylate group. Antibodies against negative charges, which presumably contain a positive charge in the combining region, are not affected by esterification indicating the absence of a carboxyl group in the combining region.

The positive charge in the combining region of antibodies against a negative group could be contributed by an amino group such as the ε-amino of lysine or the α-amino at the end of a polypeptide chain, or by the guanidinium group of arginine. In the case of antibodies against benzoate, it appears that the amino group plays a rather limited role, and the positive charge is probably entirely due to a guanidinium residue. Histidine appears to be ruled out as the contributor of the charge, because binding takes place at pH values where histidine bears no charge. On the other hand, amino groups appear to be important in some antibodies against benzenearsonate (Chen et al., 1962).

The nonpolar forces are probably contributed through the amino acids with the large hydrocarbon component such as phenylalanine, alanine, leucine, isoleucine.

The tyrosine residue seems to be particularly important in the antibody combining region. Several antihapten antibodies have been found to contain a tyrosine residue. This is shown by various chemical reactions such as iodination and acetylation (Grossberg et al., 1962; Grossberg and Pressman, 1963) and by the occurrence of tyrosine in certain peptides derived from the combining region of antibodies (Pressman and Roholt, 1961).

Heterogeneity of Antibodies

Evidence that antibodies are formed against various parts of the haptenic group was first presented by Landsteiner and van der Scheer (1938) in connection with the study of antibodies directed against the symmetrical azoisophthaloylglycine-D,L-leucine, called the GIL group (Fig. 10). Recent work in our laboratory (Kreiter and Pressman, 1964) has shown that it is possible to fractionate antibodies formed against the GIL group into antibodies directed against the L group, others against the G group. This was done by absorbing the antibodies of the anti-GIL serum on a solid absorbent containing GIL groups. It was found that a portion of the antibodies could be eluted by passing benzoylleucine through the column; another portion could be eluted by passing benzoylglycine through; and a third portion could be obtained by passing the original hapten GIL through. The binding constants for these three fractions were determined for the three haptens, as given in Table 5. It can be seen that antibody eluted by benzoylglycine was bound

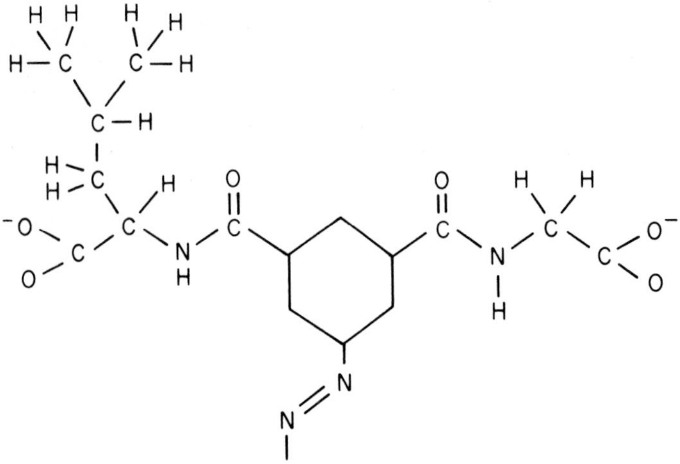

Fig. 10. The GIL hapten.

to the G-azo hapten and the GIL-azo hapten, but not to the L-azo hapten. The material eluted by the benzoylleucine did not bind the G-azo hapten but combined with the L-azo hapten. Both antibodies combined with the

Binding Constants with Haptens for Various Fractions of Anti-GIL Antibodies and for Anti-G and Anti-L Antibodies.

	Binding Const. $(\times 10^{-4})$		
	G-azohapten	L-azohapten	GIL-azohapten
Anti-GIL antibody (Unfractionated)	31	10	17
G Fraction (Eluted by benzoylglycine)	27	0	59
L Fraction (Eluted by benzoylglycine)	0	12	69
GIL Fraction (Eluted by GIL)	6	6	1106
Anti-G antibody	78	0	65
Anti-L antibody	0	46	54

GIL-azo hapten. The GIL fraction showed a very strong binding for the GIL-azo hapten, but very low binding for the G and L haptens. The antibody eluted only by the GIL hapten seemed to be directed against both the G and the L grouping and required both for good binding. The antibodies in the G fraction and the L fraction were both bound appreciably tighter by the GIL hapten than by the G and L haptens. On the other hand antibodies formed against the simpler benzoylglycine and benzoylleucine groups, anti-G antibody and anti-L antibody, respectively, were not bound more strongly by the GIL hapten than by the G and L haptens. This indicates that all the anti-GIL antibodies had a specificity toward the second grouping (Fig.11). The antibodies appear to be formed against various portions of the GIL hapten as indicated.

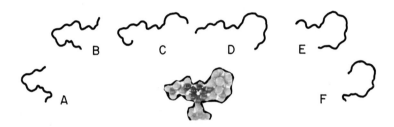

Fig. 11. Portions of the van der Waals outline of the GIL-hapten which are implicated for various antibodies in anti-GIL serum. A and B represent the portions toward which antibodies eluted in the G fraction are directed; E and F, portions toward which antibodies eluted in the L fraction are directed; and C and D portions toward which antibodies from the GIL fraction are directed.

REFERENCES

Chen., C. C., A. L. Grossberg, and D. Pressman. 1962. *Biochem.* 1: 1025.

Eisen, H. N., E. S. Simms, J. R. Little, Jr., and L. A. Steiner. 1964. *Federation Proc.* 23: 559.

Farah, A., M. Kern, and H. N. Eisen. 1960. *J. Exptl. Med.* 112: 1195.

Grossberg, A. L., C. C. Chen, L. Rendina, and D. Pressman. 1962a. *Immunol.* 88: 600.

Grossberg, A. L., and D. Pressman. 1960. *J. Am. Chem. Soc.* 82: 5478.

Grossberg, A. L., and D. Pressman. 1963. *Biochem.* 2: 90.

Grossberg, A. L., G. Radzimski, and D. Pressman. 1962b. *Biochem.* 1: 391.

Karush, F. 1956. *J. Am. Chem. Soc.* 78: 5519.

Karush, F. 1962. In *Advances in Immunology* Ed. W. H. Taliaferro and J. H. Humphrey. New York: Academic Press, Inc.

Kreiter, V. P., and D. Pressman. 1964. *Immunochem.* 1: 151.

Landsteiner, K. 1945. *The Specificity of Serological Reactions* Cambridge: Harvard University Press.

Landsteiner, K., and H. Lampl. 1917. *Z. Immunitats.* 26: 293.

Landsteiner, K., and J. van der Scheer. 1934. *J. Exptl. Med.* 59: 751.

Landsteiner, K., and J. van der Scheer. 1938. *J. Exptl. Med.* 67: 709.

Nisonoff, A., and D. Pressman. 1957a. *J. Am. Chem. Soc.* 79: 1616.

Nisonoff, A., and D. Pressman. 1957b. *J. Am. Chem. Soc.* 79: 5565.

Nisonoff, A., A. R. Shaw, and D. Pressman. 1959. *J. Am. Chem. Soc.* 81: 1418.

Obermayer, F., and E. P. Pick. 1906. *Wien Klin. Wochschr.* 17: 327.

Pauling, L., D. H. Campbell, and D. Pressman. 1943. *Physiol. Rev.* 23: 203.

Pauling, L., D. Pressman, and A. L. Grossberg. 1944. *J. Am. Chem. Soc.* 66: 784.

Pressman, D. 1958. *Serological and Biochem. Comp. of Proteins, Proc. 14th Ann. Protein Conf.* 25–39.

Pressman, D., J. H. Bryden, and L. Pauling. 1948. *J. Am. Chem. Soc.* 70: 1352.

Pressman, D., A. L. Grossberg, L. H. Pence, and L. Pauling. 1946. *J. Am. Chem. Soc.* 68: 250.

Pressman, D., A. Nisonoff, and G. Radzimski. 1961. *J. Immunol.* 86: 35.

Pressman, D., A. B. Pardee, and L. Pauling. 1945. *J. Am. Chem. Soc.* 67: 1602.

Pressman, D., and L. Pauling. 1949. *J. Am. Chem. Soc.* 71: 2893.

Pressman, D., and O. Roholt. 1961. *Proc. Natl. Acad. Sci.* 47: 1606.

Pressman, D., and M. Siegel. 1953. *J. Am. Chem. Soc.* 75: 686.

Pressman, D., and M. Siegel. 1957. *J. Am. Chem. Soc.* 79: 994.

Pressman, D., M. Siegel, and L. A. R. Hall. 1954. *J. Am. Chem. Soc.* 76: 6336.

Pressman, D., S. M. Swingle, A. L. Grossberg, and L. Pauling. 1944. *J. Am. Chem. Soc.* 66: 1731.

Schwartzenbach, G. 1936. *Z. Physik. Chem.* A176: 133.

Singer, S. J. 1965. In *The Proteins*, Vol. III, ed. H. Neurath. New York: Academic Press, Inc.

Blood-Group Substances

Winifred M. Watkins

The Lister Institute of Preventive Medicine
London, England

Erythrocyte membranes have a multiplicity of antigenic groupings on their surface, and the division of bloods into groups is possible because not all members of a given species have the same complement of antigens. The first blood groups were discovered in humans (Landsteiner, 1900), and similar divisions, based on antigenic differences on the erythrocytes, have since been established for most mammalian species (cf. Joysey, 1959). The blood-group factors are, with minor exceptions, constant throughout life and are inherited according to simple Mendelian laws. Antigens, believed to be the products of allelic or closely linked genes, are classified together in blood-group systems. In humans the number of known blood-group factors exceeds 60, and these factors have been resolved into some 14 genetically independent systems (cf. Race and Sanger, 1962). Chemical investigations of the human blood-group factors have so far been limited to the ABO, Lewis, MN, P, and Rhesus systems; this review is concerned with various aspects of the work on these five systems.

The ABO Groups

The first blood-group system to be discovered, and the one of greatest importance from the point of view of blood transfusion, is the ABO system. Individuals are divided into four blood groups, A, B, AB, and O according to the presence or absence of two antigens, designated A and B, on the red-cell surface; the antigens are detected by two antibodies, anti-A and anti-B, which always occur in the serum or plasma when the corresponding antigen is missing (Landsteiner, 1900, 1901; von Decastello and Sturli, 1902). The A and B antigens are termed blood-group substances because of their association with erythrocytes. It is now known, however, that they are present on the cell surfaces of probably all endothelial cells and many epithelial cells (Wiener, 1943; Glynn and Holborow, 1959; Szulman, 1960, 1962; Holborow et al., 1960) and substances with the same serological specificity occur in a water-soluble form in tissue fluids and secretions (Yamakami, 1926; Yosida, 1928; Lehrs, 1930; Putkonen, 1930). It is evident therefore that the term "blood-group substance" is somewhat misleading, as applied to the A and B factors, and that the genes controlling the appearance of these serologically active structures express themselves at many different sites throughout the body. In an elegant study of the histological distribution of blood-group antigens in embryos and fetuses, Szulman (1964) showed that the A and B antigens are very widespread as epithelial cell-wall antigens in early intrauterine life. The survival of antigens beyond the twelfth week is restricted to stratified or simple confining epithelia, while epithelia proceeding to further morphological or functional complexity lose the antigens. The secretion-borne antigens first appear approximately eight weeks after ovulation, and the antigens of cell walls of the gastrointestinal tract begin to wane at about the same time.

Of considerable interest, from the point of view of evolution and comparative biochemistry, is the occurrence of A and B serological activities not only in man, but also in many other mammalian species (Kabat, 1956), in certain plants, and in bacteria (Springer, 1958; Springer et al., 1961). Substances with related specificities have even been reported in marine invertebrates (Cushing, et al., 1963). The chemical groupings responsible for A and B specificities, and hence the synthetic mechanisms leading to their formation, are therefore present in nearly all plant and animal life.

Although erythrocytes were the obvious source from which to isolate active substances for investigations on human blood-group specificity, the earlier attempts to obtain A and B materials from these cells met with little success. One outcome of these attempts, however, was that A and B antigens on the red-cell were designated alcohol-soluble as opposed to the water-soluble substances found in secretions. The first serious studies on blood-group substances were performed mainly with materials from animal sources such as the mucosal linings from the stomachs of pigs, which are strongly A active. (For references to this early work see Kabat, 1956.) The work on the animal blood-group substances in turn led to investigations on the water-soluble substances secreted by humans whose ability to secrete A and B substances is inherited as a Mendelian dominant character. About 80% of Caucasians are "secretors;" the proportion of secretors and non-secretors is slightly different in other ethnic groups (cf. Race and Sanger, 1962). Among the normal body fluids and secretions saliva, gastric juice, and meconium are the most potent sources of A and B substances, but a fluid that frequently has a higher content than any of the normal sources is the pathological secretion found in pseudomucinous ovarian cysts (Yosida, 1928; Morgan and van Heyningen, 1944). The secreted blood-group substances isolated from ovarian cysts have been subjected to the most rigorous purification procedures and the chemistry of the purified product has been studied in the greatest detail (cf. Morgan, 1960; Watkins, 1966).

The purified A and B substances isolated from ovarian cyst fluids are glycoproteins, i.e., compounds containing carbohydrate and amino acid moieties held together by primary valency bonds. They are macromolecules with average molecular weights ranging from 2×10^5 to 1×10^6. Carbohydrate accounts for about 85% of the molecule; therefore, although these substances can be grouped under the general heading of glycoprotein they represent one extreme end of the classification, because the amino-acid moiety is quantitatively the minor component. The over-all structure of the molecules is not yet elucidated, but their general properties and behavior appear consistent with the view that a large number of relatively short oligosaccharide side chains are joined at intervals to a peptide backbone.

The A and B substances are qualitatively similar in composition. Each contains the same five sugars, L-fucose, D-galactose, N-acetyl-D-glucosamine, N-acetyl-D-galactosamine and N-acetylneuraminic acid. The same fifteen amino acids, aspartic acid, threonine, serine, glutamic acid, proline, glycine, alanine, valine, isoleucine, leucine, tyrosine, phenylalanine, lysine, histidine, and arginine (cf. Pusztai and Morgan, 1963) are also present in substances of both A and B specificity. Typical analytical figures for preparations of A and B substances isolated from ovarian cysts are given in Table 1.

TABLE 1

ANALYTICAL FIGURES FOR SPECIMENS OF HUMAN A AND B SUBSTANCES
ISOLATED FROM OVARIAN CYSTS
(Compiled from Gibbons et al., 1955; Pusztai and Morgan, 1961; 1963)

Component	Blood group	
	A	B
Nitrogen %	4·7– 5·3†	4·5– 5·1†
Fucose %	17·0–19·5†	16·2–20·8†
Hexosamine* %	27·8–36·3†	23·9–27·6†
Reducing sugar* %	51·0–57·0†	50·0–60·1†
Sialic acid %	1·3– 2·9†	1·9– 5·1†
Total amino acids %	13·5–15·7†	10·4–16·4‡

* Estimated after hydrolysis with 0.5N HCl at 100° for 18 hrs.
† Range of values for four specimens.
‡ Range of values for three specimens.

In general quantitative composition the preparations are very similar and since small variations occur in the composition of highly purified substances having the same specificities, any differences between A or B specimens could only be regarded as significant if they fell outside this range of variability. The one difference between A and B observed consistently is that the ratio of galactosamine to glucosamine in A is higher than in B substances (Rondle and Morgan, 1955; Morgan, 1965). This finding, as will be clear later, has some bearing on specificity. The content of individual amino acids in preparations of A or B specificity is very similar, and the most striking feature of the amino acid composition is that about two thirds of the total are made up of four amino acids, namely, serine, threonine, proline, and alanine (Pusztai and Morgan, 1963). The nature of the linkage joining the carbohydrate to the peptide moiety in the blood-group substance is not yet firmly established, but there is some evidence to suggest that O-glycosidic linkages to the hydroxyl groups of seryl or threonyl residues are involved (Anderson et al., 1964; Kabat et al., 1965; Adams, 1965; Donald and Morgan, 1965).

The blood-group substances isolated from human saliva are closely similar in qualitative and quantitative composition (Kabat, 1956; Carsten and Kabat, 1956; Hiyama, 1962) to the ovarian cyst materials and appear to be glycoproteins built up on the same general pattern. The materials with A or B specificity isolated from animal sources such as pig or horse gastric mucosa are also essentially similar types of macromolecules containing both carbohydrate and amino acids (Kabat, 1956). Recently, however, A and B active preparations have been obtained from human red cells, glycolipid in nature and not containing any amino acids (Yamakawa, et al., 1960; Koscielak and Zakrzewski, 1960; Hakamori and Jeanloz, 1961; Koscielak, 1963; Handa, 1963). The A and B substances from red cells and secretions are thus associated with macromolecular entities of differing general composition. The glycolipid A and B substances contain fatty acids, sphingosine, and a carbohydrate moeity composed of the same five sugars as those present in the secreted substances, plus glucose, which is not found in the glycoprotein molecules. Analytical values for active glycolipid preparations isolated in two different laboratories are given in Table 2. It is the opinion of Koscielak (1963) that 1) the activity of the blood-group substances from red cells in hemagglutination inhibition tests depends largely upon their state of aggregation in aqueous solution and that 2) specific precipitation is probably a more reliable method for measurement of activity.

Despite the difference in macromolecular composition the glycoproteins from secretions and glycolipids from erythrocytes have the same serological specificity, which suggests that they must share identical, or closely related, chemical groupings. In double diffusion tests, glycoprotein and glycolipid A substance give single lines of precipitate which join in a pattern of fusion when rabbit anti-A red-cell serum is used as the test reagent, and give a pattern

TABLE 2

ANALYSIS OF BLOOD-GROUP A- AND B-ACTIVE GLYCOLIPIDS
FROM HUMAN RED-CELLS
(After Koscielak, 1963 (a); Handa, 1963 (b).)

Group	A (a)	A (b)	B (b)
Hexose %	43·0	36·8	38·9
Hexosamine %	15·8	14·5	12·9
Sialic acid %	10·4	4·7	0·8
Fucose %	1·2	2·8	0·6
Nitrogen %	2·46	——	——
Sphingosine N %	0·81	——	——
Glucosamine/galactosamine ratio	· 3·0:1	——	——
Galactose/glucose ratio	3·1:1	——	——
Blood-group activity*			
1. Hemagglutination inhibition	50	40	30
2. Precipitation	100	30†	

* Expressed as percentage of activity of ovarian-cyst substance.
† Estimated from precipitation curves given in Handa (1963).

of partial fusion when the serum is produced against glycoprotein A substance (Handa, 1963; Watkins *et al.*, 1964). Such patterns of fusion are normally interpreted as indicating chemical identity of the antigens, or at least of the serologically reactive groupings.

So far, little structural work has been carried out on the glycolipid A and B substances, and it is not possible to say how far inferences drawn from the glycoprotein substances can be applied to the red-cell substances. There is, however, certain indirect evidence to show that the primary determinants of specificity are the same for the two types of substance. The first indication that A specificity was associated with a carbohydrate structure, and that a single sugar was an important determinant of specificity, came from the observation that N-acetyl-D-galactosamine inhibited the agglutination of A cells by an anti-A reagent, whereas a large number of other sugars had no such inhibitory effect (Morgan and Watkins, 1953). N-acetylgalactosamine was thus competing with the A receptor on the red cell for combination with the antibody. Inhibition of precipitation (Kabat and Leskowitz, 1955) and of the enzymic destruction (Watkins and Morgan, 1955) of glycoprotein A substance by N-acetylgalactosamine strengthened the inference that this sugar was important for specificity. Later, when the glycolipid A substance isolated from red cells was available, it was found that precipitation and enzymic destruction of this material was inhibited by N-aceytlgalactosamine in the same way as the A active glycoprotein (Watkins *et al.*, 1964). These indirect tests therefore pointed to N-acetyl-D-galactosamine as the primary determinant of specificity in both the glycoprotein and glycolipid A substances. In an extension of the hemagglutination inhibition tests, methyl-*N*-acetyl-α-D-galactosamine was shown to be a better inhibitor than the simple sugar, indicating that the *N*-acetylgalactosamine is joined to the next sugar in α-linkage. By a similar series of experiments an α-D-galactosyl grouping was implicated as a primary determinant of B specificity in both the glycoprotein and glycolipid B substances (Kabat and Leskowitz, 1955; Watkins and Morgan, 1955; Watkins *et al.*, 1964).

Structural studies on the glycoprotein A and B substances, however, have given considerably more insight into the chemical basis of blood-group specificity and the possible ways that these molecules are constructed under the influence of the blood-group genes. Partial acid hydrolysis of A substance has yielded three fragments, serologically A active (Table 3), and each of these contains a terminal nonreducing *N*-acetylgalactosaminyl unit joined in α-(1→3) linkage to galactose (Côté and Morgan, 1956; Cheese and Morgan, 1961; Schiffman *et al.*, 1962). Similarly three B-active oligosaccharides have been isolated from the partial acid hydrolysates of B substance (Table 3), and each of these contains a terminal non-reducing D-galactosyl unit

TABLE 3*

OLIGOSACCHARIDES ISOLATED FROM THE PARTIAL ACID HYDROLYSIS PRODUCTS
OF GLYCOPROTEIN A AND B SUBSTANCES

1) A-active oligosaccharides occurring only in hydrolysates of A substance.

α-GalNAc-(1 → 3)-Gal
α-GalNAc-(1 → 3)-β-Gal-(1 → 3)-GNAc
α-GalNAc-(1 → 3)-β-Gal-(1 → 4)-GNAc

2) B-active oligosaccharides occurring only in the hydrolysates of B substance.

α-Gal-(1 → 3)-Gal
α-Gal-(1 → 3)-β-Gal-(1 → 3)-GNAc
α-Gal-(1 → 3)-β-Gal-(1 → 4)-GNAc

3) Oligosaccharides common to the hydrolysates of both A and B substances.

β-Gal-(1 → 3)-GNAc
β-Gal-(1 → 4)-GNAc
β-GNAc-(1 → 3)-Gal
β-Gal-(1 → 3)-GalNAc
β-Gal-(1 → 3)-β-GNAc-(1 → 3)-Gal
β-Gal-(1 → 4)-β-GNAc-(1 → 3)-Gal
β-GNAc-(1 → 3)-β-Gal-(1 → 3)-GalNAc

* Abbreviations: Gal   = D-galactopyranose
                     GNAc   = *N*-acetyl-D-glucosaminopyranose
                     GalNAc = *N*-acetyl-D-galactosaminopyranose

joined in α-(1→3) linkage to galactose (Painter *et al.*, 1962; 1963). The role of *N*-acetyl-D-galactosamine in A, and D-galactose in B specificities is thus confirmed.

In addition to the serologically active oligosaccharides, four di- and three tri-saccharides (Rege *et al.*, 1963) were isolated from both A and B substances (Table 3). On the basis of these units it is proposed that there are two types of active carbohydrate chain in both A and B substance, and the simplest sequences which can be built up from the isolated oligosaccharides are given in Table 4. The necessity for proposing two types of active

TABLE 4*

PARTIAL STRUCTURES PROPOSED FOR THE CARBOHYDRATE CHAINS IN
GLYCOPROTEIN A AND B SUBSTANCES
(After Rege, *et al.*, 1963)

1) A substance
α-GalNAc-(1 → 3)-β-Gal-(1 → 3)-β-GNAc-(1 → 3)-β-Gal-(1 → 3)-GalNAc
α-GalNAc-(1 → 3)-β-Gal-(1 → 4)-β-GNAc-(1 → 3)-β-Gal-(1 → 3)-GalNAc

2) B substance
α-Gal-(1 → 3)-β-Gal-(1 → 3)-β-GNAc-(1 → 3)-β-Gal-(1 → 3)-GalNAc
α-Gal-(1 → 3)-β-Gal-(1 → 4)-β-GNAc-(1 → 3)-β-Gal-(1 → 3)-GalNAc

* Abbreviations are the same as in Table 3.

chain arises from the isolation of the two active trisaccharides from both A and B substances (Table 3) differing in the nature of the linkage—(1→3) or (1→4)—joining the subterminal galactosyl residue to *N*-acetylglucosamine. It is to be noticed that all the linkages in the chains are β apart from the α-linkage joining the terminal nonreducing sugar—the one of greatest importance for specificity—to the rest of the carbohydrate chain.

The fragments isolated from the partial hydrolysis products of A and B substances frequently do not contain fucose, because this sugar is readily cleaved from the molecules under conditions of mild acid hydrolysis. Oligosaccharides containing this sugar have been obtained, however, from the products of alkaline degradation (Schiffman *et al.*, 1964a; b; Lloyd and Kabat, 1964; Painter *et al.*, 1965). The reduced pentasaccharide fragment (see 1(a), Table 5) isolated from the products of alkaline borohydride degradation of A substance is considerably more active in A-anti-A precipitation inhibition tests than the most active trisaccharide isolated from acid hydrolysis products. The A and B active tetrasaccharides (Painter *et al.*, 1965) (Table 5) isolated from the products obtained by degradation of A and B substances, respectively, with aqueous methanolic triethylamine are also more active than the corresponding trisaccharides without fucose. Therefore,

TABLE 5*

SEROLOGICALLY ACTIVE FRAGMENTS ISOLATED FROM ALKALINE-DEGRADATION
PRODUCTS OF A AND B SUBSTANCES

1) A-active
  a) α-GalNAc-(1 → 3)-β-Gal-(1 → 3 or 4)-GNAc-R
            ↑ α 1,2
        Fuc
	Lloyd and Kabat, 1964

b) α-GalNAc-(1 → 3)-β-Gal-(1 → 4)-GNAc
            ↑ α 1,2
        Fuc
	Painter et al., 1965

2) B-active
    α-Gal-(1 → 3)-β-Gal-(1 → 4)-GNAc
         ↑ α 1,2
       Fuc
	Painter et al., 1965

* Abbreviations: Fuc = α-L-fucopyranosyl.
                      R   = Reduced sugar or sugar fragment.
                      The other abbreviations are the same as in Table 3.

although not a primary determinant of A or B specificity, the fucose on the
subterminal galactosyl residue must contribute to the complete serologically
determinant structure.

The general similarity in qualitative and quantitative composition of A
and B substances and the isolation of many fragments from hydrolysis products common to the two substances support the idea that the A and B active
structures are built on a common precursor glycoprotein molecule. The
immediate precursor of A and B is believed to be H substance (cf. Watkins,
1966). H serological activity is found on the red cells and in the secretions of
individuals belonging to all four ABO groups, but the activity is strongest in
group O persons. Although at one time H was thought to be the product
of the O gene, it now appears likely that H is the product of an independent
gene system Hh. Moreover, it seems that the accumulation of H substance
in group O persons occurs because the product of the O gene does not change
the H substance, whereas in A and B individuals H undergoes further conversion to A and B substances.

H substances isolated from ovarian cysts are identical in qualitative composition to A and B substances in both carbohydrate and amino acid components, and are very similar in general quantitative composition (c.f. Morgan,
1960). Serological and enzymic inhibition tests with simple sugars showed that
of the five sugars present in H substance, L-fucose is of primary importance in
the H serological determinant structure and that this sugar is joined in α-

glycosidic linkage. Partial acid hydrolysis of H substance (Rege *et al.*, 1963) resulted in the isolation of the same seven inactive fragments obtained from A and B substances (Table 3) and of a very small amount of an H active fucose-containing trisaccharide (Table 6a). A second H active trisaccharide isolated from the alkaline degradation products of H substance (Rege *et al.*, 1964a) was identical in structure with the first trisaccharide apart from the linkage, (1→4) in place of (1→3), joining the galactosyl unit to N-acetylglucosamine (Table 6b). This trisaccharide is identical with the unit formed by removal of the terminal nonreducing N-acetylgalactosamine or galactose residues from the A and B active tetrasaccharides, respectively (Painter *et al.*, 1965) (Table 5, 1b and 2).

TABLE 6*

SEROLOGICALLY ACTIVE OLIGOSACCHARIDES ISOLATED FROM
GLYCOPROTEIN H-SUBSTANCE

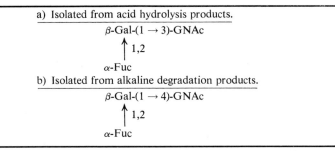

a) Isolated from acid hydrolysis products.

β-Gal-(1 → 3)-GNAc
↑ 1,2
α-Fuc

b) Isolated from alkaline degradation products.

β-Gal-(1 → 4)-GNAc
↑ 1,2
α-Fuc

* Abbreviations are the same as in Tables 3 and 5.

The isolation of the same series of oligosaccharides from the acid hydrolysis products of H substance as from A and B substances, apart from the A and B serologically active units, supports the idea that H substance is the substrate converted into A and B substances. Additional evidence obtained from enzymic decomposition experiments revealed that removal of the terminal-N-acetylgalactosamine or D-galactose units from A or B substances, respectively, resulted in loss of A or B specificity and a concomitant enhancement, or development, of H activity (Iseki and Masaki, 1953; Watkins, 1956; Iseki and Ikeda, 1956; Watkins, Zarnitz and Kabat, 1962; Harrap and Watkins, 1964). H active groupings are therefore present as underlying structures in both A and B substances; they are revealed by the removal of the terminal nonreducing sugar from the carbohydrate chains. The function of the *A* and *B* genes is therefore envisaged as the production or control of enzymes (glycosyl transferases) which in so far as the glycoprotein substances are concerned, add N-acetylgalactosamine in the case of A, and D-galactose in the case of B, in *a*-(1→3) linkage to the terminal nonreducing ends of H active carbohydrate chains (cf. Watkins, 1966). The presence of a certain amount of H activity in the secretions of A, B, and AB persons would result from incomplete conversion of the H active structures.

It is not yet clear whether H specific structures on the red-cell surface can be invoked as the recipients of the sugar additions controlled by the *A* and *B* genes. Iseka and Furukawa (1959) and Marcus, Schiffman, and Kabat (1964) reported that the action of specific A- and B-decomposing enzymes on red cells results in loss of A or B activity with a rise in H activity; Fujisawa, Furukawa, and Iseki (1963) also claim that the H activity of isolated A and B glycolipids is enhanced, although to a lesser extent than in intact red cells, by enzymic destruction of A and B activity. The glycolipid preparations isolated by Koscielak (1963), however, have no demonstrable H activity and the very low fucose content of these preparations makes it a little doubtful whether H active structures are present in the molecules. Nevertheless it should be borne in mind that the activity of the isolated glycolipids is difficult to measure in hemagglutination tests owing to the variations in activity brought about by changes in the state of aggregation of the molecules. Therefore the failure to detect H may result from technical difficulties in measurement rather than from the absence of active groupings.

The Lewis System

The Lewis blood-group system, first discovered by Mourant (1946) is of considerable interest in relation to the ABO groups because of its close association with the secretion phenomenon. The system was discovered by an antibody reacting with red cells. However, it is now believed that the substances on the erythrocyte are not integral parts of the red-cell membrane, but are acquired from the surrounding plasma (Sneath and Sneath, 1955). The factors are thus analogous to the J factor in cattle (Stormont, 1949), and the R factor in sheep (Rendel *et al.*, 1954).

Two antibodies, designated anti-Le[a] and anti-Le[b] (Race and Sanger, 1962) gave almost reciprocal reactions when tested with red cells and were at first thought to be detecting the products of allelic genes. It is now believed, however, that anti-Le[a] serum is detecting the product of a gene *Le* and that anti-Le[b] reacts with an interaction product of the genes *Le* and *H* (cf. Watkins, 1966). The first observation linking the ABO and Lewis systems was made by Grubb (1948), who observed that nearly all nonsecretors of A, B, and H substances are secretors of Le[a] substance, and have Le[a]-positive red cells. Le[a] substance is also secreted by most ABH secretors, although the amounts are usually considerably smaller than in ABH nonsecretors. Ceppellini (1955) observed that Le[b] activity is invariably associated with secretions in which both A, B, or H *and* Le[a] activities are present. He concluded that Le[b] specificity is an interaction product of two genes and not the product of an allele of the gene forming Le^a. The allele of *Le* is designated *le*.

The close interrelationship of the ABH and Lewis specificities in secretions can be explained if it is assumed that the *A*, *B*, *H*, and *Le* genes all control changes in the same precursor glycoprotein. Schemes for the later stages of the biosynthesis of the blood-group active glycoproteins, which attempt to reconcile the serological, genetical, and biochemical data, have been formulated (Watkins, 1958; Watkins and Morgan, 1959; Ceppellini, 1959). In these schemes the conversion of the precursor glycoprotein to H substance is assumed to be under the control of the secretor genes *Se se*, that is, the *H* gene cannot function in the presence of two nonsecretor genes *se se*. The formation of H active structures is a necessary prerequisite for the formation of A and B structures, and therefore failure to form H results in the absence of A and B in secretions, even when the *A* and *B* genes are present. The *Le* gene, conversely, is not under the control of the secretor genes, and the changes induced by *Le* take place on the precursor glycoprotein whenever this gene is present. The function of the genes is taken as the addition of sugar units to the carbohydrate chains in the precursor substance; *H* and *Le* are both considered to control the addition of L-fucose, but the additions take place to different sugars in the precursor and through different linkages; *A* adds *N*-acetylgalactosamine and *B* adds D-galactose to the H active structures. An outline of the additions to the carbohydrate chains in the precursor substance controlled by the *H* and *Le* genes and the specificities formed are given in Table 7. The scheme implies that the Le^b specificity arises from the addition of two fucosyl units to adjacent sugars on the backbone chain. Such a unit has not yet been isolated from blood-group substances, but compounds containing the proposed structure (Table 8b), have been isolated from human milk (cf. Kuhn, 1957) and found to be inhibitory in the Le^b agglutination system (Watkins and Morgan, 1957b, 1962). The Le^a-active trisaccharide formed by the addition of fucose to the chain ending in β-galactosyl-(1 → 3) *N*-acetylglucosamine (Table 8a) was originally proposed as the Le active structure on the basis of agglutination inhibition experiments (Watkins and Morgan, 1957), and is now confirmed by the isolation of this trisaccharide from the alkaline degradation products of Le^a substance (Rege *et al.*, 1964b).

Biosynthesis of a blood-group active substance from an inactive precursor has not yet been achieved. For simplicity in the schemes, a preformed glycoprotein is envisaged as the acceptor of the sugar units. There is, however, evidence from the biosynthesis of lipopolysaccharides in bacteria, that in some instances oligosaccharide intermediates are formed and subsequently joined as units to the macromolecule (Weiner *et al.*, 1965; Wright *et al.*, 1965). A similar mechanism could also be operating for the biosynthesis of the oligosaccharide side-chains in the blood-group substances; this would not mitigate against the sequences indicated in the biosynthetic schemes, but would

TABLE 7*

PROPOSED ADDITIONS TO CARBOHYDRATE CHAINS IN THE PRECURSOR
GLYCOPROTEIN CONTROLLED BY THE H AND Le GENES

Carbohydrate chains in precursor substance				
Type I	β-Gal-(1 → 3)-β-GNAc-(1 → 3)-β-Gal-(1 → 3)-GalNAc—			
Type II	β-Gal-(1 → 4)-β-GNAc-(1 → 3)-β-Gal-(1 → 3)-GalNAc—			

Additions to nonreducing ends of basic chains				
Gene	Sugar added	Chain type	Structure formed	Specificity
——		I	β-Gal-(1 → 3)-GNAc—	——
——		II	β-Gal-(1 → 4)-GNAc—	Type XIV
H	L-fucose	I	β-Gal-(1 → 3)-GNAc— $\uparrow$ 1,2 α-Fuc	H
		II	β-Gal-(1 → 4)-GNAc— $\uparrow$ 1,2 α-Fuc	H
Le	L-fucose	I	β-Gal-(1 → 3)-GNAc— $\uparrow$ 1,4 α-Fuc	Le^a
		II	β-Gal-(1 → 4)-GNAc—	Type XIV
H and Le	L-fucose	I	β-Gal-(1 → 3)-GNAc— $\uparrow$ 1,2 $\uparrow$ 1,4 α-Fuc α-Fuc	Le^b
		II	β-Gal-(1 → 4)-GNAc— $\uparrow$ 1,2 α-Fuc	H

* Abbreviations are the same as in Tables 3 and 5.

merely imply that the sugar additions take place to an oligosaccharide intermediate rather than to the formed glycoprotein.

The following evidence supports the inference that the same precursor
glycoprotein is used by the Le gene as by the A, B, and H genes: 1) Le^a
substances isolated from ovarian cysts are identical to A, B, and H substances in qualitative carbohydrate and amino-acid composition, and are
also similar in quantitative composition apart from the fucose content which
is usually lower in Le^a preparations (cf. Morgan, 1960). 2) On partial acid
hydrolysis the same fragments are isolated from Le^a substance as from H
substance (Rege, Painter, Watkins and Morgan, 1963) indicating an essential
similarity in the structure of carbohydrate chains. 3) In group A preparations,

TABLE 8*

SEROLOGICALLY ACTIVE TRISACCHARIDE ISOLATED FROM ALKALINE-
DEGRADATION PRODUCTS OF HUMAN Le^a SUBSTANCE AND
STRUCTURE PROPOSED FOR Le^b DETERMINANT

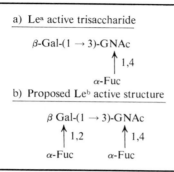

a) Le^a active trisaccharide

β-Gal-(1 → 3)-GNAc

↑ 1,4

α-Fuc

b) Proposed Le^b active structure

β Gal-(1 → 3)-GNAc

↑ 1,2   ↑ 1,4

α-Fuc α-Fuc

* Abbreviations are the same as in Tables 3 and 5.

the presence of Le^a active groupings on the same macromolecules as the A active groupings has been demonstrated (Watkins, 1958; Brown et al., 1959). 4) Le^a structures not detectable in the undegraded molecules are revealed by the sequential enzymic degradation of certain A, B, and H substances (Watkins, 1962; Furukawa et al., 1963).

The relationship between the Le^a and Le^b active glycoproteins in secretions and the substances taken up from the plasma that confers Le^a and Le^b reactivity on erythrocytes is not yet established. Presumably, however, the groupings responsible for Le^a and Le^b specificity are the same, even if these groupings are associated with different molecular entities. The position of Le^b is interesting because although hybrid antigens formed by the interaction of two genes have been described in doves (Irwin and Cumley, 1945) and in rabbits (Cohen, 1956), no other examples of hybrid antigens have yet been recognized in man (cf. Race and Sanger, 1962).

The MN System

The MN system, discovered by Landsteiner and Levine (1927a, b), is of minor importance from the point of view of practical blood transfusion, but it has been extensively used as a "marker" in genetical and anthropological investigations. Three main groups are recognized, M, N, and MN, and these are considered to represent three genotypes, *MM*, *NN*, and *MN*, determined by the presence or absence of two allelic genes *M* and *N*. Since the time of the discovery of the MN system, many related antigens and subgroups of the MN system have been found (cf. Race and Sanger, 1962).

M and N activity has been reported in tissue cells (Kosjakov and Tribulev, 1939), but does not occur in significant amounts in saliva or ovarian cyst fluids. N activity is found in human meconium (Springer and Hotta, 1963) and an N-like receptor is present on horse red cells (Levine et al., 1955). Hohorst (1954) first isolated M and N substances from red cells by application of the hot phenol-water method originally introduced by Westphal, Lüderitz, and Bister (1952) for the isolation of the specific lipopolysaccharides from gram-negative bacteria. Other workers (Baranowski et al., 1959; Stadler and Springer, 1960; Klenk and Uhlenbruck, 1960; Kathan et al., 1961) have since found that with slight modifications, this is the most successful method for obtaining active M and N preparations for chemical studies. The materials isolated contain carbohydrate and amino acid constituents and are free from lipid. Their general behavior indicates they are glycoproteins in which the carbohydrate and amino acid components are joined together by primary valency bonds. The preparations contain galactose, glucosamine, galactosamine, mannose, fucose, and sialic acid (N-acetylneuraminic acid), and fourteen amino acids. Typical analytical values for M and N preparations isolated in different laboratories by the phenol extraction method are given in Table 9 (preparation numbers 1 to 4).

TABLE 9

TYPICAL ANALYTICAL VALUES FOR M AND N PREPARATIONS
ISOLATED FROM HUMAN ERYTHROCYTES

| | Preparation No. | | | | | |
	1*	2†	3‡	4**	5††	6††
	MN active	MN active	MN active	N active	M active	N active
Nitrogen %	7.5	7.5	10.1	7.1	—	—
Hexose %	10	15	12.4	17	22	13
Hexosamine %	6.5	5.8	12	9	29	22
Sialic acid %	20	14	21	24	18	38
Fucose	1	—	1.1	1	—	—

* Baranowski, et al. (1959).
† Klenk and Uhlenbruck (1960).
‡ Kathan et al. (1961).
** Hotta and Springer (1965).
†† Cook and Eylar (1965).

An alternative method of obtaining M- and N-active fragments from red cells is treatment with proteolytic enzymes. Nondialyzable materials can be recovered from the cell-free supernatant obtained after incubation of red cells with trypsin, ficin, bromelin, papain, or pronase (Uhlenbruck, 1961a).

The materials recovered by this procedure, however, are less active than those obtained by the phenol method. Lisowska (1960) suggests that treatment with proteolytic enzymes of the materials isolated by the phenol method results in the splitting of the macromolecule into smaller fragments. If the blood-group receptors are considered as integral parts of the red-cell surface, it is difficult to say how much of the associated molecules can legitimately be considered as part of the blood-group substance. If the aim, however, is to study the biological activity of the isolated product, it is obviously desirable to attempt to isolate fragments with as high an activity as possible. M- and N-active glycopeptides richer in carbohydrate than those previously described were recently isolated (Cook and Eylar, 1965) from red cells by treatment with pronase followed by fractionation of liberated material on Sephadex G25). The M glycopeptide (Column 5, Table 9) had a lower sialic acid and higher galactose content than the N glycopeptide (preparation number 6 Table 9), and the authors concluded that M and N antigens differ in primary structure. Although it is undoubtedly true that to account for their independent serological specificities M and N antigenic groupings must be chemically different, it can only be accepted with reservation at present that such differences are reflected in the analytical values of the two glycopeptides described.

Sialic acid (N-acetylneuraminic acid) appears to play no part in the serological specificity of A, B, H, Le[a] or Le[b] substances, although it is present to a variable extent in all the preparations isolated from ovarian cysts; in M and N substances, however, there is a considerable body of evidence to suggest that this sugar plays a vital role in the specificity measured by human anti-M and anti-N reagents. Springer and Ansell (1958) and, independently, Mäkelä and Cantell (1958) demonstrated that treatment of red cells with influenza virus or the receptor destroying enzyme (R.D.E.) from *Vibrio cholera* destroyed the M and N activity of the cells. Treatment of the isolated M and N substances with influenza virus (Romanowska, 1959) or R.D.E. (Klenk and Uhlenbruck, 1960) similarly resulted in loss of M and N specificity; N-acetylneuraminic acid was shown to be the only component of the glycoproteins liberated by the action of these enzymes. Therefore unless the enzyme preparations are bringing about changes in the secondary structure of the M and N substances that result in loss of reactivity, it must be assumed that N-acetylneuraminic acid forms part of the serologically active structures detected by human anti-M and anti-N sera.

The M and N substances isolated from red cells by the phenol extraction method are potent inhibitors of influenza virus hemagglutination, whereas the preparations isolated by treatment of red cells with proteolytic enzymes are inactive (cf. Kathan *et al.*, 1963). N-acetylneuraminic acid is an integral part of the prosthetic group of influenza virus inhibitors and is the grouping which binds the virus to the surface of red cells. There is evidence, however, that a certain minimum molecular weight is essential for a glycoprotein to

function as a viral inhibitor irrespective of structural aspects of the carbohydrate moiety (cf. Gottschalk, 1960). The sialic acid present in the M and N
substances may therefore contribute to the influenza virus receptor sites on the
red-cell surface, but the ability of the isolated materials to act as viral hemagglutination inhibitors may be related to the size of the fragment liberated
from the cell.

Preparations isolated from MM red-cells frequently show inhibitory
activity with anti-N sera, whereas preparations obtained from NN cells are
usually specific for anti-N and fail to react in tests with anti-M sera (Uhlenbruck, 1961b). Moreover treatment of isolated M substance with swine
influenza virus, or by mild acid hydrolysis, destroys M activity with a concomitant increase in N activity (Nagai and Springer, 1962). Several workers
have therefore suggested that N is a basic substance bearing the same relation
to M as H does to A and B substances (cf. Prokop and Uhlenbruck, 1963).
The N substance would thus not be the product of the gene allelic with *M*,
but the product of genes lower down on the assembly line of glycoprotein
synthesis. The plant seed anti-N reagent *Vicia Graminea* does not react with
a sialic acid containing structure in N substance (Springer and Hotta, 1964;
Romanowska, 1964), and there is evidence from experiments with this reagent of two carbohydrate chains in N substance—one of which is substituted with sialic acid, responsible for the reactivity with human anti-N sera
and, a second chain, which carries the *Vicia graminea* specific groupings.

P_1 Substance from Hydatid Cysts

The basis for the P blood-group system was laid down in the same series
of experiments in which the MN system was discovered (Landsteiner and
Levine, 1927). The P system for many years was considered as a monofac-
torial system and bloods were differentiated simply into P + or P − according to whether they reacted or failed to react with an anti-P serum. Two antigens are now recognized, P and P_1, which give rise to three phenotypes, P_1, P_2,
and p (cf. Race and Sanger, 1962). Antigens associated with the P system have
not yet been isolated from red cells, and substances related to this system have
not been demonstrated in saliva or human tissues (cf. Weiner, 1943; Pettenkofer, 1955). A water-soluble source of P_1 active substance is found in hydatid
cyst fluids (Cameron and Staveley, 1957) of human or animal origin; this
substance specifically inhibits human anti-P_1 sera, but is believed to originate
from the infecting organism *Echinococcus granulosis*. Materials isolated
from dried cyst fluids by extraction with cold 95% phenol are highly active
serologically and appear to be glycoproteins containing galactose, hexosamine,
and amino acids (Morgan and Watkins, 1964). Hemagglutination inhibition
tests with simple sugars indicated that P_1 specificity on the red-cell surface

is associated with an α-D-galactosyl structure and enzymic inhibition tests on the hydatid cyst P_1 substance also pointed to the role of D-galactose as a determinant of specificity (Watkins and Morgan, 1964). Therefore, although the chemical evidence on the nature of P_1 is still rather fragmentary, a carbohydrate structure is once again implicated in specificity. On the basis of serological and genetical data, a scheme has been proposed for the sequential development from a precursor substance of the different specificities associated with the P system (Kortekangas et al., 1965).

Rhesus (D) Inhibitors

Great interest centers on the Rhesus blood-group system because of its importance in clinical medicine, and many attempts have been made to isolate the $Rh_o(D)$ antigen from red cells and to determine its chemical nature. It has been variously reported as lipid, protein, or carbohydrate. Attempts have recently been made to determine the nature of the serologically active groupings in Rh antigens by the method of hemagglutination inhibition with low molecular weight inhibitors of known structure, or with macromolecular substances isolated from sources other than human red cells. These studies have implicated so many compounds of diverse chemical nature that an interpretation and evaluation of the results is rendered extremely difficult. Specific inhibition of $Rh_o(D)$ antibody by sialic acids and compounds containing sialic acid has been claimed by some groups of workers (cf. Dodd et al., 1961; Boyd and Reeves, 1961), and recently Dodd, Bigley, Johnson, and McCluer (1964) proposed that the structure given in Table 10 represents

TABLE 10*

PROPOSED IMMUNOLOGICAL DETERMINANT OF Rh_o (D) ANTIGEN

Gal-(1 → 3)-GalNAc-(1 → 4)-Gal-(1 → 4)-Gluc-1 → R

$$\begin{pmatrix} 3 \\ \uparrow \\ 2 \end{pmatrix}$$

NANA (2 → 8) NANA

* Abbreviations:	Gluc	= D-glucose.
	NANA	= N-acetylneuraminic acid.
	R	= Remainder of molecule.

Other abbreviations are the same as in Tables 3 and 5.

the immunological determinant in the $Rh_o(D)$ antigen, on the basis of inhibition tests with gangliosides isolated from human brain. The similarity of this structure to the types of structure present in A, B, H, and Le^a substances will at once be evident. The backbone chain is composed of alternating galactose and N-acetyl hexosamine residues and the sialic-acid residues take the place of the fucosyl branching units. The $2 \rightarrow 8$ linked sialic acid residues are neuraminidase-resistant and such a structure would therefore explain how sialic acid could be involved in $Rh_o(D)$ specificity and not be destroyed by treatment with the *Vibrio cholera* or influenza enzymes. The presence of readily accessible sugar units would also explain the extreme sensitivity of the Rh antigen to treatment with periodate (cf. Morgan and Watkins, 1951). A ganglioside identical in structure, apart from the terminal nonreducing galactosyl unit, was much less inhibitory in the $Rh_o(D)$ test than the one containing the structure in Table 10; it was concluded that this terminal galactose contributes to the full determinant structure. The structures proposed for these compounds, however, seem to be based on analogies of composition and chromatographic behavior with a similar series of gangliosides isolated from bovine sources by Kuhn and Wiegandt (1963), rather than on rigid structural proof. Wolff and Springer (1964) reported failure to obtain inhibition with any of the gangliosides prepared by Kuhn and his colleagues. Acceptance of this structure as the $Rh_o(D)$ determinant must therefore be reserved until confirmatory evidence has been presented.

Summary and Conclusions

Far less is known about the chemistry of the blood-group antigens than about their serology and genetics. Isolation of the substances from the red cells in a serologically active, and chemically homogeneous, condition presents technical problems that, as yet, are only partially solved. The most detailed information on the relationship between chemical structure and blood-group specificity has been obtained for the ABO and the closely related Lewis systems. Substances associated with these systems occur, however, not only on the red cells but as surface components of many tissue cells and in a freely soluble form in certain secretions. It is the purified blood-group substance derived from secretions that have received most study. The isolation of serologically active fragments from their partial acid and alkaline degradation products has confirmed the inferences drawn earlier from indirect tests — that specificity is associated with carbohydrate structures, and more especially, with the nature of the sugars at the nonreducing ends of the carbohydrate chains. The immuno-dominant sugar in the A-determinant structure was characterized as N-acetyl-D-galactosamine and the immuno-dominant sugar in the B-determinant structure as D-galactose. Schemes have been put forward to suggest ways in which the complete A and B determinant structures can be built up by the addition of these two sugars, respectively, to H-active structures, and it is proposed that the A and B genes control the formation, or functioning, of specific glycosyl transferases. The close relationship between the Lewis (Le^a and Le^b) groups and the ABO system is thought to arise from the fact that in the secreted blood-group substances the Lewis *Le* gene controls the addition of fucosyl residues to the same precursor molecule, as is used for the formation of H, A, and B substances. The recognition that more than one genetic locus may be involved in the formation of a blood-group specific structure has enabled a clearer understanding to be obtained of the serological relationships between genetically independent systems and indicated the ways in which interaction products may arise.

In the secreted A, B, H, Le^a, and Le^b substances the carbohydrate chains are joined to a peptide moiety, and the molecules are classified as glycoproteins. Recent work has revealed that the A and B substances isolated from erythrocytes are glycolipids in which the carbohydrate is joined through sphingosine to fatty acids. Little structural work has been carried out on these substances, but there is indirect evidence to suggest that the groupings responsible for specificity are similar to those in the glycoproteins with the corresponding blood-group activity. It is possible that in the two types of molecules the peptide or lipid moieties serve similar functions in maintaining the correct orientation and spatial arrangements of the serologically active carbohydrate groupings.

In contrast to the A and B substances isolated from red cells, M and N substances from this source are glycoproteins. Sialic acid appears to play a dominant part in both M and N specificity as measured by human or rabbit anti-M or anti-N sera, but this sugar can be eliminated without loss of the specificity measured by certain plant seed anti-N reagents. The chemical and serological evidence would seem to favor the interpretation that the M and N substances have many common structures and that N may be the immediate precursor of M substance rather than the product of a gene allelic with the *M* gene.

A scheme similar to that proposed for the formation of A, B, H, Le^a, and Le^b antigens has been advanced to explain the interrelationships in the P system. This scheme is based only on serological findings, as knowledge of the chemistry of the antigens in this system is still fragmentary. P_1 specificity does, however, again appear to be associated with a carbohydrate structure and an α-D-galactosyl residue is implicated as the immuno-dominant sugar in the serological determinant.

A carbohydrate structure has been advanced as the serological determinant of the $Rh_o(D)$ antigen, but this is still the subject of some controversy. Of the other ten or so blood-group systems, no chemical information is available at present. The fact that specific groupings identified so far are all associated with carbohydrate structures may be fortuitous, or it may suggest that blood groups arise from genetically controlled variations in the disposition and nature of sugar residues attached to structures on the surface of erythrocytes.

REFERENCES

Adams, J. B. 1965. *Biochem. J.* 97: 345.

Anderson, B., J. G. Riley, P. Hoffman, and K. Meyer. 1964. *Proc. 6th Internatl. Congr. Biochem. New York.* P. 138.

Baranowski, T., E. Lisowska, A. Morawiecki, E. Romanowska, and K. Strozecka. 1950. *Arch. Immunol. Terapü Doswiadczalnej* 7: 15.

Boyd, W. C., and E. Reeves. 1961. *Nature (London)* 190: 1123.

Brown, P. C., L. E. Glynn, and E. J. Holborow. 1959. *Vox Sanguinis* 4: 1.

Cameron, G. L., and J. M. Staveley. 1957. *Nature* 179: 147.

Carsten, M. E., and E. A. Kabat. 1956 *J. Am. Chem. Soc.* 78: 3083.

Ceppellini, R. 1955. *Proc. 5th Internatl. Congr. Blood Transfusion, Paris,* P. 207.

Ceppellini, R. 1959. *CIBA Found. Symp. Biochem. Human Genetics* London: Churchill P. 242.

Cheese, I. A. F. L., and W. T. J. Morgan. 1961. *Nature (London)* 191: 149.

Cohen, C. 1956. *Science* 123: 935.

Cook, G. M. W., and E. H. Eylar. 1965, *Biochem. Biophys. Acta* 101: 57.

Côté, R., and W. T. J. Morgan. 1956. *Nature (London)* 178: 1171.

Cushing, J. E., N. L. Calaprice, and G. Trump. 1963. *Biol. Bull.* 125: 69.

Dodd, M. C., N. J. Bigley, and V. B. Geyer. 1961. *Science* 132: 1398.

Dodd, M. C., N. J. Bigley, G. A. Johnson, and R. H. McCluer. 1954. *Nature (London)* 204: 549.

Donald, A. S. R., and W. T. J. Morgan. Unpublished observations.

Fujisawa, K., K. Furukawa, and S. Iseki. 1963. *Proc. Imp. Acad. Japan* 39: 319.

Furukawa, K., K. Fujisawa, and S. Iseki. 1963. *Proc. Imp. Acad. Japan* 39: 540.

Gibbons, R. A., W. T. J. Morgan, and M. Gibbons. 1955. *Biochem. J.* 60: 428.

Glynn, L. E., and E. J. Holborow. 1959. *Brit. Med. Bull.* 15: 150.

Gottschalk, A. 1960. *The Chemistry and Biology of Sialic Acids and Related Substances.* London: Cambridge University Press.

Grubb, R. 1948. *Nature (London)* 162: 933.

Hakamori, S. I., and R. W. Jeanloz. 1961. *J. Biol. Chem.* 236: 2827.

Handa, S., 1963. *Jap. J. Exp. Med.* 33: 347.

Harrap, G. J. and W. M. Watkins. 1964. *Biochem. J.* 93: 9P.

Hiyama, N. 1962. In *Biochemistry and Medicine of Mucopolysaccharides.* ed. Egami and Oshima. Tokyo: Maruzen. P. 161.

Hohorst, H. J. 1954. *Z. Hyg. Infecktionkrank* 139: 561.

Holborow, E. J., P. C. Brown, L. E. Glynn, M. D. Hawes, G. A. Gresham, T. F. O'Brien, and R. R. A. Coombs. 1960. *Brit. J. Exp. Path.* 41: 430.

Hotta K. and G. F. Springer 1965. *Proc. 10th Internatl. Congr. Blood Transfusion,* Stockholm 1964. P.

Irwin, M. R., and R. W. Cumley. 1945. *Genetics* 30: 363.

Iseki, S., and K. Furukawa. 1959. *Proc. Imp. Acad. Japan* 35: 620.

Iseki, S., and T. Ikeda. 1956. *Proc. Imp. Acad. Japan* 32: 201.

Iseki, S., and S. Masaki. 1953. *Proc. Imp. Acad. Japan* 29: 460.

Joysey, V. C. 1959. *Brit. Med. Bull.* 15: 158.

Kabat, E. A. 1956. Blood Group Substances. Academic Press Inc., New York.

Kabat E. A. and S. Leskowitz 1955. *J. Am. chem. Soc.* 77: 5159.

Kabat, E. A., E. W. Bassett, K. Pryzwansky, K. O. Lloyd, M. E. Kaplan, and E. J. Layug. 1965. *Biochem.* 4: 1632.

Kathan, R. H., L. J. M. Riff, and M. Real. 1963. *Proc. Soc. Exp. Biol. Med.* 114: 90.

Kathan, R. H., R. J. Winzler, and C. A. Johnson. 1961. *J. Exptl. Med.* 113: 37.

Klenk, E., and G. Uhlenbruck. 1960. *Z. Physiol. Chem.* 319: 151.

Kortekangas, A. E., E. Kaarsalo, L. Melartin, P. Tippett, J. Gavin, J. Noades, R. Sanger, and R. R. Race. 1965. *Vox Sanguinis* 10: 385.

Koscielak, J. 1963. *Biochim. Biophys. Acta* 78: 313.

Koscielak, J., and K. Zakrzewski. 1960. *Nature (London)* 187: 516.

Kosjakov, P. N., and G. P. Tribulev. 1939. *J. Immunol.* 37: 283.

Kuhn, R. 1957. *Angew. Chem.* 60: 23.

Kuhn, R., and H. Weigandt. 1963. *Chem. Ber.* 96: 866.

Landsteiner, K. 1900. *Zentr. Bakteriol. Parasitenk.* 27: 357.

Landsteiner, K. 1901. *Wien. Klin. Wochschr.* 14: 1132.

Landsteiner, K., and P. Levine. 1927a. *Proc. Soc. Exptl. Biol. Med.* 24: 600.

Landsteiner, K., and P. Levine. 1927b. *Proc. Soc. Exptl. Biol. Med.* 24: 941.

Lehrs, H. 1930. *Z. Immunitätsforsch.* 66: 175.

Levine, P., F. Ottensooser, M. J. Celano, and W. Pollitzer. 1955. *Am. J. Phys. Anthropol.* 13: 29.

Lisowska, E. 1960. *Arch. Immunol. Terapü Doswiadczalnej* 8: 235.

Lloyd K., and E. A. Kabat. 1964. *Biochem. Biophys. Res. Commun.* 16: 385.

Mäkelä, O. and K. Cantell. 1958. *Ann. Med. Exptl. Biol. Fenniae* Helsinki 36: 366.

Marcus, D. M., E. A. Kabat, and G. Schiffman. 1964. *Biochem.* 3: 385.

Morgan, W. T. J. 1960. *Proc. Roy. Soc. (London)* B. 151: 308.

Morgan, W. T. J. 1965. Unpublished observations.

Morgan, W. T. J., and R. van Heyningen. 1944. *Brit. J. Exptl. Pathol.* 25: 5.

Morgan, W. T. J., and W. M. Watkins. 1951. *Brit. J. Exptl. Pathol.* 32: 34.

Morgan, W. T. J., and W. M. Watkins. 1953. *Brit. J. Exptl. Pathol.* 34: 94.

Morgan, W. T. J., and W. M. Watkins. 1956. *Nature (London)* 177: 521.

Morgan, W. T. J., and W. M. Watkins. 1964. *Proc. 9th Internatl. Cong. Blood Transfusion, Mexico City,* 1962. P. 225.

Mourant, A. E. 1946. *Nature (London)* 158: 237.

Nagai, Y., and G. F. Springer. 1962. *Federation Proc.* 21: 67.

Painter, T. J., W. M. Watkins, and W. T. J. Morgan. 1962. *Nature.* 193: 1042.

Painter, T. J., W. M. Watkins, and W. T. J. Morgan. 1963. *Nature.* 199: 282.

Painter, T. J., W. M. Watkins, and W. T. J. Morgan. 1965. *Nature (London)* 206: 594.

Pennell, R. B. 1964. In *The Red Blood Cell.* ed. Bishop and Surgenor. New York: Academic Press, Inc. Ch. 2.

Pettenkofer, H. J. 1955. *Proc. 5th Internatl. Congr. Blood Transfusion, Paris,* 1954. P. 91.

Prokop, O., and G. Uhlenbruck. 1963. *Lehrbuch der Menschlichen Blut- und Serumgruppen.* Leipzig: Georg Thieme. P. 348.

Pusztai, A., and W. T. J. Morgan. 1961. *Biochem. J.* 80: 107.

Pusztai, A., and W. T. J. Morgan. 1963. *Biochem. J.* 88: 546.

Putkonen, T. 1930. *Acta Soc. Med. Fennaie* A.14: 107.

Race, R. R., and R. Sanger. 1962. *Blood Groups in Man,* 4th Ed. Oxford, England: Blackwell.

Rege, V. P., T. J. Painter. W. M. Watkins, and W. T. J. Morgan. 1963. *Nature (London)* 200: 532.

Rege, V. P., T. J. Painter, W. M. Watkins, and W. T. J. Morgan. 1964a. *Nature (London)* 203: 360.

Rege, V. P., T. J. Painter, W. M. Watkins, and W. T. J. Morgan. 1964b. *Nature (London)* 204: 740.

Rendel, J., A. Niemann-Sorensen, and M. R. Irwin. 1954. *Genetics* 39: 396.

Romanowska, E. 1959. *Arch. Immunol. Terapü Doswiadczalnej* 7: 749.

Romanowska, E. 1964. *Vox Sanguinis* 9: 578.

Rondle, C. J. M., and W. T. J. Morgan. 1955. *Biochem. J.* 59: xiii.

Schiffman, G., E. A. Kabat, and S. Leskowitz. 1962. *J. Am. Chem. Soc.* 84: 73.

Schiffman, G., E. A. Kabat, and W. Thompson. 1964a. *Biochem.* 3: 113.

Schiffman, G., E. A. Kabat, and W. Thompson. 1964b. *Biochem.* 3: 587.

Sneath, J. S., and P. H. A. Sneath. 1955. *Nature (London)* 176: 172.

Springer, G. F. 1958. In *CIBA Found. Symp. on Chem. and Biol. of Mucopoly-saccharides*. London: Churchill. P. 200.

Springer, G. F., and N. J. Ansell. 1958. *Proc. Natl. Acad. Sci.* 44: 182.

Springer, G. F., and K. Hotta. 1963. *Federation Proc.* 22: 539.

Springer, G. F., P. Williamson, and W. C. Brandes. 1961. *J. Exptl. Med.* 113: 1077.

Stalder, K., and G. Springer. 1960. *Federation Proc.* 19: 70.

Stormont, C. 1949. *Proc. Natl. Acad. Sci.* 35: 232.

Szulman, A. E. 1960. *J. Exptl. Med.* 111: 785.

Szulman, A. E. 1962. *J. Exptl. Med.* 115: 977.

Szulman, A. E. 1964. *J. Exptl. Med.* 119: 503.

Uhlenbruck, G. 1961a. *Nature (London)*. 190: 181.

Uhlenbruck, G. 1961b. *Z. Immunitätsforsch.* 121: 420.

von Decastello, A., and A. Sturli. 1902. *Munch. Med. Wochschr.* 49: 1090.

Watkins, W. M. 1956. *Biochem. J.* 64: P. 21P.

Watkins, W. M. 1958. *Proc. 7th Internatl. Congr. Blood Transfusion, Rome*. P. 622.

Watkins, W. M. 1966. In *Glycoproteins*. ed. A. Gottschalk. Amsterdam: Elsevier. Ch. 11.

Watkins, W. M., J. Koscielak, and W. T. J. Morgan. 1964. *Proc. 9th Congr. Internatl. Soc. Blood Transfusion, Mexico, 1962*. P. 213.

Watkins, W. M., and W. T. J. Morgan. 1955. *Nature (London)* 175: 676.

Watkins, W. M., and W. T. J. Morgan. 1957a. *Acta Genetica Statistica Med.* 6: 521.

Watkins, W. M., and W. T. J. Morgan. 1957b. *Nature (London)* 180: 1038.

Watkins, W. M., and W. T. J. Morgan. 1959. *Vox Sanguinis* 4: 97.

Watkins, W. M., and W. T. J. Morgan. 1962. *Vox Sanguinis* 7: 129.

Watkins, W. M., and W. T. J. Morgan. 1964. *Proc. 9th Internatl. Congr. Blood Transfusion, Mexico, 1962*. P. 230.

Watkins, W. M., M. L. Zarnitz, and E. A. Kabat. 1962. *Nature (London)* 195: 1204.

Westphal, O., O. Lüderitz, and F. Bister. 1952. *Z. Naturforsch.* 7b: 149.

Weiner, I. M., T. Higuchi, L. Rothfield, M. Saltmarsh-Andrew, M. J. Osborn, and B. L. Horecker. 1965. *Proc. Natl. Acad. Sci.* 54: 228.

Wiener, A. S. 1943. *Blood Groups and Transfusion*. 3rd Ed. Springfield, Ill.: Thomas Publishing Co.

Wolff, I., and G. F. Springer. 1964. *Federation Proc.* 23: 296.

Wright, A., M. Dankert, and P. W. Robbins. 1965. *Proc. Natl. Acad. Sci.* 54: 235.

Yamakami, K. 1926. *J. Immunol.* 12: 185.

Yamakawa, T., R. Irie, and M. Iwanaga. 1960. *J. Biochem. (Tokyo)* 48: 490.

Yosida, K. 1928. *Z. Ges. Exptl. Med.* 63: 331.

Index